Soldier

A Sniper's Story of Vietnam

An Original, Intense Story of That War Like it Really Was

James Gibbore

BP

Soldier
A Sniper's Story of Vietnam
An Original Story of That War Like It Really Was

By

James Gibbore

Published by:
Brundage Publishing
74 Front Street
Binghamton, NY 13905

ISBN Number: 0-7394-2694-X

This book is dedicated to

Jesus
and
All the men I served with
in Vietnam

The Briefing

This book is about Vietnam in all its gory reality for me as a soldier and for many others who served there.

It is a miracle that this book has been written or published. I never read books. In school I read only enough to get by but never read any assigned reading. As a soldier, I read only manuals required for the course I was taking.

All my life I loved movies and attended as many as possible. This may explain why I felt compelled to write about my experiences in the Vietnam War. I saw it all as a movie playing over and over in my head and I wanted to tell the world about it.

When I first wrote about Vietnam I included in every conversation all of the filthy language common to the soldiers in that war. Although I was a participant in this language during my service, still, when I wrote it all down, I was so embarrassed and shocked by its sheer ugliness that I didn't know what to do with it. So I set the story aside.

Only after a drastic near-death experience and the vision that came to me as a result of it, did I, as if by magic, know what to do. Once I took out all the meaningless curse words, the uncluttered truth of the story was magnified and I felt completely at ease with it.

This story is about a soldier. I have been many different kinds of soldier. Even in the rebellious and destructive part of my youth, I was quick to defend the weak and innocent as well as myself from perceived wrongdoing. Perhaps this is a clue as to why my story turned out the way it did.

As an Airborne-Recon and a Sniper, my experiences were very unique but very typical of much of that war. I hope it will help those that were not there to better understand the unusual traumas that haunted those who served there. To the reader, my story may be gruesome and brutal, but is the true reality that I experienced in Vietnam.

Some names of persons and places have been changed to provide anonymity, which many veterans who suffer PTSD would desire, and because of the sensitivity of some events. I fully understand this need for I was once a part of it.

Table of Contents

CHAPTER 1

In The Beginning

Many times during my life I was about to be snuffed out but I was inexplicably saved just in the nick of time. It all started with me at a very early age. In the year 1950, I lived with my parents, my grandfather, and my younger brother (born a year and a half after I was). We lived on a large farm in Greene, New York. One day when I was about five, while playing in the barn, I climbed on piled bails of hay. Suddenly, the hay bails fell and literally buried me alive. After some time, my father noticed that I was no longer by his side and started to look for me. Eventually he began to get worried because he couldn't find me. He then noticed all the hay toppled and scattered. He called for my grandfather and a hired man and they worked hard to dig me out. I still remember feeling squashed, not being able to breathe well, and feeling very scared. My father told me years later that I was half dead when they unburied me.

Even at an early age I did all kinds of crazy and outrageous things on the farm. My mother once told me that I crept out of the house completely naked in the wintertime and almost froze to death before they found me. I know what you're thinking, I was just born stupid. I know…yeah yeah.

A short time ago I saw a special report on the news about other kids that have done this same kind of thing many times before. It makes me wonder if things are planned by someone or something that has the power to know how all of us will eventually turn out.

I remember sneaking into the old attic and dismembering dolls someone had left up there before we moved in…not playing with them, dismembering them and pulling their heads off. One day while in kindergarten, I somehow talked a girl into getting off my bus and running off with me for the day. Her parents were crazy with worry searching for her by the time she and I finally came wandering into my house that evening. My childhood activities were only the beginning.

My family stayed on the farm until 1957. When I was seven years old we moved to Vestal, New York where my dad found employment after losing the farm. That was the fifth move in seven years.

I never knew until I grew to adulthood that my father was chasing women…and their husbands were chasing him. I used to think he had gypsy blood in him. But that wasn't the case. He was one hundred percent Russian and brought up hard. He was taught by his father back in Russia that kids were for use as free hired help or a tool that could make his work easier. He was something! Mean most of the time. He was very abusive to my mother, my brother and I. I saw my mother with more than one black eye. I couldn't even begin to count the lumps I received on my head. But there were times that he would become very soft hearted and I could tell that he really did love us but just had a very hard way about him. In the '50's & '60's the man was the undisputed "King of the castle."

He was a Ranger in the Army during World War II and now when I look back at how he acted I can see some of the violent things in him are also in me. I believe he was suffering from P.T.S.D., (Post Traumatic Stress Disorder) as I suffer myself because of the Vietnam War. He never went for help as I've done and they didn't know anything at all about P.T.S.D. then anyway. He drank a lot which didn't help any with his attitude.

We stayed in Vestal about three years. During that time I was nearly killed one day while crossing the street. As I ran across the road I was hit by a pick-up truck. I was knocked thirty feet and out cold, but I had no scratch on me anywhere. My mother saw the whole thing happen herself. Once again I came out of it without a scratch.

Then we moved yet again to my Grandmother's house in Endicott, New York. I was ten years old at the time and soon fell in with the wrong company. Within a week I was smoking cigarettes with a gang I hung out with. We stole cigarettes from car glove compartments and our folks. We soon began to steal from any store that would let us through the door on Washington Avenue, the business district of Endicott. We would also throw eggs, apples, or whatever else we could find at cars to get chased; just for the thrill. For three years I got my education on how to live on the streets. I was stealing, fighting, smoking and raising Cain any way I could think of. Every time I got caught, my father would beat me. But so what?! I would heal! He would call me all kinds of names. "No good for nothin' pup! You ain't worth a damn." You name it. So what?! I would heal!

Soon the old man's gypsy blood took over and we moved again when I was thirteen years old to Endwell, New York a few miles away. My father bought his own house and we hoped we'd stay a while and we did. I stayed until I was eighteen years old and joined the Army. But it was long before I joined the Army that Satan had me doing all kinds of evil and destructive things. For some reason I always had to be the ringleader and always had to be the toughest guy in the crowd. I would have rather died than taken orders from anyone!

Soon I found out that on the "camp outs" we would have in the back yard, numerous people would leave their keys in their cars over the visor or under the front seat. Car stealing was then added to my list of things to do. We would steal cars and completely destroy them. Sometimes the car would even make it back and I would park it where I had just stolen it from. That is how bold I was! Every chance I got I stole cars, drank, got into fights and did whatever I could dream up. My friends followed me like they were on a leash. They trusted me completely!

On one camp out we all headed out to where a new dam was being built. I thought the construction was invading the privacy of the fort we had built nearby in the woods. So I decided to take it upon myself to do a little "destruction" of my own. My friends and I found all the keys to all the trucks, dozers, and graders. We figured out how to start and run all the equipment, by trial and error, and had a demolition derby! By the time we had finished, we had demolished everything. To this day, I still don't see how some of us didn't get killed!

When we left, we drove away in the only dump truck that was still running. We drove up the road to a golf course and did burn outs and doughnuts all over the greens before the truck died. The next day we read about it in the papers. That was as good as a badge of valor to all four of us. We were all very proud of what we had done. We laid low for a while and were never caught. Satan takes care of his own…for a while.

Soon I was itching to rob a car again. We camped out and stole a car from a driveway. There were two cars parked there. There were only two of us there that night and we pushed one of the cars out of the driveway and down the street. My friend and I quickly started the car, the keys were over the visor as usual and we drove away. We both took turns driving the car and beat the tar out of it. We drove all over town having a ball then we took the car back…at that point it was still in one piece. Carefully I pulled the car into the driveway behind the other car parked there and I went to shut the motor off. Suddenly, a man quickly sat up in the front seat of the other car in front of us and he started to get out to come after us. I quickly put the car in reverse and floored it back out onto the street. I flew up the street and to the left up a steep hill.

Halfway up the hill I could see in my rear view mirror the second car coming up fast. At the top of the hill, the road turned left very sharply. I spun out and stopped broadside in the road. The motor had stalled out. I yelled to my friend to get out. We jumped out and ran as fast as we could.

Just then I heard a loud screeching noise. I turned just in time to see the man chasing us lose control of his car and slam into the side of the car I had been driving. The man totally demolished both of his own cars. For the longest time, I thought that was the funniest thing I had ever seen! I was laughing so hard I could hardly run. But we just kept going and never got caught.

I cheated death many times behind the wheel of a car in those days. Strangers' cars were not the only ones at risk. Our parent's cars were in mortal danger as well.

All through junior high and high school, I would fight daily. Someone always wanted to see how tough they or I was. They all quickly found out it was not them. I never lost a fight! Not even one!

Then one day in tenth grade, my fighting went from students to teachers. I had a gym teacher that thought he was really tough. One day, while not paying attention to him as he instructed us, he slapped me in the head and told me to run ten laps around the ball field. I told him to forget it. He looked at me as though he was going to slap me again, so I kicked him as hard as I could right in the groin. He bent over, holding his stomach and gasping for air. I uppercut him in the face with as much force as I could and down he went. Every boy present cheered loudly. I walked down to the school and into the principal's office and told the vice-principal what had happened. He was very angry, to say the least. His decision was to throw me out of school until a conference with my parents was held. As I left school, I saw my gym teacher coming up the hall holding his face and stomach. To me, that was the second funniest thing I had ever seen. Outside, I bummed a cigarette off the janitor and went home.

Soon my reputation was widely known. There was a fraternity called "The Brown Coats." The majority of the members were in eleventh and twelfth grade. But, since I was knocking out most of their tougher members, they decided to let me join. After becoming a "Brown Coat," very few guys from my school tried to pick a fight with me.

There were teachers at my school that hated me for what I was, and hated my younger brother just because he was my brother. He wasn't a fighter at all. He was nothing like me! He was a good kid.

One day, just as school was letting out, I saw a scuffle down the hall and ran to watch. Soon I recognized my younger brother. He was in a fight with a man...a teacher! I broke through the crowd and pulled them apart. I was so angry I screamed at the teacher saying, "If you want a fight...here I am!" Before he could say a word, I beat him bad and threw him over the stair railing onto the stairs below. He hit hard and injured his spine on the stairs when he landed. I was immediately expelled from school and the teacher was whisked off to the hospital with serious injuries.

During my day at the parent-teacher conference I talked my way back into school. I forced people to come in and falsely testify that the teacher was going to and did attack me first, as well as my younger brother. All I ended up with was a few days suspension. The teacher ended up with a broken back and he was never the same again.

Then one day in my twelfth year of high school, we got a new assistant gym teacher. He was a young and very large man who played football for Cornell University at one time. He disliked me right away...it is no wonder why! He rode me like a horse, trying to get me to break, but his size kept me from going after him...for a while.

Then he went too far. He was left as our substitute biology teacher one day. After we all sat down and got settled in class he said that he wasn't going to teach, but we were to use the time as a study hall. He said he didn't want to hear one peep out of anyone or else! After he put his head down, the room got dead quiet. Then a friend sitting next to me, who was a real instigator, let out a loud "Peep!" I looked up and saw the teacher looking right at me. "It wasn't me!" I said. He quickly got up and ran over to me. He stopped in front of me and said, "You asked for it," and slapped me in the face. Instantly I lost my temper and punched him right in the nose with the hardest most perfect punch I ever threw up to that time. Instantly his nose started to gush blood like I hit him with a ball bat. His eyes watered up and he was blinded. I knew then that I had to do this man up but good because if I let him come back to his right mind or come to he would most likely kill me right there. I beat him unmercifully.

Soon he went down. When he did, I watched as my friend kicked the teacher in the face and head several times. He was hurt really bad and he went quickly out cold! The room full of kids went wild and turned into a riot. I walked out and reported what had happened to the principal. Again, I was expelled from school. That teacher went to the hospital. He later pressed charges against me.

CHAPTER 2

In the Army

A few days before I had to go to court, the district attorney told me I was in a lot of trouble with only one possible way out. He told me he may be able to talk the judge into letting me join the Army rather than pulling jail time. And so it was. The judge let me join the Army for three years instead of jail.

I found in the Army a perfect place to unleash the hatred I felt inside myself. I was forced to join because of my brutality to others. This brutality in me made me a willing soldier and it was in fact reinforced by my training. Instead of concentrating on simply fighting people, which I was already good at, the Army taught me to enjoy killing people. Our training discipline regarding the Army was,

Q: What are you?
A: Airborne.
Q: What is your job?
A: To kill people.
Q: How do you feel?
A: I love it, Sir!

Because I was already filled with hate, acceptance of this discipline was easy for me. I now felt I had a license to kill and I truly loved the idea of killing my enemy. I quickly became a good soldier. This raging hatred became even more intense as I was involved in the war. It just seemed to feed upon itself within me and to grow in response to the horrors I was caught in.

Because it all came so naturally to me, the Army offered me every infantry school they had and I went for it. I went to every school except Officers Candidate school. I mistrusted mandatory leaders so I didn't want to be an officer. I had an attitude against people in authority from high school, perhaps arising from the harshness of my father's authority. This caused me to steal cars and show disrespect for my teachers. If you wanted to follow me, fine! If not, see you around, Bubba! I didn't want to be someone to be followed because of a title, I believed people had to earn respect.

I went through Army training and became a master paratrooper. Then while in Vietnam, I went to Recondo/Ranger school, then Pathfinder school, and finally Sniper school. I qualified expert in every weapon I ever fired in the army. I was told I was a natural born dead shot.

All the schools that I ever went to in the army always made sure that we were physically fit in every way. Perfect sight, hearing, feet, and all the parts of the body had to be perfect just to get into the schools. I'm not talking about the marks or the grades we got in the schools, which had to be high to pass. At these schools I went through, any flaw, any blemish, could cut us from ever even making it into the first day of class. All others that were not absolutely perfect in every way were made into anything but an infantry airborne soldier.

5

It never really dawned on me until later in life that to do the job of an infantry soldier, to die for our country in combat duty, you had to be in perfect physical health. It reminded me greatly of the fact that the only sacrifices deemed worthy of God or the gods of the past had to be physically perfect. The best sheep was always chosen as the ultimate sacrifice.

We went to war because man's laws said we had to. God's law says, "Thou shalt not kill!" It makes me wonder what god men serve. I believe we were all sacrificial lambs, blameless and without blemish.

After seven or eight months of training in the states I was sent to Vietnam. I was assigned to the 173rd Airborne Special Operations group working with a Recondo/Ranger team in the central highlands of Vietnam. The place where I was stationed was called Landing Zone Uplift or L.Z. Uplift. I was unleashed and given a ticket to ride by Satan himself. For one year, four months and twenty-eight days I went into Hell on Earth…I was completely immersed in the madness of a place called Nam.

In this story I will take you there. But first, it was New Year's Eve, 1969.

U.S. Army Training Center
Fort Gorden, GA

Private James Gibbore

CHAPTER 3
Two Short Weeks

I was home on leave on my way to Vietnam. Two weeks leave is all the Army gave me before going. The last thing my two friends and I said to each other before leaving Fort Bragg, North Carolina was that we were going to spend one more New Year's at home before going to the Nam. We were supposed to report to Fort Louis, Washington on the 31st of December, 1969. But we made a pact not to meet until January 2, 1970. That was my birthday and it would also make us two days A.W.O.L. But what the heck, it looked like we would be shot sooner or later anyway.

The party was at my friend's house. Everyone looked like they were having a good time. Just then I heard my girl friend ask, "What's wrong?" I turned around and saw her standing behind me.

"Oh nothing...Sort of in a day dream I guess," I replied.

"Thinking about Nam?"

"I guess. But to heck with that awful place. It's New Year's Eve and we're going to party!"

And we did! As long as I had two days left I thought, I might as well kill myself having fun and maybe beat Charley to it.

The next day I felt sick so I kept a buzz on all day. I spent that day saying goodbye to all my family and friends. Everywhere I went people kept stuffing me with things to eat and drink. They must have thought it was going to be my last meal or something.

The two days I had left wore down to hours. The last two or three hours seemed like forever. I was sitting around at home with my Mom, Dad, and girlfriend Deb. My father would just pace around saying things like, "Dumb bell kids! Bring them up right and look what you get. They want to join the Army Rangers and go off to fight a blasted war that don't even belong to us. Even after I told him not to." I think at that time I had finally become a man in my father's eyes and maybe we were finally seeing eye-to-eye. He knew he could no longer kick my butt and that I had become too tough for him to push around anymore. Still, he had to let me know how he felt about the whole thing.

My mother was all choked up and sobbing. She was usually tough and not often would she let her emotions show. But not that day. She was tough as nails and never took any bull from me. I guess she is where my "religion" (not my belief in God) came from because during my early years she was the one that would make sure none of us missed church. She believed in going to church and that whole religion thing. She wanted all of us to go to church and get "religion"...but none of us could have told you why or what it was all about. It was just the thing that we all had to do on Sunday morning, like it or not. That was the way she was raised and that was the way my brother and I were going to be raised even if it killed her or us in the process. That was one of the few things the old man let her get away with, no questions asked. As time went on the family grew apart. We really never were a kissy huggy type of family anyway. At least after the age of six or eight.

7

As for my girl…she clung to me like I was the last thread of life. She was a very beautiful little Italian girl who loved me big time! While everyone was trying to say last minute things all at once, I just sat on the couch with my girl thinking of all my Army training and common sense. Would it ever get me back alive?

Just then my father said, "Well, if you're going to make your flight we'd better get going." My mother got up and put her arms around me and said, "Jim, please be careful and don't take any unnecessary risks. I love you very much and I'll pray hard and say the Rosary for your safe return." She hugged and kissed me goodbye. Though she never took any s*#& from me and would give me a whack when I needed it, (and at times I did have it coming), I always knew she loved me big time. I had a lump in my throat so big I thought I would choke to death. I kind of pushed her away and said sadly, "I love you Ma. I'll see ya soon. Most of all don't worry because I know you're a worry wart!" I turned around and I walked out the door.

My father and my girl friend drove me to the airport. All the way there my chick kept trying to say something but she could only start to choke out a word or two. I kept saying, "Don't worry baby, it's just a year and I'll be back, no sweat," knowing every minute that I was only kidding myself. I was going to a place where little people you never see shoot and kill you. My old man kept saying, "Just use your head and don't volunteer for anything. I know – I made it through three years of World War II. I taught you many things in the woods about hunting all your years as a kid. I know you will make it back okay, you always was a good hunter." He looked at me with a half smile. "Yeah, but I never had anything hunt me back before," I said with a sick smile.

Just ahead was the airport sign. Dad parked the car and I got my duffel bag and we went in. There were people moving everywhere. I checked on my flight. They said we would be loading in fifteen minutes. All three of us sat and said nothing. My girl and I kept smiling at each other, just nervous I guess. Soon the P.A. System came on and a voice said, "Flight #209 to Syracuse, and on to Washington State, loading at Gate Number Four." We stood up. My old man's hand was out. He said, with tears in his eyes, "Jim, you're my first son. You mean the world to me. I'll never forget how you look at this minute, so strong and brave. Thank God you don't really know what you are in for yet. But I'm sure you'll make it back no problem. Take it easy son and keep in touch. I'll miss you a lot!" That was one of the few times my old man ever got mushy like that and the only time I ever saw him with tears in his eyes. I believe he was looking at himself and feeling inside what he felt the day he went off to war many years ago.

My chick Deb jumped up and put a choke hold on my neck. She kissed me all over my face then she cupped her mouth trying not to cry and then she threw me a kiss goodbye. I said, "I love you baby."

Then I turned and walked away. I felt so alone and empty inside I thought I would die! As I turned to go I heard my father say, "You give them Commies hell, Jim." I waved and thought, I just hope those Commies weren't thinking the same thing about me.

CHAPTER 4

Fort Louis, Washington

I was soon aboard Flight #209 headed for Syracuse, New York, just a short stop for more passengers. I had just left Broome County Airport. This is a small airport in Upstate New York near Binghamton. I was born and raised in that area, but felt soon I would be growing up in a very strange and different place called South Vietnam.

During the flight from Binghamton to Syracuse, I thought of many things. My childhood, my high school, which I was only out of for about six months. And my Army training – Basic, A.I.T., Jump school, etc. There I was, just an eighteen year old kid out to get blown up. I must be nuts, I thought.

After the stop in Syracuse and after many hours of flight I got bored thinking of all that stuff and I tried to relax. I guess about four or five hours went by and I was awakened by a voice on the P.A. System. "Ladies and Gentlemen, we are about to land at Seattle Airport. Please extinguish all smoking material and fasten your seat belts, thank you." I looked out the window and I saw it was dark outside. All I could see were millions of lights down below.

In a few minutes we were on the ground. I kept thinking of my two friends that should be there waiting for me, like we all agreed on back at our last duty station at Fort Bragg. I felt very excited with anticipation of meeting those two screw ups. If they were there, we would all have to face the music of being two days A.W.O.L. together, instead of just me alone.

When I got into the terminal I looked around trying to get my bearings. That was the fastest moving place I'd ever seen. We had said we would meet in the airport bar. I walked around for awhile then thought I would ask someone before I got lost. A black baggage handler was coming my way so I stopped him and asked where the main bar was. He told me and I went on. After a few minutes I finally found it. It was packed at the bar, about three deep. Just then I could see Becham. There's that bald headed nut, I thought. I walked over and slapped the side of his head.

I said, "Hey sucker! Want to get knocked out wise guy?"

The bar quieted down as Becham turned around.

Jokingly he said, "Why you sawed off piece a rat dodo! I thought you turned yellow and wasn't going to show up!"

"What me? Turn yellow? No way! Where's Brad?" Brad Feelen was my other friend that was going to meet up with us.

"Right here, you dummy!" A voice sprang up from behind me. I knew it was him right away. "I just had to go take a leak," Brad said.

Then we all sat down to four or five beers and got up enough guts to go report into Fort Louis. After a while we picked up our bags and headed for the main entrance. Once outside a cab driver yelled out, "Hey soldier boys! Need a ride to Fort Louis?" We said we did and he loaded our bags into the trunk. We all got in the cab and we talked about how they would probably hang us for being A.W.O.L. and things about our girls back home and what we did on leave.

Soon we were entering the fort. We were all going to the Out of Country Processing Station. The building was about half way across the fort. Finally we got there and stood in front of the building with our bags in hand. I asked, "Well, should we go face the music?"

They both replied, "Let's go."

It was night time so we went up to the E-4 at the desk inside and asked what we should do. The guy was as ambitious as a blind man at a turkey shoot. He put us through a bunch of bologna about being late but he finally assigned us quarters and bunks. The building was filled with guys going to Nam. Even though it was after 10 o'clock lights out, everyone was up and buzzing with excitement. We all sat up and talked about anything and everything.

The next day we were up at 0500 in the morning. We were awakened early to get chow and formation out of the way, so we could start our out of country processing. The whole day and most of the night we went from building to building. We got physicals, clothing checks, needed shots, all that. Then we were told we would be there four to six days waiting for our final orders, to be shipped to whatever place in Vietnam. They gave us complete post privileges. That meant we could go anywhere on post. To movies, E.M.'s or Enlisted Man's clubs, etc. We were told to just relax and wait. All three of us took full advantage of our post privileges and kept a good buzz on all the time. Becham had some good Mexican pot that he brought with him from his home in Texas. So between that and E.M. club beer and whiskey we weren't even thinking about Nam for a few days. We all got a chance to call home and tell everyone about what had happened so far. Except for me, I just couldn't.

The day before we got our orders we all acted like we just came down with a bad case of hysteria. We were all very nervous about the big day. All three of us decided to go for a walk after chow. It was about 2000 hours that night. As we walked we heard a lot of shouting and happy cheering going on a few barracks ahead. This area was the staging area for the guys coming back from Nam. So we got the brilliant idea of going over and asking some of the guys about Nam and what to expect. I wish we had went the other way instead.

The closer we got to the guys sitting on the steps outside the barracks the more hesitant I became. These guys looked grubby with very long hair for being in the Army and a general screw-the-world attitude. Just then one of them saw we were coming over to them and he said, "Hey looky here! A bunch a cherries!"

I said, "Oh no! These guys are going to bust us but good!"

One of them said, "Yeah, you guys, come here. So tell us what's been happenin' back here in the world?"

We all looked at each other and I said, "I don't know, the same old thing I guess?"

When the vets heard that and stopped laughing one said, "Dudes, when you come back from where you're goin' you'll love the same old thing!"

Then they all started telling us about the excitement of a fire fight and all the death and destruction, 'till all three of us were so nervous, we didn't know whether to faint or go blind!

We talked for a while then one of the vets said, "Hey cherries…I got somethin' for yah." He tossed a bottle of Seagrams 7 at me. I grabbed it out of the air almost dropping it.

He said, "Now then…take that and get drunk! This will be the last drunk that you'll really enjoy. After tonight always stay straight and always keep your head clear!"

We said, "Goodbye."

They yelled, "Lots of luck!"

Walking back to the barracks Bec said, "Screw it all. Let's get drunk!" So we did. All three of us drank the whole quart of Seagram's and got smashed. I ended up throwing up everywhere in the barracks, which I had to clean up the next day before going onto my flight. Becham ended up putting his fist through a glass window and Feelen got homesick and cried all night. I didn't really know for sure what that Vietnam Vet meant by what he said, but I wish he would have kept the Seagram's for himself! God, I was so sick and I had to catch a flight that morning for Vietnam which made me feel sicker with just the thought.

By the time noon came we all felt better and made noon formation. We all had our bags and things waiting for the bus to take us to the airplane. Soon the bus came and we were packed on board. Next stop was the airfield. We got off the buses we were loaded onboard a very large four engine jet. After we were settled in I looked out and thought, is this the last time I will ever see the United States? Will I land here when I get back, if I get back? How many other men thought the same thing, but never came back?

About 100 yards away out the window I could see men unloading large silver boxes from another jet like this one. I heard a voice say, "Best hope you're not on that plane coming back!"

The guy in the seat in front of me was an E-5. I could see the combat infantry badge on his coat that told me he had been in combat before. He was going back for another tour in Nam, I thought.

So I said, "Yeah why not?"

"Only dead men fly that airline. They're all caskets, them silver boxes," he replied.

I looked with my eyes wide open. There must have been at least two hundred by the looks.

He said, "They come and go all day long…planes like that. Get used to dead things dude! You are gonna see lots of death." He asked if I knew where I was going once I got to Nam.

I said, "My orders are for Company E. Recondo 173rd Airborne."

He just shook his head and said, "Man! You got to be nuts. If you're smart, don't ask what their life expectancy is – you won't like it."

I asked him what he would be doing there. He said he was an M-60 gunner on a chopper. He also said that it was a good job but his butt was in mortal danger at all times. Bec, Feelen and I all laughed. The E-5 said, "Don't laugh! Just wait 'till your first drop into a hot landing zone, then you'll see it's not so funny!"

Little did we know then but we would all find out he wasn't wrong at all. As a matter of fact, Feelen ended up as an M-60 gunner on a chopper and learned first hand what this guy meant. He told us it was a long plane ride to Nam, about twenty seven hours. During the flight there were many guys that we all talked with throughout the airplane. We talked about things like where we were from and where we were going. It kind of made the time pass by quicker. All the stewardesses were very pretty and friendly. They brought us coffee and sandwiches, most anything you could want. Maybe they felt sorry for us, who knows? From time to time the pilot would come over the P.A. and tell us to look at certain ships, islands, etc. over the ocean. It was the first time I ever saw an ocean, especially from up that high. The pilot told us we were up 28,000 feet! All we could see in any direction was blue sky and blue ocean. Soon my ears started to pop open and closed. I thought we might be changing altitude and I was right. The pilot said, "Buckle up, we're going to land in Hawaii for fuel and a short rest."

CHAPTER 5

Short Stops

The smell of warm and humid air was even more refreshing than the stretch. The air was filled with all kinds of flowery and spicy smells. The airport looked like many others I'd seen but there was still something special about that one. The one main difference was that it was hot and humid outside, where back home it was cold with snow butt deep. Being in Hawaii for the first time, I acted like a tourist, snapping pictures of everyone that even looked Hawaiian and buying postcards which I later threw away. My friends and I ate some hamburgers and fries then waited to hear the call of our flight. But that didn't come for six hours. They said they had some problems with the air brakes. So for six hours we watched people come and go from all parts of the U.S. and overseas.

After six hours of hanging around we were all ready to take off for anywhere. Finally the call came for us to go back to the buses for a ride back out to the plane. Once back on board the pilot said he was sorry for the delay but it couldn't be helped. So we all relaxed for the long flight ahead. More hours went by and the night sky turned to day. Outside the sight was breathtaking as the sun came up with all its colors reflecting against the miles of open ocean. Up that high it was beautiful. Breakfast was served and it amazed me to see how all the men could be fed by such a small group of women.

More time passed. Then lunch was over and we were told by the pilot we would be landing in the Philippines. That stop would be about one hour for fuel. All around me I heard mumbles referring to our over-long stop in Hawaii. But by that time we were all happy about the thought of any kind of rest stop.

The first thing I saw at the air field in the Philippines was a plush tropical foliage everywhere outside the gates of the airport. The air felt damp and very hot. We went into the airport terminal for lunch. It took about an hour, just enough time to stretch and walk around a bit. Next thing we knew we were loaded back onto the plane and we were off again. By that time I had about had it with plane rides. I couldn't wait to get to Nam already! A few more hours of boredom and we were going down for our second to last stop, Guam. Some of the guys that had been on that trip before said Guam was almost like Vietnam. Same atmosphere, but not quite as primitive.

We got off the plane and went into the terminal. Inside there were people moving everywhere. There were many food and souvenir shops, barber shops, and vendors of all kinds. Even a Hong-Kong tailor shop to buy a three piece suit…tailored while you wait. Most of the people were Oriental looking, but not all. Some were G.I.'s coming and going. To get away from the hustle and bustle the three of us took a walk outside for awhile.

All over the airfield there were jets taking off in every direction. But the planes that fascinated me were the huge black six engine jets that kept taking off, one after the other. I yelled to a worker inside the airfield fence. "Hey guy! What are those big, black jets for?" They did not look at all like passenger planes. The man replied, "They are B-52 Bombers, leaving to dump their loads on Charley Cong." In just the fifteen or twenty minutes we stood there watching, I lost count of planes taking off. Man! I thought, just imagine the amount of bombs they must be dropping on those people! I could hardly believe it.

I bought a couple of things and we wandered around looking at everyone until our flight was called. Back on board for the last leg of the journey to Vietnam, we were all tense with excitement and anticipation of what was yet to come. All the way from Guam we heard more war stories from the guys on their second tour to Nam. After a while the excitement of war tales gave way to a sick, lost and empty feeling. I think we all just wanted to get there and get it over with. After what seemed like a century, the pilot's P.A. system came on for the last time. The pilot said, "Gentlemen, if you look out the window you will see the final airfield on this trip. This is Cam Rhon Bay, Republic of South Vietnam. We hope you'll have a nice stay in Vietnam and good luck!" Out the window we could see the airstrip and the South China Sea below us.

CHAPTER 6

Welcome to Vietnam

Wow! This is it, I thought. I'm finally here! My gut was all tensed up with thoughts of what was to come. The plane landed and the engines stopped. They said to start unloading and not to forget any personal baggage. The first thing I saw were the U.S. Air Force people outside the airplane. There were no other people except military personnel everywhere. I thought, what the heck…no V.C.?

But soon after we entered the main terminal they were everywhere and we didn't even know it. We saw people in uniform, some in civilian dress. In the Nam you never knew who was who. Friend and enemy all looked the same.

Most women had big round sand dollar-shaped hats, black silky looking pants, and white button up shirts, all wearing sandals or flip-flops. Most of the young girls were dressed in very short mini-skirts so short your…well, anyway. Most middle-aged men were dressed in regular pants with colorful shirts. The younger men wore army pants, tiger fatigues or regular clothes.

In the front of the terminal we were loaded into still more buses to be shipped to the In Country Processing Stations. The station was only about twenty minutes away from the airport. All the way my friends and I talked and made cracks about how the people looked and acted. There were people walking everywhere on the road. A lot of them walked hand in hand. Two and three abreast they walked in the road, as though there was no one on the road but them. There were army vehicles coming and going very fast on those narrow dirt roads. With all the congestion in the streets it was a miracle those people weren't run over more often. Like I said, more often. I've seen drivers hit walking pedestrians more than once, sometimes deliberately.

There were S.V.N. civilians selling everything you could think of…from dope to women. They had tables and little hand carried shops set up all over the street. The only way to walk down the road without being hassled and pitched to death was to keep walking and push them away. Even as our bus drove down the road they clung to the sides of it, trying to sell us anything. I even saw a young boy about fifteen fall off the side of another bus, and the tire crushed his foot flat.

The Vietnamese people traveled these roads mainly by foot. But some either had small 90 or 100 cc motorcycles or drove what they called Lambrettas. These were French-made motorized carts, sort of like what a meter maid would drive. They looked like a cross between a three-wheel motorcycle and V.W. bus.

After our short ride, we finally reached the U.S. Army In Country Processing Depot. We were told earlier that this was going to be our temporary home until we got transported to our Republic of Vietnam Refresher training. This was sort of like a weeklong boot camp all new troops had to go through to be refreshed on the army's operations in Vietnam.

We all got off the buses and filed into formation. Each section was marked with the name of the unit to which we were eventually going to be assigned. Becham, Feelen, and I fell into the formation marked 173rd Airborne. We knew this from the orders given to us at Fort Louis.

15

Along the formation areas were long buildings with roofs but no sides. Inside these buildings were long tables, about chest high, with partitions spaced about three feet apart. We were ordered to file in and stop at a booth or partition.

After everyone was placed inside his own booth we were given ten or fifteen papers to fill out. These papers were a part of our permanent records while in Vietnam. These papers told the whole story; who you were and where you were going.

After five or six hours of filling out paperwork and processing, we were all assigned to a barracks, bunk, and footlocker. The barracks where we were placed were like the rest of the buildings; no sides, just a roof. The sides were only mosquito netting. Most buildings were two levels high. They housed about two hundred G.I.s each. It was very tight and unorganized, but we all got along and made the best of it.

After doing all of the settling-in chores, we headed out for chow. It was about 1600 hours, or four o'clock in the afternoon, and we noticed that all the locals were being herded into a big line and led off the compound and off the post. I found out later that they weren't allowed to stay on post after 1600 and not allowed back until 0600 in the morning. I was told they didn't want any possible Viet Cong or enemy around camp at night.

After chow we went over to the E.M. club. This was a small wooden building with a pool table and a banana crate bar. There were all kinds of really weird posters and paintings that some G.I.s had put up on the walls. I guess they tried to make it look as close to a bar as they could. It looked like a place you wouldn't want to go into unless you were already drunk or nuts. There was deafening music coming from every corner of the place with a few guys bobbing and dancing to it. It was so smoky inside you couldn't see the guy next to you. We all sat down with a beer and we tried for awhile to talk. But forget it! The noise and smoke finally got to us and we left.

We hadn't seen many combat troops yet except for the ones on the road from the airport that morning that were marching up and down the road. But way off in the far distance you could see flashes of light and the sound of cannon fire. We walked along for awhile very slowly, kicking stones and things, just chatting about how we really felt about being there and wondering if we would all make it home in one piece. Feelen asked, "I wonder what my girl is doing right now."

"Probably going off to work yesterday," I replied.

He asked, "What do you mean?"

"Well, from what I hear there is a twenty-four hour difference between here and home."

Becham said, "Yeah man, you're right. We've already lived the day people at home are waking up to."

"Man! That's weird," Feelen said. "We could be dead a whole day here before people at home wake up to the day that it happened."

We walked on to our barracks. There were lights lit up all over the barracks. Guys were smoking joints everywhere. It seemed so funny to smoke a joint right out in the open with no fear of being busted. You just had to be cool around lifers or M.P.s.

In Nam there were two groups of people. Pot heads and juicers, with very few in between. Almost no one stayed straight, everyone was either stoned on all kinds of dope or alcohol. Alcohol was more expensive to buy than dope. But alcohol could only be bought at a P.X. at 4 or 5 bottles a month. Even though whiskey was harder to get than pot, you could get a quart of top-shelf American whiskey for four or five dollars M.P.C.

M.P.C. was the money the U.S. Army printed up. It looked like stage money, only smaller. It was also known as "Monopoly" money. They would change it every so often to make it harder to counterfeit. During In Country processing that morning we all had to exchange our U.S. currency for M.P.C. This meant Military Payment Certificate. The U.S. Army would pay us $5.00 M.P.C. for $5.00 U.S. currency. Later we found out downtown in the black market you could get a twenty-to-one ratio for green backs. If they caught you though, they would nearly hang you. Lots of guys got one big nest egg built up doing this.

The black market was very big business in Nam. With cash in hand you could have or do anything. And I mean anything…dope, women, investments on goods, etc. The Vietnamese people would buy cigarettes, tape players, radios…you name it. All you had to do was buy these things at the P.X. for nearly nothing, then turn around and sell for five or six times what you paid for it. Trading for dope of all kinds was a good investment because most every G.I. did dope like there was no tomorrow. Dope, whiskey, or Salem cigs in particular would go fast.

Most everyone was all stoned out by the time we got to our barracks. Soon everyone finally started to settle down to sleep. All I could think of the first night as I lay there was home.

The next morning came fast. We were all awakened at 0500 in the morning. We all ate breakfast and had to report after chow to the orderly room to find out whose orders came in to leave that day. Three days of this went by before one of our names was called.

It was Feelen that was the first to go. He said, "Oh nuts! You guys aren't coming with me. We're all broke up already man!"

"Don't worry," I replied. "You will just get to the 173rd ahead of me and Bec, that's all. We'll catch up with you there."

"Yeah I guess. I still wish you guys were coming with me."

The next morning we said goodbye to Feelen. He said, "I am gonna miss you two dopes, but don't think you've lost me yet. I'll find you wherever you go!"

We shook hands and said goodbye as he ran to his chopper.

"Watch your butt!" I yelled as he ran out of sight.

"I wonder if we'll ever see that dude again?" Becham asked.

"No sweat!" I replied, with hope anyway.

That night it seemed like one of our eyes was missing now that Feelen was gone. Bec and I missed him already. All three of us had come a long way together. We all met in Basic Training back at Fort Dix, New Jersey. It was strange that these two guys had been assigned to that post so far from their homes. Feelen was from a small town in California and Becham was from Texas. They should have done their basic out West, not way out East. But anyway, we stayed together from Basic Training through A.I.T., Airborne school, N.C.O. school, and all the way to

Nam. We constantly lived, worked and played together for the past six or eight months. Each one of us knew the other inside out. In the Army, people quickly become very close friends because the only family you had left, right there and then, was whoever you could call "friend." We were more like brothers than just friends, being in the same boat as we were. It seems a big part of you dies when you lose a friend and brother; either by transfer or worse yet, death.

The next two days that followed were days of hot, sweaty work details - picking up the grounds and doing odd jobs. Mostly, they were filled with boredom.

Finally the day came. Bec and I got our orders. Both of us got the same orders for our R.V.N. Refresher course. Early one morning we were on our way, just like Feelen.

CHAPTER 7

Fall in Troop!

With bags in hand Bec and I got into our chopper and took off for R.V.N. training. This was our first time flying with crazy people. What a rush when that chopper took off! It was only seconds and we were way up. It was faster than anything I've been up in before. There were about six or seven of us in the chopper all hanging on for dear life.

The pilots and crews on the choppers were crazy. The pilots flew those ships like they were little sports cars or something. These guys were only nineteen or twenty years old. Believe me, these guys were expert pilots but totally nuts! Our crew chief asked, "How do you cherries like this ride?" Wide-eyed and white-knuckled we all just nodded yes. So the crew chief said, "Good, let's have some fun." The pilot looked back at him and smiled. They could hear every word the other said by the built-in microphones in their helmets.

The next thing we knew we were on the most breathtaking roller-coaster ride we could imagine! Up, down, sideways and all around we went. I don't know about anyone else, but I nearly wet my pants. Man, what a ride. How we ever got to where we were going is beyond me.

After the pilot came back to his right mind and leveled out the chopper, the ride was very enjoyable. The scenery below us was beautiful. The jungle down below looked like a big ball of green hair, so thick you couldn't see down into it. The land was green, brown and had various shades of brownish-red, with rice patties etched in every direction as far as I could see. The land was covered with tropical plants that were a beautiful sight from up that high. There were tiny human figures running about down below in the rice fields. The main road, and there was only one, was called Highway #1. It looked like an endless centipede winding its way along.

In a short time we were landing on a small flat-topped hill overlooking a large Army post. There were men and jeeps running everywhere around the whole compound. That was our first sight of barbed wire. It was about six or eight feet high and ten to fifteen feet wide. From up in the air I could see that it enclosed the whole post. Every forty to fifty yards all around the post were lookout towers about twenty feet high with an M-60 or .50 caliber machine gun sticking out toward the jungle. The base was an armed sanctuary, completely surrounded by jungle. There were bunkers with sandbags piled up in front, on top, and in between each lookout tower. Most of the guys on these towers and bunkers seemed to be sitting around relaxing. This was not so at night. If there is one place you don't relax or sleep at night, it was in the Nam.

Soon the chopper was down and stopped. I told the pilot to forget the tip and I jumped out. There were jeeps for us to jump in and take us down to the main post. Down on the main post the dust blew around at all times. Everything was very dry. The only time things weren't dry was during the Monsoon season, which turned the whole country into a mushy moving mudslide. All I could smell was dust and smoke from the people burning human dung.

There were no bathrooms like we have at home at the compound, just old-fashioned outhouses. Under these out houses were 55 gallon oil drums that were cut in half that the waste would fall into. When the drums were full they would have some dude on "s*#*! detail" pull these drums out and pour fuel oil in them and burn the waste. Man, talk about stink! Anywhere I went on post, burning waste was about all I smelled.

I remember one morning I was sitting down inside of an outhouse doing my morning thing. Suddenly from up out of one of the potty seats or holes the huge head of a eight foot long lizard came up, with its very long tongue lashing in and out. It almost gave me and one other dude sitting two seats down from me a heart attack! It startled the guy next to me so bad he dove out the screen door. From a seated position, pants still down and all, he went bursting through the door smashing the door to splinters as he dove through it. The lizard looked just like a Kamono dragon I saw on T.V. a couple times. They were huge! And very dangerous looking. The lizards would hang out under there to catch flies and other bugs to eat. They had a head that looked like a monster snake. That lizard was something else.

Our first day at the training center was much like all of the other military posts before. We were herded into formation after formation, building after building, finally to our barracks. There Bec and I grabbed our bunks and footlockers right next to each other and we sat down to rest until chow time.

After chow at noon we all had to attend an orientation class. This was to tell us about our week in the refresher course. They told us about the practice maneuvers and basic survival techniques that would help keep us alive while we were there. They said from then on we would be pulling bunker guard, Kitchen Police duty, tower and fire watch. The rest of the day would be set aside for us to get orientated with the post or to see where everything was. We were told to fallout for formation at 1800 that afternoon for our first night on guard duty.

At 1800 we fell into formation. The 1st sergeant that was assigned to us told us we would be put on guard duty all night long; either in a tower or bunker with a number of his staff. So each of us would be assigned with someone that knew what the heck was going on. He said if anyone fell asleep, he would shoot that man in the head if Charley didn't do it first. He said it convincingly enough that we all believed him. No one had any reason to doubt him, being in a war zone and all. We were then headed for the real thing, no more screwing around!

There were three men assigned to each post along with an N.C.O. The guy Bec and I got was an E-5. His name was Sergeant Horton. He was only twenty years old and had been in the country for eleven months. He was getting short and really didn't give a hoot about anything except for getting high. (Short means your time left in country was coming to an end.)

As the evening grew dark I felt a bit restless. Becham and I were assigned to a lookout tower. For weapons, we were each issued one M-16, six clips of ammunition, three rounds of M-79 grenade launcher ammo and two hand grenades. Sergeant Horton carried the M-79 grenade launcher. In the tower there was an M-60 machine gun mounted with all the ammo you could shoot already stored in boxes in the top of the tower. The field of fire out in front was clear out to about 400 yards. Any Viet Cong caught out there would be dead; there was no place to hide.

We all had to share the time on guard equally. That was two hours on and four hours off. You could doze off on your off hours if you wanted. I picked the third shortest straw, which meant I was on the third watch, sometime in the middle of the night. Sergeant Horton stayed up smoking pot and talking to anyone that was awake and listening, which all of us did 'till about midnight or so. Then I said, "I don't know about you guys but I am crashing big time. If something happens wake me up." Bec was on watch then so I laid back to rest for awhile 'till I had to get up.

About an hour went by and I heard Sergeant Horton talking. He was down below talking to someone. I think it was one of the guards from the next bunker. They were talking so quietly that I really couldn't hear what was going on. So I got up and asked Bec what was up. He said Horton told him to be on the lookout for sappers. They were Viet Cong that would sneak through the wire by themselves with a big bag of explosives and blow up anything they could.

Just then Horton came back up and said, "The next bunker saw some movement out front about a half an hour ago, so be on your toes." We sat down except for Becham. He stood up and kept a good eye out. Sergeant Horton said, "Screw this. Man, I'm so sick of this…right up to my ears! I've been here eleven months and I'm tired of it all. Man, I want out of this hole!"

With that he lit a big, I mean a big, joint. He called it a Bon Song Bomber. This was a joint of Cambodian red pot laced with tar opium. He started passing it around until it was gone. I've smoked pot before but that pot was strong! I was so stoned out I couldn't even talk. I only had three or four good hits and it was the worst buzz I ever had. All I could do was sit there and look stupid. Becham's shift was about over and it was my turn. Stand guard! I thought, Man, I can't even stand up!

I slowly got up and acted like I was all right but I near floated right off the tower. Sergeant Horton said, "Hey Jim, you know what to do?"

I said, "Oh yeah, if I see anything, anything at all, I'll call you!"

Horton replied, "The watch is all yours." They lay down and went to sleep. Well, let me tell you, being as stoned as I was I near saw the whole Viet Cong Army coming at me all at once. I kept telling myself not to flip out, just be cool and watch… just like deer hunting. Be quiet and just watch.

About an hour into my shift I saw a V.C. – or what at that time I thought was a V.C., slinking all over the ground. Am I seeing gremlins or what? I asked myself. There! I saw him again. I grabbed the bolt of the M-60 and I cocked it. I did this very quietly so as not to make any noise. I saw him crawling slowly across the ground. When I was sure it was a V.C. I started shaking so badly I could hardly stand up. I started to whisper out Horton's name but he didn't move. I kept watching that V.C. to make sure he didn't slip out of my sight.

"Horton," I whispered, "Wake the heck up!"

I stretched my leg out to try to kick him in the butt but I couldn't reach him. Looking back to see if that V.C. was still there, I heard Horton ask, "What's wrong?"

I said, "Outside of the wire I've got some movement!"

He just lay there for a moment then said, "If there's someone outside that wire, shoot um'!"

I looked at him then I looked back at the V.C. I said, "He is still there, just lying still on the ground about three or four feet under the wire."

Horton said, "That's good enough for me."

I drew down on that little sucker and let go. That M-60 rang out so sharp it must have woke up the dead. I lay on that trigger long and hard. All I could see down range was dust and fire flying everywhere. The barrel of the M-60 was red hot and smoking. Horton jumped up like a cat shot in the tail and shouted, "Stop firing you dumb @#$%!!" He looked out down range long and hard but we couldn't see anything but dust and smoke.

Horton yelled, "Hoooly molly! If Charley was out there he's just a pile of hamburger now. The old man's gonna want to know what all the shooting was about. Just say I had to go take a dump and wasn't here at the time to confirm your sighting. Or...or they'll hang me for not checking it out myself. Man! I thought you were kiddin' me."

I said, "I wouldn't kid around about somethin' like that!"

Horton said, "It figures. I would have to run into someone that tells the truth. Around here you can't believe anybody!"

Just then the radio came on. It was the 1st Sergeant. The voice yelled, "Is everything okay out there?"

Horton grabbed the mic. and said, "Everything's okay here, just an over anxious cherry."

"Is there anything out front?" asked the 1st Sergeant.

"Not that I can see." Horton answered.

The top Sarge said, "In the morning I want to meet the cowboy that's seeing things!"

Horton replied, "10-4...out!"

"Man, I hope you're ready for that. Just don't forget what I told you, I wasn't here, I was taking a dump!" Nervous as a cat in a dog pound I sat down and tried to stop shaking. The next man on watch was Horton so he told me to take it easy and relax. But I felt like the biggest bonehead in the army. I felt the old man would probably hang me for that one!

Horton went downstairs for a while then he came back up. He said they didn't see anything down on the ground but told me not to sweat it. He said it could have very well been a V.C. out there because they love to hit the training center just to scare the tar out of new troops.He said, "Try to get some sleep, see ya in the morning."

With all that was going down I couldn't sleep for nothing! So I got up and talked to a guy that came up with Horton. He was a tall skinny redhead from St. Louis. Seemed to be a very calm pleasant sort of guy. We talked for a while about what happened. He said, "Screw it! It don't mean nothin'! It don't mean nothin' at all."

The night was very long, but it finally started to get light. About a half hour after sun up I saw a guy from the next bunker looking around out front. He walked over to the wire where I thought I saw the V.C. the night before. He checked around for a couple of minutes then stopped. He was leaning out over the barbed wire looking down at the ground hard. Just then he turned and ran past his bunker all the way back up to the C.O.'s office.

About five minutes later he came back with our 1st Sergeant. I turned around and got Horton up. I said, "Look at this."

He looked up and asked, "What's up?" I told him about the guy checking out the wire and everything, so he went down to see what was up.

Soon they were all down by the wire talking about something. A few minutes later Horton turned around and he gave me the A-okay sign and he was smiling. I thought, what the heck was this all about?

Just then the guy that was looking over the wire first that morning ran back up to the Orderly Room office. The First Sergeant turned to Horton and said, "Get the men down and in formation."

Horton ran over to the tower and said, "Get everyone down here and line up."

Once on the ground and in formation the First Sergeant called us to attention. He looked at Horton and said, "Get me that cowboy!" I darn near choked. Here we go I thought. He is going to bust my rocks bad! Right in front of everyone!

Before Horton got to me, I did a right face and marched right up to my First Sergeant. The sergeant said, "Nice work soldier."

He told me to do an about face, and face the formation. He started to walk around slowly rubbing his chin then stopped. He said, "Last night I was ready to chew this man out for shaking me out of my bunk with that M-60. But this morning I see I was wrong." Out of the corner of my eye I could see two M.P.s and a guy all dressed up in a steel helmet and flack jacket headed our way fast.

The 1st Sgt. went on, "Last night a sapper tried to get through this wire. This man standing right here was the one that stopped him." He turned to me and said, "Soldier, I want to be the first one to commend you on the action you took against an enemy force. For a new man you handled this possibly deadly situation expertly. Charley got away, but he dropped the bomb he carried." He told me that I must have learned my army training well. He then stood at attention and saluted me. I was numb with pride. I thought I was dreaming!

The sergeant looked over at an Sp-4 standing nearby and called him over. Later I found out he was the company clerk. He then unbuttoned the Sp-4's (Specialist 4) rank pins from his shirt collar and put them on me. I would have had my orders for Sp-4 anyway in a month or so, because whatever your rank is, as soon as you land in Vietnam you automatically make the next rank higher, which was Sp-4 for me. I was only a PFC right then. I was so happy and proud I could have jumped for joy right there. From what I thought was going to be a big chewing out, I got commended instead. The sergeant said, "It's not official yet but it's just as good. From now on you will be grade E-4. Congratulations soldier! You've done an outstanding job." He then turned to Sergeant Horton, smiling from ear to ear and said, "Dismiss your men for chow."

After formation Horton, Bec, and I walked down to the wire where the two M.P.s and the bomb squad man was. They had just finished picking up a five-pound satchel charge the enemy dropped the night before. I thought, last night I was stoned, but I knew what I saw was real! I turned around with Horton and Bec and we walked toward the chow hall. Horton patted me on the back and said, "Man am I glad you had your stuff together, 'cause I sure didn't. Good job Jim! Good job!"

The rest of the week of training went as well as it could have. Running, firing weapons at the range, etc. But I really couldn't wait to move on to my permanent unit. Most of the other guys were put on loads of details, but for me things were a lot easier. My E-4 rank helped keep me away from such things as waste burning, K.P. and some other duties. Usually I was in charge of keeping the barracks cleaned up, which was pretty easy.

Finally all the orders came in. Bec and I would still be together. We were assigned to the 173rd Airborne Special Operations Group at Landing Zone Uplift. Most places out in the front lines were called L.Z. or Fire Bases because that's about all they were, Landing Zones or fire support bases - very small compounds with just enough supplies to keep the war going. From these places troops could be re-supplied with men and equipment.

The last night at formation our drill sergeant said we were all invited…except for men on detail, to report at 1900 to the E.M. club for our last night's party. None of us had seen a party for quite some time. Luckily Bec and I were off duty for the night so we headed for the barracks to clean up. After we were all cleaned up and ready for fun Horton came in and asked, "You mind if I go with you guys?"

Bec replied, "Heck no man! Let's go."

The party was already going strong when we got there. There were guys playing pool, cards, arm-wrestling, etc. Everyone was having a good time. Every once in a while you would see a couple of guys heading outside for a joint break. Bec and I figured we would join them. I walked over to Horton, who was playing pool and asked him if he wanted to go with us. He said he just smoked some and was good for now. So we just told him we would see him in a little while. I looked up at the clock on the wall; it was a little after twelve. It was late but it was our last night's party and all so I said to heck with it!

Bec and I walked about sixty yards away from the E.M. club where a couple of guys we knew were smoking a joint. Bec asked, "Hey men, what's up?"

"Oh, not much, just catchin' a buzz. Want some?" one asked.

We sat down with them and talked 'till we finished the joint. Then Bec said, "Let's go back for one more beer, then I'm gonna' crash."

Suddenly there was a very noisy hissing sound that seemed to rush right past us. It was sort of like the noise of a sky rocket or something. For an instant I saw a flash of light headed for the club. Then…the biggest blast I ever heard.

The E.M. club exploded like an enormous bomb. All of us hit the ground. I could see most of the roof of the building about fifty feet in the air. Boards and bodies flew everywhere. I couldn't believe my eyes. I knew right then a rocket had hit that place. Charley somehow knew we were having a party that night and it would be packed with men.

After the blast all that could be heard was men screaming and crying. The club was a big ball of fire. Bec screamed out, "Horton!" Bec and I got up and ran over to what was left of the place and we tried to help. There were body parts all over the place. Bec asked, "What can we do?" By that time firemen were rushing to the scene and starting to hose everything down.

The fire was quickly put out but bodies were everywhere. At the time I didn't think of anything, I just helped carry men still alive to ambulances. I had never seen anyone dead before, especially like that. But it wasn't the dead guys that really got to me then. It was the ones who were still alive. They yelled, cried and screamed so badly that it made me sick! Seeing guys you lived and worked with twisted and burned still screaming and crying was something I'll never forget. It took all night to get everyone out of the rubble, but we kept at it. The dead guys were pieced back together the next morning.

As for Horton, we never did find all of him. Our Commanding Officer delayed our departure until noon that day so we could help with the clean up of the E.M. club. After things got under control all of us left….thank God. All I had were bad memories left of that awful place. But I was just thankful that I still had a memory.

CHAPTER 8

Landing Zone Uplift

The chopper ride from R.V.N. Training school to L.Z. Uplift was about thirty minutes. The pilot seemed to be able to fly the chopper on an even course so we all sat back and relaxed, enjoying the scenery below. We flew over many small grass hut villages and jungle.

After awhile we could see in the distance puffs of white-gray smoke coming out of the jungle. The guy next to me asked the gunner what it was. He said that it was eight-inch gunfire. It was some line company getting some cannon support. I thought to myself, Man! There it was, the real thing right out there. The battle ground. My belly full of butterflies, I looked at Bec and knew he was thinking the same thing. We both smiled and shook our heads.

Just then the pilot turned to us and pointed out the window about two o'clock. It was a camp much like the one we just left, with all the black human waste smoke and barbed wire. There were a few watchtowers and piled sandbags in front of many bunkers. As we got closer we could see some half-tent, half-wood buildings. "Here we are boys," the crew chief said, "Your new home."

Down below we could see six or eight men standing around on the fairly large landing zone. Jeeps were parked just outside the fence of the landing field. So this is L.Z. Uplift, I thought. Mostly what I expected, but not what I had hoped for. For the next year this was what I would have to call home.

But as time went on, I would find out this was a lot better place than being in Charley's back yard…the jungle. Home is where you hang your hat, I guess.

We finally touched ground and left the chopper. We were all instructed to climb into one of the waiting jeeps to take us to our company. We rode down the dusty path to the main compound. When we got to the post we were told to get into formation inside the large bunker twenty or thirty feet away from where we stood. When we got inside and lined up, an E-6 sergeant came up in front of us and called us to be at ease. "Welcome to L.Z. Uplift. I will read your names off one at a time. When I do, I'll tell you what company you will be assigned to. Stay awake, I'll not tell you again."

The first name he read was mine. I answered and moved to where he told me to stand. He then read off four more names. Once we were in line he said, "Your company will be Company E. Recondo. When you go back outside you should look up on the hill, across the road and outside the gate. The mountain you see is called Recon Hill. You are to move up the hill and report to E. Co. Recon orderly room. All of the other men whose names were not called will be staying down on the main post to be replacements for the badly depleted line companies."

I said to myself, there goes Bec! We both looked like we just lost our best friend, because we did! The E-6 came up to me and said, "Seeing's how you're E-4 and the rest of the men E-3, I want you to lead these men up Recon Hill to your company. You will be in charge of these guys. Now move out troops!"

I looked at Bec and nodded my head goodbye. He just looked down. It would be quite some time before I saw Bec again.

As I marched the men and myself up toward Recon Hill I thought, well, I got what I wanted anyway. I wanted to be a Recondo Scout and I got it. But Bec! He was stuck in a no-mind Line Company. The difference between a Line Company and Rangers, Recon, or Scout is that Recon/Rangers all work in small teams being very quiet and sneaky. Hit and run operations only. Line troops are just massive numbers of moving targets. Line companies work with many men...up to one hundred twenty or more. You can hear that many men coming a mile away! It was a very good way of being spotted and ambushed easily. They were all sitting ducks! It might seem more secure being with over one hundred guys. But for Charley...they were just more targets to hit. The V.C. would swoop down on these poor dudes, kill as many as possible, then disappear into the jungle again.

I thought, it's every man for himself now! I felt very empty inside, once again as though I just lost another brother. But all I could think of was...Good luck Bec. Survivors, survive.

It was a long steep march up to the top of Recon hill. The place was built on the side of a mountain. The buildings were about fifty feet long and ten feet high. They were all built of big beams about one foot square. We marched past 1st....2nd....3rd and 4th platoon Recon, Ranger and other buildings until we got to the Orderly Room of E. Company Recon. I stopped the men out front and I went in to report.

Once inside I walked up to an Sp-6 sitting at a desk. He wore a tiger-striped camouflage uniform and an old beat up boony hat. He was a big dude with a mean look. He said, "Well, what can I do for ya?"

I replied, "Sp-4 Gibbore reporting with new troops sir!"

He said, "Oh good!...More cherries."

I just said, "Yes sir!"

He replied, "Wonderful...just wonderful! By-the-way....stop with that sir jazz. The name is Peppavich. They call me Sergeant Peppy or just Peppy. Got that?"

I said, "How about just Sarge?"

He replied, "Cherries! Come on....let's go pick some cherries." Later on I found out that he was nick named Peppy because he was a speed freak.

I turned and followed Peppy outside. When we got outside, I saw the men were all fidgety and restless. I looked up and saw three men sitting on the bunker roof above us. One guy laughed and said, "This one looks real bad, don' he!" The others just laughed then all moved back out of sight.

"What happened?" I asked. The men told me the guys on the roof were busting them real heavy. Telling them how we wouldn't last two days out there, like that.

Just then Peppy came up from behind me and said, "Don't pay any mind to those guys, they're just messin' with ya! You'll find out around here cherries get picked on a lot so get used to it. It won't last forever anyway." Back home I used to pick and eat a lot of cherries. I loved them, but just the sound of the word was starting to really get to me.

Peppy stepped up and said, "I'm your acting first Sergeant, anything you need or want, you come to me for it. I'll give you whatever you need except a piece of ail….You get that downtown if you're brave or dumb enough." Syphilis was a very big problem in Vietnam, but that's not the only thing he meant. Many times guys went into the villages for sex but never made it back.

Sgt. Peppavich said, "From here we'll go into the barracks and get you guys cot and settled in. Then we'll go to the armory for weapons and ammo. Every day outside on the bulletin board in front of the orderly room will be listed everyone's duties for the day. Check this board first thing each day, so you'll know what your jobs are while back here in the rear. It will also tell who's going out on mission and what six-man team you'll be working with. After you get your bunks and weapons, you will fall back out front here and I will take you down to the main post for an orientation class. This block of instruction will last for most of the day. Now!…fall out into the barracks."

The barracks, or "hooches" as they were called, had large wooden doors on them. It was as dark as a cave inside. Only a small light burned overhead. There were six men inside with belongings scattered everywhere. You couldn't even walk without falling on your face. Peppy yelled out, "You pigs…clean this out house up. First, get out 'til we're done." The guys got up, turned off the tape player they had going, and packed up the letters that they were reading or sending home. Slowly they walked toward the door. We got an ice-cold stare from each of them as they left. Naturally, the last guy had to say, "@#$#%@! cherries!"

Peppy then directed us to find a cot that wasn't made up. You couldn't really tell if the cot was being used or not, there was so much stuff piled up everywhere. We all started to sort through the mess as we kicked rats out of our way (and the rats were not at all frightened of us). Soon we all had a place to sleep. That place was something! M-16s hanging on the wall, hats, shirts, knives stuck all over the walls, even a camping hatchet stuck into a beam. It looked like they had been throwing the hatchet for quite some time. The beam was about one foot square, and it was all splinters and torn up bad. It was hot and moist inside, just a total stinking mess. But that's what we called home from that day on.

After all of the in-processing and orientation was over, we all got to eat chow. The chow hall was just a big tent with no sides. The meals were cans of sea rations heated in hot water. Not bad if you are starving to death or had your taste buds up your…

After chow the first night none of us had any duties except getting acquainted with all of L.Z. Uplift. We were told to go anywhere we wanted on the main post or on Recon Hill but we were warned to stay around the post. Peppy said if we went to the main post across the road at the bottom of the hill, to make sure we got back on the hill before dark. Once they closed the gates down on the road between the post and Recon Hill, you would have to stay there until morning when they opened the gate again. He said not making formation in the morning would be considered A.W.O.L., around there they consider A.W.O.L. desertion. They can hang you for that in a combat zone.

With all of that in mind, we wandered off in different directions. I had time to kill so I walked back down the hill to the main post to try to find Becham. I felt as though I stuck out down there because everyone wore plain green Army fatigues

with a steel helmet and I had brand new tiger fatigues and a boony hat. Being a
decked out in new clothes I stuck out. There I wanted anything but that.

I wandered down by the L.Z. where we first landed at noon. I thought I migh
pick up Bec's trail there. I asked, but no one knew anything. Finally I came acros
the E-6 that talked to us first thing that morning. He remembered right away tha
Bec was assigned to B. Company 503rd infantry. I asked, "Where would thos
guys be?"

He said, "About six clicks out or about 6,000 meters over that mountain tha
way."

I said, "He's out in the jungle already?"

He replied, "You go to wherever your company is, even if you're a cherry."

I thanked God for getting me into a Recondo company and I bid that E-
goodbye. Holy cow, I thought, Bec is at Charley's doorstep right now! He mu
be wettin' his knickers!

I had a few M.P.C. dollars on me, so I looked for the E.M. club for the sh
and beer I needed bad. All I could think of was Bec. God, I hope he is all right,
thought. After a while of wandering aimlessly around the post, I finally found th
E.M. club. I went in and ordered a beer. I felt edgy just remembering the last E.M
club I was in. Just then two guys came barging through the door looking like deat
warmed over. Ragged, sweaty clothes, they had belts of ammo strapped all ove
them and stoned to the bone! I looked at the one coming closest to me and aske
myself, are my eyes playing tricks on me or is that Westmore? Westmore was
friend of Becham, Feelen and I. We all went through A.I.T. and jump school togethe
He was sent right over to Nam from jump school, but Bec, Feelen and I went on t
other schools.

I yelled out, "Hey Westmore, is that you dude?"

He stopped and looked real close at me and smiled. "Why looky here!
brandy new spit shined cherry Recondo! I don't believe it....how ya been? Whe
did you get to this place?"

I replied, "This morning."

He asked, "So what do you think of the hot vacation spot so far?"

I said, "It all seems so strange to me so far. Everything is moving so fast,
can hardly keep up with all of it."

He said, "You ain't seen nothin' yet dude."

Just then the guy that Westmore came in with said, "I'll see you guys late
I'm going to sit down and eat something."

Westmore said, "Yeah! Go ahead on...we're gonna suck some suds and ra
awhile. Jim....how about another beer?"

I replied, "Yeah man!...I'll buy."

He replied, "Sounds good to me."

He called the bartender over and ordered up two more beers. I paid for th
beer and we walked over to the table where Westmore's friend was sittin
Westmore said, "You'll never guess who I saw about a half hour ago."

"Who?" I asked.

"That bonehead Becham," he replied.

I yelled, "Bec! You saw Bec? Where?"

He said, "Yeah, my company came in for stand down today. We got relieved by his company. As I was getting into my chopper, Bec was one of the guys just jumping out. We tried to talk for a minute but the chopper made so much noise, I couldn't hear him very well. I told him I would see him back here in the rear someday. Bec told me they were going out for twenty-five or thirty days. No kiddin' that's strange…now I run into you. How about Feelen? Have you seen him?"

I told him the story about Feelen getting his orders a couple of day before Bec and I and how we lost track of him at the In-Country Processing Station. Westmore said, "I get sent all over the country and I'll probably run into Brad somewhere. And Bec…he's really going to be in for a surprise out there because Charley's really active where he is. I just hope he stays down and doesn't volunteer for anything."

I said, "Have you ever known Bec to volunteer for anything?" We both laughed. Bec was very laid back and quiet).

Just then Westmore asked, "Hey man have you had enough of this warm beer?"

I said, "Yeeeeah! Tell me about it."

He said, "Let's go catch a buzz."

Westmore and I said, "Later," to his buddy who was stuffing hamburgers and fries down like there was no tomorrow and we left.

We walked outside and down the powdery dirt road. The road had about three inches of fine dust like dirt on it and every step made a cloud. Westmore said, "I've been here three months and I'll never get used to this dust. It's everywhere! That and the smell of burning…."

I interrupted, "That's one big thing I've noticed too, how bad the burning waste stinks."

We wandered around for awhile just talking. As we walked he showed me different things around the lower post area. The barber shop, P.X. and most of the bigger attractions on post. Not really very many things to rave about, that was for sure. He pointed and said, "See that field over there?"

I said, "Yeah…."

He said, "That's where we have shows every once in a while. They sometimes get a Vietnamese song and dance act or some Korean musicians. One time, they even had a U.S.O. show there. I was out in the boonies at the time and I didn't get to see it. They even had real women from the world with them. I heard they were looking good enough to eat! Man…I miss real women! I'd give a whole months pay for some of that. You must have had some of that sweet smellin' stuff not too long ago? Hey!" I just looked at him and licked my lips. He laughed, "You….It must be nice."

"It was," I replied.

"Well…just remember that long and hard 'cause there ain't any of that good stuff here!"

By that time he led me to a bunker out on the perimeter of the post. All it was was a big hole in the ground about ten feet in diameter and about six feet deep. It

had sandbags piled all around and over the top about two feet thick. We walke
down the five dirt steps inside.

Inside there was a guy sitting on a pile of ammo boxes taking the tobacco ou
of a cigarette. This was called shelling. In Nam you could buy a sandbag full of po
without a seed or stick in it. The cost was about twenty dollars M.P.C. The othe
way to get pot was to buy it already rolled up in cartons at the same price. Nea
Bon Song, a small village down the road, you could buy Bon Song Bombers. The
were big six-inch long by three eighths of an inch wide joints of Cambodian re
pot with opium laced all through it. The same kind that Sergeant Horton had th
night I got so ripped in the tower back at R.V.N. School. They sold for five dollar
M.P.C. for ten joints. Let me tell you that a five-dollar pack of bombers coul
keep the city of New York high for six months. Real strong stuff…Dope of a
kinds could be found and seen anywhere. It was easier to get dope than good foo
or water. Most everyone did some kind of thing or another.

Westmore and I walked up to the guy sitting on the ammo boxes and I wa
introduced to him. Everyone called him O.B., short for O'Banyon. He was a shor
stocky guy with wire rimmed glasses. He was from Canada. He spent six years i
the Canadian Army but the Canadian army wasn't into Vietnam. So he became
U.S. citizen to join the U.S. Army and to come to Nam. He didn't look like muc
but he was a smart soldier. At that time he had twenty-five confirmed kills. H
later joined my Recondo company on the hill where I was stationed.

Westmore said, "Well, light that sucker up."

O.B. said, "Don't get shook up, it's coming…Cut me some slack! This ain
the real good stuff." So he whipped out an aspirin bottle full of tar opium an
painted the joint black with the stuff.

I asked, "What's that black stuff?"

O.B. replied, "Tar…tar O…You ever been high on that yet?"

I replied, "I think so. Back in Cam Rhon Bay R.V.N. Training school."

O.B. said, "Well if you haven't…hang on to your slats."

Westmore just smiled and said, "It's good…you'll love it!"

Well, after that joint there I was again. Back in the Twilight Zone. We sat the
for about two hours. I listened to those two guys telling stories about the differe
missions they'd been on and what I was in for. Westcott got up and said, "He
Jim…it's getting dark outside." I got up and looked outside.

Westcott said, "You better get back on the hill. Even now…I don't think you'
make it in time."

I said, "Nut's! Now what?!"

He said, "No sweat, if you can't get back, just walk down six bunkers fro
here. That's where I'm staying. I'll get you a bunk for the night. But you best g
moving fast."

Man…I was so screwed up I couldn't even see, plus it was dark out. The
wouldn't turn any lights on outside because of the fear of Charley mortaring th
fort at night easier. Westmore asked, "You know how to get back to the gate don
ya?"

I said, "I think so."

Westmore said, "Just go straight up this road, fourth set of barracks turn right, keep going till you see the P.X. and barber shop. From there you'll see the chopper pad. You'll know the way from there, won't you?"

"Yeah…I guess…look I gotta swoop! See you guys tomorrow."

Westmore said, "Yeah…if I don't have to go back out tomorrow I'll see you around."

I never saw Westmore again.

I started off. Being as screwed up as I was I soon had no idea where I was. It was pitch dark by then and I knew I was in trouble. I had to walk very slowly because it was so dark. I couldn't see anything. I was stumbling all over big tent ropes and stakes, I about broke my neck. All around me I could hear men talking, inside and outside of tents and hooches, but I could only see shadows and dark images. Every once in awhile, a flare from the perimeter bunkers would go up and I could see for a couple of minutes. At these times, I would move fast toward where I thought the hill was. Landing Zone Uplift was in the central highlands and there were very big hills and mountains all around. I couldn't tell which hill was Recon Hill for sure.

After I found my way back to the chopper pad, I could start to tell where I was. I moved quickly toward the gate. When I got there I saw it was locked. I said, "Now what?" I saw an opening in the wire, just enough room to squeeze through. I was now outside the gate on the road, somewhere I knew I wasn't supposed to be. I looked both ways to see if anyone was watching and I ran across.

All of a sudden, I heard the sound of rifle bolts closing. I gasped. "Don't shoot," I yelled.

A voice on the other side of the road said, "Halt! Advance to be recognized!"

I walked up to the gate on the hill side of the road and I was looking down the barrels of four M-16's. I about fainted. "What the !@#$$%!? do you think you're doing out there?" One of them asked.

"You best get your young sorry m#*%##! butt in here boy." I went up that fence like a monkey.

On the other side one of the guys on guard said, "Let me tell ya pal you almost traded in your m##@^$** butt for a harp!"

I replied, "Man, I had to get back any way I could."

Another one of them said, "Don't you know the rules?"

I replied, "Yeah….But I had to get back."

The guy said, "You were real lucky this time, next time you might get your f*$@*! rocks blown off!"

As I thanked them all for not turning me into dog food, I walked away toward my hooch. A few steps away, I could hear them saying things like, "Dummy…must be a cherry or somethin'."

Now I had to find the right hooch. I walked up on the hill and recognized the motor pool full of jeeps I passed that afternoon. My hooch was just about another fifty yards or so. Sure enough, there it was, home at last.

As I got closer, I could hear loud music and men talking. In those days the Stones, Iron Butterfly, Cream and songs from Woodstock were constantly being played. Everyone had a small portable cassette player with them. Some had one everywhere they went, like a camera. Music wasn't the only thing these players were used for. Most everyone hated to write letters, so they would send tapes back and forth from there to home. You could say a lot more and could hear each other's voice. Tapes were much better than writing letters.

As I got close to the door, I could see it was well lit inside my hooch. It was still a stench filled dungeon to me. I saw ten or twelve guys inside, none of whom I recognized. They were two teams that just came back in, late that afternoon. "Well, come on in," one guy said. So I did.

The guy sitting by the door asked, "Looking for someone?"

I said, "I just came in today and I was late getting back across the road."

Just then another guy jumped up and asked, "Are you the cherry from Binghamton?"

I said, "Yeah….I'm from the Binghamton area all right."

He walked over to me with his hand out and said, "My name is Updike…I'm from Owego."

"No way…" I replied.

He said, "Man I don't believe it. Finally I found a homey." A homey was a guy who came from the same place or close to where you came from back in the world.

Everyone else went on talking and unpacking their rut sacks. Updike started asking me all about home and what was happening in our area. We talked as he went on with his unpacking. He said, "Soon as I get done…I'll show you our club. We'll suck some suds or something."

I said, "That's fine with me."

As I sat there, I watched the other guys doing their own thing. Some making a tape to send home, some just resting on their cots. Some were playing "split" with a Gerber dagger. The object of the game was to see which one of two guys had the guts enough to keep playing and not quit or flinch, when the distance between your feet got too close to go on. You start out with your feet spread two feet apart. The first guy throws the dagger between the other man's feet. Wherever the dagger sticks into the floor is where that man has to put one of his feet. With each shot, the distance keeps closing. Then it's the next man's shot and so on until one man's feet are so close together he get's scared of being stuck with the dagger and he gives up. They played for money.

I remember the one time I played that split game….Once! The guy that I was playing with would not give up when his feet were only inches apart. I asked him if he was sure he wanted to go on. He just stood there looking tough and said, "Don't forget that it's my turn next!" We were both getting real close. But the dope never thought if I missed there wouldn't be another turn. I would only lose a few bucks, not a foot. Well I missed slightly and the razor sharp dagger hit the inside of his foot near his big toe. The dagger went into the side of his big toe, through the toe and out the side of his boot and stuck his foot to the floor! He was stabbed bad! It took him out of action for a few days and it almost got me busted for doing it. Like I said, I played the game….Once!

The guys were all crazy for the most part! I could just tell. One guy about my size kept looking at me with very cold eyes. His name was Moran. He was from a small town in Pennsylvania. He was a real wise, mean jerk! He hated near everyone except for his three butt boys that looked just as mean. Around his neck was a string of dead Viet Cong ears all dried out. They looked like dried apricots. I thought I was seeing things, but that's what they were. Not too many guys would do this, but there were always a few dopes around. It was no wonder I later heard stories of dead Americans found with their rocks cut off and sewn up in their mouths. Charley was just getting back at us for all of the Morans in Vietnam.

On their way out, Moran and his friends just had to stop at Updike's bunk and say, "So…I see you're hanging out with f@#$#! cherries now Updike?"

I stood right up in Moran's face and said, "Take a walk…Moron!"

He looked down at his name tag on his shirt and said, "The name's Moran."

I said, "I like it better the way I said it."

He looked long and hard at me and said, "Watch your back mother f@#$#!"

I looked right back and said, "Looking at you….I would believe that's the only place you would have the guts enough to shoot someone!"

He and his friends turned and walked out. Updike said, "I hope you know he meant that."

I replied, "He best hope he don't miss!"

Updike said, "For a cherry, you're all right pal."

About an hour went by since I had the misfortune of meeting Moron and his butt boys. During that hour I got acquainted with a bunch of the other guys in the hooch. They were all real nice guys. They were from every state in the U.S., even Hawaii. There was a guy called Cowboy from Texas. He was a professional bull rider back home. There was Babbles from California. He was very smart and well educated. He went to school most of his life, but had little common sense. He just thought he was some sort of philosopher or whatever and babbled all the time about everything. Babbles was a real nice guy though. The guy from Hawaii was about six feet tall and solid muscle. I never saw a real weight lifter before. I mean not like this guy anyway. He looked like Mr. America, dark tan and all muscle. His name was Kabbatt. He very seldom said a word. He just worked out all the time with the barbell set he made out of cement filled coffee cans.

When most everyone was unpacked they all wanted to go to the club. So Babbles, Updike, Kabbatt and I walked out of the hooch and headed for the club. Some of the other guys said they would be there shortly. We walked down the long wooden walkway, sort of like the wooden sidewalks seen in an old Dodge City cowboy movie.

We went around the corner and there it was. It looked like an old wooden building someone put together out of scrap wood and nails. Counting the bar, it would hold about twenty or maybe thirty guys. Right in the middle of the room was a very unbalanced pool table. They had the right amount of balls, but two or three with the same number.

Everyone fought over the only good cue-stick they had. Naturally Moron and his boys had total command over the pool table, so forget that. Everyone was getting pretty screwed up after awhile. Most of the time all you could hear above the deafening music was Moran's voice bragging about all the "gooks" he slaughtered single handedly on the last mission.

After he was drunk and crazy enough he said, "I want my team lined up right here! Come on! It's toast time." He walked over to the wall where a steel helmet hung on a nail and brought it over to the bar.

He demanded, "Bartender!…make me some Ranger Punch." The bartender started pouring into the helmet shot after shot of every kind of whiskey there was. Then he handed the helmet back to Moran. Moran then walked slowly back toward the other five men in his team and stopped in front of each of them. As he stopped, they each pulled out their….Pistol…and urinated a squirt or two into the helmet. I thought, here we go…I think I'm seeing things again.

After they each squirted a little in the helmet Moran held the helmet up high and said, "E. Co. Recon is the toughest…meanest…bunch a mother f@#$%^&! Charley ever ran into and he f@#$%^&! knows it. To another successful mission and more dead gooks!" They all passed the helmet until the punch was all gone. Man…I thought, these guys must be nuts! Or more like turning into animals. I just wondered if I would ever flip out that bad.

I looked at Babbles and Kabbatt shaking my head. "Do you guys do that?" I asked.

They both said, "No!"

Babbles said, "Most of that team are left over old guys. They used to do that all the time. Most of those guys have spent two or three tours over here. Their brains are getting soft. After a while…you'll see yourself wandering away from reality too. Don't mind them….they're really a bunch of pretty good guys. I know one thing for sure…they're about the best in the world to have on your side during a firefight. They really know their stuff!"

I said, "Yeeeeah…Well guys, it's been a long one for me…so I'm going to crash out! See you later."

They said, "See ya," and I left.

I got back to my hooch and saw all the guys I came in with that morning. They said that Peppy told them that there was a movie up at the day room earlier and that is where they'd been. I told them about the party at the club and the Ranger punch toast. I think they thought I was nuts!….I said, "You should have been there! That was a good one…" I laid down on my cot and I was out like a light.

I must have been out for a couple of hours when I woke up to very loud blast noises. Guys were running everywhere! They were yelling, "Get your weapon and get to a perimeter bunker… it's a mortar attack." In a state of panic I jumped up, grabbed my M-16 and flew out the door.

I ran as fast as I could to the nearest bunker I could see. The area was all lit up with arial flares almost like daylight. Mortar rounds were hitting everywhere! One hit somewhere near me as I ran but only the back blast hit me. It felt like a car plowed into me. It knocked me about twenty feet high. I thought I was blown apart. My whole body was numb. I was half knocked out as I quickly looked myself over…I saw no blood. I was sitting right on top of a bunker, so I scrambled down inside. My M-16 was gone!

Once down inside some guy said, "Man…I thought you bought the farm, friend." He said he saw the mortar round hit and then me flying through the air.

I yelled, "I'm still not sure I'm not dead! Man…was that a weird feeling."

I sat down. The guy said, "Just sit and rest awhile I'll keep watch. Charley usually doesn't attack in full force. This is probably just a harassment attack. But, you never know." I told him that I lost my M-16 and had nothing to fight Charley with anyway.

Just then another guy said, "Here take mine! I ain't f@#$% in' moving." It was so dark in that bunker you couldn't see anyone, just hear voices. That voice was familiar.

"Who the heck was that?" I asked.

"The name is Brad…Brad Feelen."

I said, "Brad! you bonehead…you! Where are ya?"

"Who's that?" He asked.

"It's me…Gibbore."

Brad yelled, "Jim! I'm over here." So I crawled over to where the voice came from and I could finally see him.

We both yelled at the same time. "I thought I'd never see you again."

The guy I first talked to in the bunker said, "Yeah-yeah! It's a small f*#$**! world…..Now get over here and keep an eye out."

By then most of the shelling stopped except some small arms fire out on the edges of the hill. Brad and I got caught up to date on everything that had happened while we watched out the firing holes of the bunker. I told him about Becham and I getting split up and everything else. He then told me about his landing at Uplift. He said, "Guess what?"

I asked, "What?"

"I'm going home!" He replied.

"What?….already?" I asked.

He said, "Yeah…I got here a few days ago and after I saw some of the stuff I saw, I knew I had to get out-a-here or get my butt blown away."

I asked, "But how are you going to get out of here this early?"

He said, "Easy…I just went down to the re-enlistment N.C.O. down on main post and re-upped for three more years!"

I gasped, "Three more years!"

He said, "Yeah! If you re-up over here for three or more years you get to change your M.O.S. and get a thirty day leave." M.O.S. meant Military Occupational Specialty. He said his M.O.S. could be changed, giving him a job on a gun ship instead of pounding the bush for V.C. and getting shot at. Plus, starting day after tomorrow, he was going back home for thirty days leave. I personally told him I thought he was nuts but to do whatever he thought best for himself. I just wanted to stay and get it over with. He also said the re-enlistment N.C.O. told him if you pulled an extra six months there in country after your first tour was over you could get an early out from active duty once you got back to the world. That way you wouldn't have to pull a whole three years in the army, but would be immediately discharged when you got back home. Now to me that sounded good then, because once my tour was over in Nam, I still had a year to pull in the States. That meant an early out for me. I said, "I'm going to have to make it through this year first, before thinking about six more months in this nut house."

Brad then asked me who I was assigned to. I said, "Co. E. Recon." He said that he was in the hooches just below mine in Co. C. Recon. Recon is long range reconnaissance patrolling. Mostly watching enemy movements and gathering information for the big shots.

Everything was quiet outside by then. But Brad and I just stayed there in the bunker where it was safe. We smoked a joint of pot that Brad had and we both fell asleep until morning. Everything was quiet the rest of the night so I slept pretty good. Man I was beat!

The next morning the sun beat down on that bunker so hard and hot it was stifling inside at 0600 A.M. We both left for formation. I said, "See ya later." We both said good-bye and went off to our own companies. That was the last time I saw Brad for a long time.

By the time I got to my platoon the men were starting to gather in the formation area. I walked over to the formation where the other new guys were and waited for the rest of the men. Soon I saw the Peppy coming. He called everyone to attention and started handing out details.

Once again my bad luck struck! I was stuck on burn detail with another guy that had done it before...Moran! First thing he said was, "How did you like the fireworks show last night....homey?" I told him to get choked and I walked away. He said, "Come on we got lots of s!*# to burn." So I followed.

All day long in that hot sun we burned smelly waste. That jerk Moran didn't do a thing all day! I knew if the work didn't get done it would be my neck. Moran was in charge but was getting short so he didn't care about anything.

By about 1600 we were done with all the johns we had to work on so we decided to go to the club for a drink. We walked all the way up Recon Hill to the club and went in. Five or six guys were just sitting around "rapping."

One of Moran's friends was sitting on a stool at the bar. He laughed and said, "Well well...If it ain't the terd jockeys."

Moran pushed him out of the way and ordered up a couple of beers. "Here." He said, sliding a can of warm beer toward me. "You can't work for beans, let's see if ya know how to drink."

I slid the beer back at him and walked out. I really didn't want a warm beer anyway. Not only that, but I was splattered with liquid poop from head to toe and couldn't stand the smell of myself.

I walked into my hooch and got some clean clothes. Then I asked Kabbatt, who was doing push-ups on the floor where the showers were. He said, "Up the hill behind the Radio shack...You can't miss it."

"Thanks." I said and started to walk out.

Kabbatt asked, "Do you know anyone that lost an M-16 last night?"

I said, "Yes! I know someone!"

Kabbatt said, "If you find the guy tell him Babbles found one outside last night."

I said, "Thanks a lot!" And I left.

I walked up the hill to the Radio shack and around the corner, to the showers. It was a platform about ten feet high with four 55 gallon drums up on top. They would fill the drums every night and throughout the next day, the sun would heat the water. There were no sides on the place at all. You would just strip and stand out in the open and take your shower. A sign on one of the platform post read, "Pull a rope for water, but don't forget to leave enough for the next guy." After pulling all four ropes, I finally figured out no one gave a snort about the next guy. I wet a rag with what dripped out of the four valves and washed up the best I could. I got dressed and went down the hill for chow. Man, I was starved!

When I got down to the chow hall they asked me where I was when chow was on. I said, "I was on detail."

The big fat, sweaty slob who was supposed to be the cook said, "If you're not here by chow call…forget chow." So I walked out.

I wandered down to the E.M. club where I had met Westmore yesterday afternoon, because I remembered Westmore's friend stuffing down burgers and fries. That sounded like a Thanksgiving dinner to me right then I was so hungry. I went in and sat at the bar. I asked the bartender if I could get something to eat and he said, "Sure!" I ordered two burgers and fries.

"How about something to drink?" he asked.

I said, "A double of Jack Daniels."

By the time my food came I had three doubles of Jack Daniels and I was three quarters in the bag from the Jack and the heat. Even late afternoon and night, the temperature stayed around 98-100. I gulped down my burgers and left.

I walked around for awhile looking for Westmore or anyone I knew, but found no familiar faces. It was starting to get dark, so I went back up on the hill. As I walked up toward the hooch, I ran into my first Sgt. Peppy. He stopped me and asked where I was during evening formation. I explained about the shower and meal I needed and what I had to do to get both. I said I was sorry about not being there and all but I was so hungry that I never even remembered formation. He said not to miss formation again. Then he said I was on guard duty that night and I was to get my weapon and ammo, then report to bunker #14. As I started walking away, he asked if I had my orders for Sp 4. I told him I didn't have orders yet, but told him about the sergeant at R.V.N. school pinning them on me. He said he was proud of what I had done, but if our company commander, a captain, saw them, he wouldn't be so understanding. He told me to take the Sp 4 pins off for now. I said I would and walked away.

I felt as though I had my face slapped, but he was right. In the army you learn to just take another bite of the big green poop sandwich and choke it down and shut your mouth. "It don't mean nothin'…..it don't mean a thing!" I whispered to myself.

Back at the hooch, I saw Babbles sitting on his cot making a tape to send home. I asked him about the M-16 that he found. He said, "Yeah…I got it….it's right here under my bunk. Do you know who it belongs to?"

I said, "Oh yeah!…..I'm going to see the dude in a few minutes. So I'll give it back to him."

He smiled and handed it over. He said, "Tell your buddy this is one friend he should never lose track of."

I said, "I'll make sure the guy gets the message!" I grabbed some ammo and a poncho liner and I left.

It was a short walk to bunker 14. There were six men at the bunker including myself. Four guys were just sitting around making tapes to send home and getting high. The guy that was on guard was called "The Cookie Man" because he did Bonoctals. They were a big pill about the size of a nickel. They were "downs" and also called Cookies. Most guys that did drugs would do speed because we normally got so little sleep that it was the only way to stay awake and alert. Why a man would do downs in that depressing place was far beyond me.

As I stood on the ground I looked up at the Cookie Man and asked, "Is this bunker 14?"

He said, "I guess so duuuude, but who gives a dump? Jump on even if it ain't!" I chuckled to myself and thought, this was the man we had on guard? If so, we will probably get overrun.

I heard other guys voices say, "Come on aboard! The more the merrier. What's a party with just five guys anyway?" I set my M-16 down on top of the sand bag second floor and I jumped up on top. Everyone started to introduce themselves and so did I. After about twenty minutes, I knew everyone's life story. All of the guys were nice and friendly. They explained about the shifts of two hours on and four hours off. They said if I could not stay awake…to wake someone else up. But never!…fall asleep…never!

First thing I was taught the job of shelling cigarettes. They said the new guy gets to shell the joints. I guess this was just all part of the initiation. After the first ten or twenty joints, I was a pro at it. And stoned to the bone as well!

All of that night, we just smoked pot and joked around. They played music on their tape recorders and from the looks of things, you would think we were all on vacation and not in a war zone. We had a lot of fun that night just getting buzzed out and rappin'.

By the time morning came we were all about beat from partying all night and we all left for our hooches. The only time you could miss formation while in the rear was if you were on guard duty. Most of us would usually make formation anyway just to get the latest info. about all kinds of stuff.

That morning I was bushed from partying all night and I just walked back to the hooch to get some sleep. Inside there were two teams getting ready to go hunting. There was an E-6 in there that I hadn't met yet. His name was Schriff. He had been on R & R for two weeks in Tokyo. He got back last night. He walked up to me and said, "Hi…my name is Schriff. You must be Gibbore?"

I said, "Yep."

He said, "Get your stuff ready…you're goin' huntin' with us!" Suddenly the blood rushed into my head so fast and hard it seemed to dull my hearing. I was in shock!

"Me!" I gasped. I just stood there looking dumb.

He said, "Well move out, we only have about an hour." I kind of felt faint, but I did what I was told.

First I went over to my cot and got my rut sack. Then I started watching everyone else, to see what they were packing. Schriff said, "You can grab eight or ten L.R.R.P. meals over there in that box. The ammo is over there too." He pointed to a pile of M-16 ammo boxes on the floor. "Take as many as you have room for. Your gonna' need um."

Trying to watch everyone to see what they packed was a job in itself. No one really wanted to help, so I used my common sense and finished packing.

There were six men counting myself on the team. Schriff, Babbles, Jackson, Updike, and Lori, who was Spanish and I never could pronounce his last name. Naturally the only new guy was me!

After we got packed and loaded with water, food, ammo, fragmentation grenades, Claymore mines and all the other stuff we needed…we had eighty or ninety pounds of stuff. We headed down the hill for a briefing on the mission. Down the hill on the main post was our 173rd Airborne Brigade Special Operations Group Headquarters at Uplift. There were a few more L.Z.s around the country with 173rd Airborne stationed at them. We were led down into a big bunker where there were some long benches to sit on and maps everywhere on the walls. Up in front was a chalkboard.

After we were seated our Recondo Company Commander and two intelligence men came in and walked up front. The C.O. sat down and the two intelligence men started telling us about our mission. There was another team going out too. But we were told they were going somewhere else and they would be briefed later. One of the intelligence men said they were sending us out to meet a Line Company about six clicks out. We were going to be dropped out during the Line Company re-supply. He said we were going to be hidden from sight by the bodies of the men in the Line Company as they came up to our chopper for re-supply goods. They didn't want Charley to know Recon would be left in the area after the Line Co. moved out early the next day. The V.C. already knew the Line Co. was there and everyday the V.C. would set up ambushes for them. They were raising heck with those guys. After the Line Co. moved out we scouts were supposed to set up ambushes on the V.C. as they picked over the area of the Line Co. Every time a Line Co. moved on the V.C. would come into the area and look for anything dropped or left behind by G.I.s. They would make use of anything left behind…such as lost or dropped ammo, half eaten cans of sea rations, anything.

The briefing lasted about twenty minutes or so and then we moved out. Outside our chopper was being loaded with ammo, water, and food for the Line Co. we were about to rendezvous with. Soon the aircraft was loaded and it was time for us to get on board. My gut was so tense I could hardly breathe and I thought I would go in my pants. But it was too late for a trip to the john, so I just jumped in. Inside the chopper everyone just sat quietly and looked around. Up like a rocket we went. Well God, I thought. I'm in your hands now…..

L.Z. Uplift - South Vietnam - 1970

Heavy Recondo Team- L.Z. Uplift R.V.N.
Hunter 2
(photo taken by Author)

CHAPTER 9

Hot Landing Zone

On the ride out, I thought about what my father told me just before leaving home. I thought about hunting with him and all he had taught me. I also thought about all the training I'd had for this kind of thing. At that moment, I really started to wonder if it was enough to help. Right then, all I felt would help was a plane ticket back home to my favorite fishing hole.

Just over the mountain to our right was a big wide-open flat area between two mountains. There was some green smoke coming from the ground. Schriff pointed and nodded his head. That was it, I guessed. Hang on to your rocks, I thought.

Down we went circling the L.Z. once to see if we would draw some enemy fire. V.C. loved to shoot at choppers. Down we went till we were on the ground. Green smoke blew everywhere as about twenty men ran up to our chopper. The door was open and we all jumped out mixing toward the center of the group of men. The men grabbed as many boxes as they could carry and the chopper started to lift.

Just then I knew I heard small weapons fire above the sound of the chopper blades. The men around us started to yell, "Move fast we're being shot at!" We all ran as fast as we could within this group of men. We scouts tried to stay hidden but guys were getting hit all around us and falling out. Finally we broke out of the pack and ran for the cover of the jungle ahead.

At the edge of the jungle on the base of the mountain was the main body of the Line Co. Out of the group of about twenty men that came out to meet us there were three guys wounded and one man dead. As soon as we reached the Line Co. their C.O. was calling in helicopter gun ships and a medivac chopper for the wounded and dead. After we were in the brush and out of sight we were able to relax a while until the air strike and medivac was over.

Man! I thought, that was so close I didn't believe it. As I ran from the chopper one of the guys who got hit was so close to me he was squashing me until he took a round in the chest. I'll never forget the sound. It sounded like he was hit in the chest with a baseball bat. My head was only inches away from where the round hit him. I walked into the brush about ten feet away and took that long overdue leak.

It was about noontime before the Line Co. got its stuff back together and bid us goodbye. It felt real spooky out there with only six guys. What if, I thought, Charley knew we were only six men strong and he felt full of fight that day. Well, let's just hope not, I thought.

Sgt. Schriff was the team leader and he had the map. He looked it over for awhile, then said, "Let's move out!" Moving through the jungle was very very hard. The plants and vines made it almost impossible to walk through. The jungle was like walking through hair - very strong hair. Many times guys would get so hung up by their rut sacks in the bush and with the heat they would just fall limp. We would have to come over and cut them free with a knife. Elephant grass was a bummer, because it was six or eight feet high and sharp as a knife blade. Every time you got cut it would fester up and get infected. Infection was a big problem because of the moist, very hot climate. Open sores and jungle rot were with us at all times. Nothing would dry out and heal up. During the monsoon season it was so wet and hot you would just about rot alive.

We moved about an hour then we took a rest. The Line Co. commander had told Schriff that they ran into a small V.C. base camp the day before in the direction we were going. He thought that would make a good ambush area, or at least a good place to start.

After reaching the V.C. camp Jackson and Updike moved into the V.C. camp area to look for enemy. The place was empty, so we were told. Those two guys weren't gone for more than five minutes before shooting started. I didn't know it at the time but the team knew each other very well, inside and out. As Jackson and Updike drew enemy fire the rest of us were getting an ambush ready. They had it pre-planned to draw as many enemy as they could back to us for a welcoming party.

At that time most of our Recon missions were called "Hunter killer" missions. They were missions more like Ranger-type missions and were used to inflict as much damage to the enemy as possible. Recon missions were usually run very quietly with as little contact with the enemy as possible. Recon is sent out usually to just watch the enemy and take notes, pictures, etc. At that time we were classified as Recon/Rangers. (Things changed big time later on when we got a new C.O.)

Schriff had us put some Claymore mines just up in front of us. Then we all got down and ready. We could hear crashing sounds just up ahead. "Hold your fire!" Schriff whispered. Just then Jackson and Updike came flying past us. They stopped and got down with the rest of us. Updike said there were about six or eight V.C. down in front and they were in hot pursuit.

"Everyone set?" whispered Schriff. My heart was about to burst! But the other guys knew just what was going down.

"Listen," said Schriff, "Here they come!" I could hear Vietnamese chatter just a few feet ahead. The brush made very little noise. Those V.C. were like a blasted cat with sneakers on.

Soon there they were, about fifteen to twenty yards down front. I saw everyone slowly bringing up their M-16s and so did I. All of a sudden an enormous blast! "Baaaaboom!" Then the whole team jumped up firing like mad! I just stayed down about to mess my drawers. About ten seconds later there were many dead V.C. stretched out in front. "Get down and watch," Schriff said, "Keep a look out….There may be more."

We stayed down for about five minutes then we all got up slowly. We walked ahead to where the bodies were. Schriff sent Updike and Jackson back to the camp to check it out again. The rest of us piled up the eleven bodies we found, checking them over for any important papers they might be carrying. Then we sat down to wait. About fifteen or twenty minutes went by before the two scouts came back. "All clear," Updike said, "The place is ours." Ours! I thought. What the heck do we want with a V.C. Base Camp? Not long from then I would know.

Schriff got on the radio to the Line Co. we met that morning. They said they would send a report back to Uplift about the dead V.C. Schriff then told them, with the use of an army radio code book, our location so they could send a couple squads there to take the dead V.C. out of the area. He said that we would probably stay in the V.C. camp for a couple of days. He told the Line Company to call back our position to Uplift so headquarters would know we were there in the camp and not shell the place, just for a day or so. Schriff said that he would contact Uplift himself later at the camp that night. The Line Co. replied that they got the message and said goodbye.

After all the guys in the team got done arguing about who killed what V.C., we were off and moving toward the base camp. In those days a confirmed body count went on your record. And after you had 21 kills you got to join an elite club called the 21 club. (What else?) At that time you could wear a gold earring in your left ear. The old Rangers started the club in the early days, and that was the first time I ever heard of such a thing. Before then I had never heard of a man with an earring.

Not far ahead we saw the camp, it was full of small grass huts. There was a small fire smoldering on the ground inside one hut. Old ragged pants and shirts hung inside. It was real creepy there. We moved very slowly around the place, looking and watching for anything.

Schriff said, "Lori...Jim back down the path and keep a sharp eye out." He told us not to fire if we could help it. If we saw any enemy coming just rush back there and tell him.

Lori and I moved out about one hundred yards back down the trail. Lori put me in one spot and before he took off he said. "Just sit and keep every sense open!" I nodded, yes! We sat there for about half an hour or so. Then behind us I saw Babbles coming down the path. He whispered, "Get Lori and come on back." I found Lori and told him what Babbles said. We worked our way back to where the other guys were inside the base camp.

Updike and Jackson showed Lori and I the bunch of spider holes they found. A spider hole is a one-man hole about five feet deep into the ground. Over the top is a bamboo net with grass woven all over it. V.C. could get down into the hole, pull the grass and bamboo top over the hole, and disappear below ground level. You could see real good out, but no one could see you - until it was too late. Schriff said we were to stay in these holes until night and to ambush any enemy that walked into the camp. Then we would come out and stay in the main hooch overnight.

For a little while we huddled together talking over what ambush plan we would use if we had to. Then we all moved into a spider hole to wait. We stayed in the holes the rest of the day but nothing showed up. It was like being in a grave. Just before dark I saw Schriff come out of his hole very slowly to look around. Everything was clear. One by one we emerged from our holes. It was so hot in there it was almost like being buried alive. I was totally soaked with sweat. All day I wondered if one of those dead Viet Cong I saw had built my hole. Most likely, I thought. Or is he still out there with my name on one of his bullets? Just the thought ran chills down my back.

When everyone was out of their hole Schriff sent Lori back down the path to watch and Jackson up above the camp to watch. The rest of us got ready to chow down. The L.R.R.P. meals (a.k.a. Long Range Reconnaissance Patrol meal) we had were very good. They were a freeze-dried meal in a sealed plastic pouch. The meals were chicken and rice, chili, spaghetti and meat sauce, and beef stew. All you had to do to make a good hot meal out of these was first to take out what they called a heat tab. This was a piece of solid alcohol that looked like a piece of blue melba toast. You set this on the ground and lit it. You then poured water into your canteen cup, brought the water to a boil, opened the food pouch, poured in the hot water and let it sit for about five or ten minutes. There you have it. A hot meal. This really was a very good tasting meal. Much better than the old canned sea rations and much, much lighter. You only needed a small space in your rut sack to carry a lot of meals.

Once the first two guys got done eating they traded places with Lori and Jackson on guard. After we got done eating we all stayed together in the biggest hooch. All night long we pulled guard duty with the radio. Two hours on, four off.

At night in the jungle it was terrible! So pitch black it would sometimes make me sick and dizzy. The darkness surrounded you so completely it was again like being in a grave alive. There were animals moving around all the time. And the bugs! They would eat us alive! All we could do was pray the sounds we heard weren't Charley sneaking in on us. After a while I guess you could tell the difference. Maybe there wasn't any difference. He lived out there at all times as an animal would. The thing that freaked me out the most at night in the dark were the tigers. They would move in close and growl. What an evil sound…and you could never see them! But they could see you!

All night and the next day we stayed there, but saw nothing. It was about three o'clock in the afternoon the second day and we all needed water. I remember one Recon mission I was on one time when we had to be sneaky and quiet not to be seen or heard. All of us ran out of water for three days and nights. We couldn't find water anywhere and Uplift or another C.O. that we had at that time would not re-supply us because sending in a chopper with water would tell the enemy that the team was working the area. The C.O. told us we would have to find our own water. We found an old bomb crater with old stagnated poop smelling green water in it, with one inch of bug larva floating on top.We scooped away the muck on top and filtered the water with a piece of cloth as it flowed into our canteens. Then we had to put iodine tabs into that nasty smelling water to kill the germs and….drink it or die! Our lips and tongue's were cracked and swollen from the lack of water and the iodine made our open sore laced mouths hurt big time. We tried catching morning dew with large leaves but it was just to slow….Remember, survivors survive!, it's our nature.

Schriff said according to the map there was a stream just down the other side of the mountain we were on. Schriff said, "Let's move on to find water before dark." Just before leaving he contacted L.Z. Uplift on the radio and said we would be moving on ahead out of the base camp about one click north. Uplift confirmed our travel plans and said that the next day they would send in an air strike and burn the V.C. camp. With that we were off.

We walked north for about two hours down the mountain. Then we came to a beautiful crystal clear stream. The area was plush and very beautiful with all kinds of plants, flowers, fruit trees, and bushes. Jackson and I sat down and got ready to fill our canteens. The rest of the guys left their canteens with us to fill. It was once again time to make some "iodine kool-aid" as we called it. We always had to be careful of getting sick from germs in the water we drank. No matter how clean it looked, it could kill you. Before filling a canteen we would have to put a few iodine tabs into the canteen to kill the germs. Then each man would put in his own lemon, orange or whatever flavor powder, a packet or two of sugar, and there you have it: iodine kool-aid. It wasn't great, but when you were thirsty, it worked.

Schriff said the rest of the team was going to scout up and down the stream. Two men went up and two went down stream to check things out and see if they could spot anything. The area was alive with many different sounds from the birds and other jungle creatures. It reminded me of the Tarzan movies I saw as a kid. I almost expected to see him dive from the high waterfalls a short way ahead and yell out his famous yell as he dove. The place where we were was just beautiful. Most of the time I never stopped to look around. But when I did I would see things that I would never see anywhere else in the world...or ever see again. Many times as I sat quietly a huge dragon fly or even a small bird would sometimes land on the end of my weapon and we would just sit there looking at each other.

CHAPTER 10

First Kill

As I filled the canteens the stream made a lot of noise, especially because of the one hundred foot waterfalls we were near. I was about thirty feet away from Jackson as I was trying to fill the canteens and keep an eye out for movement as well. The stream was about forty or fifty feet across. On the other side was another very big hill leading up the face of another mountain. The thick foliage hung down over a ten or twenty foot bank on the other side. I looked across the stream and saw small rocks rolling down the twenty foot bank into the water. I couldn't see up the bank very far because of the brush that hung down over.

Just then I saw him. It was Charley! He slid down the bank on his rear. I looked over at Jackson who was day dreaming in the water. I saw Charley look right at Jackson and I from about forty feet across the stream. He had his AK-47 strapped across his chest. He moved frantically trying to point his gun around in front at us. Never moving my eyes off him, I reached out and grabbed my M-16 that was lying right next to me. At that point I shook so badly I could hardly catch my breath. I knew one of us was about to die…and by God, it wasn't going to be me! Quickly, I brought my M-16 up and I fired one shot.

Charley flipped and kicked a couple of times. Then stopped moving. He was dead! Just that quick. Just that easy. Jackson jumped up and looked all around. He yelled, "What the f#@%$!! you shooin' at, motha f#*#*!?" He was a black dude and he was a very hyper person. I shook uncontrollably trying to point. He squinted a long stare. All the guys were rushing back from up and down stream.

Schriff asked, "What's all the shootin'?" Jackson pointed across the stream at the body lying on the rocks.

He said, "The motha' f#*#*!in' cherry done got his sef! a motha' f#**#in' dink!"

"Get your canteens picked up now! and let's check it out…slowly!" Schriff ordered.

One by one we crossed the stream. On the other side Charley lay dead. One shot right under the nose in his upper lip. I walked up to Charley and looked down at him. I felt like I would be arrested at any minute for murder. Lori walked up to the dead man and he kicked his head and it sounded like a carved out Jack-O-Lantern. His head was completely empty. The bullet blew his brains right out the back of his head. The other guys all patted me on the back and congratulated me on my first kill and said I did a great job. or some reason I felt like I was going to cry or something. It was a feeling of happiness….and sheer fright with a lot of sadness mixed in.

Schriff said, "I know one thing….They can't call you a cherry any more! Outstanding soldier! Outstanding!" From that day on….I was an Airborne Recondo. Not!…a f#**in' cherry.

Just before we moved out to find a place to spend the night Jackson came up to me and said, "I know I haven't said two mo' f#%**#in' words to you since we've met. But I didn't mean nothin' by it. It's just out here you learn not to make any close personal friends because they don't last too long. But I just wants ta' thank yawl for possibly savin' both our butts. Back there…I wasn't here, I was home…dreamin' about my ol' lady and not thinkin' about this mooo! f*##**in' place. That's when Charley usually kills yawl…when you're thinkin' about home. Thanks Bro. You is all right in my mo f* ##**in' book!" He told me that as long as he was around not to worry about my back. He said, "I knooowed! I'm speaking fo' all the other dudes too!"

We all walked just a little ways farther and we came up to the water falls that I had been hearing. Schriff said we would climb up about halfway to a big ledge we could see. He said he thought it would be a good ambush spot for the night. Once we got to the ledge the Sarge pointed at the sky. It was starting to get dark. So he sent out two guards and the rest of us ate chow.

All night long I kept thinking about Charley lying down below us dead. I just couldn't get it out of my head. It must have shown on my face. Babbles was into reading the Bible and said he had read the whole thing twice and was on his third time through. He said that each time he read it, it told him something more. He also told me about the parts in it about war. According to how he read it he said it was, well, acceptible to kill someone during a war…just like in the Crusades or any other war. I thought in my head Crusades or not…I just shot a man dead for going after a drink of water. To me that wasn't much of a reason to kill a man. Babbles was just trying to help me deal with the fact that I just killed someone and I thanked him for it. But it really didn't help at all. I just hoped someday when I met God face to face I would have something more to say to him for my actions than…Oooops!

I laid back and tried to rest until my turn on guard. On my watch that night, I neither saw nor heard anything unusual and neither did anyone else. There was a full moon in the sky that looked so big and bright it almost hurt my eyes to look at it. Down below I could almost see as clear as daytime. But I saw no movement.

The next morning Schriff said we would follow the stream down a ways. He said he wanted to follow some sandal tracks he and Lori had found in the mud the day before when I shot that V.C. So down the cliff we went.

As we approached the spot I shot the V.C., Schriff noticed the body was gone. There were drag marks leading down the creek bed. He whispered, "Easy…they found that dead V.C. and they may be hiding just up ahead with an ambush….Be careful…walk slow and watch!" I could feel something breathing down my neck…but I didn't know just what it was.

We walked downstream just about one hundred to one hundred fifty yards from the spot I shot old Charley. The creek wound its way down into a narrow valley between the two mountains. I felt very edgy and cautious. I just felt something was wrong, very wrong. On we went, about fifty yards more. On both sides of us were three hundred foot sheer rock cliffs, which was a very good place to lay down a killer ambush. Schriff said that it looked like a real good spot to get killed. The skid marks and blood spots were a definite sign Charley had gone through there. He said he wanted to move a little further and see if we could spot something.

He said maybe we could report a base camp or whatever.

There were gigantic boulders all over the creek bed. The way they were staggered you couldn't see very far up ahead. Slowly we moved on. Updike was pulling point, Jackson was next. I was behind Jackson humping the radio. Schriff behind me. Babbles and Lori were on rear guard. The creek narrowed down to only about thirty feet across. There was a sharp bend in the creek bed. As we moved around the bend, I could see Updike and Jackson looking more at the creek bed than the area ahead. Then I saw them....A whole squad of V.C. coming up the creek bed head on!

I tried to warn Updike but it was too late. A member of the V.C. squad saw us and opened fire with full auto. Updike and Jackson were hit! Updike took one in the lower leg and Jackson looked like he caught one in the lower hip. I opened up with semi-automatic fire as fast as I could get them off. I saw a V.C. go flipping before I dove for it. I got down behind a huge boulder. Schriff grabbed the radio mic. and called in our position to Uplift. Shots stopped for a minute as the enemy regrouped above to get a better shot at us. I could see them moving all over the place above us.

I got the radio off my back and ran out and I grabbed Updike who was kicking and screaming. I tried to calm him as I dragged him back behind a boulder. But I could not shut him up. Jackson was down behind another boulder. He said he was alright for now because the bullet just grazed his hip. But Updike was spurting blood everywhere from the wound on the inside of his lower left leg. Schriff said he got through to Uplift and help was on its way. We made a tourniquet for Updike's leg and tried to watch out for V.C.

All of a sudden bullets came raining down on us from up above. Bullets were hitting the dry creek bed so fast and furiously it made a mountain of dust. I could no longer see Jackson but I could hear him swearing at the enemy, so I knew he was still alive. Babbles and Lori said they would move up the bank to see if they could get a clear shot at any V.C. and vanished in the dust. I just tried to keep calm and watched. Every once in awhile a V.C. would move into sight up above and when they did I was ready. I lost count of how many I shot at. Updike screamed, "Where in the f##**!!? is that medi-evac ship?!"

I just kept telling him, "Don't worry you'll be out of here very shortly."

There were enemy soldiers everywhere up above us. How they didn't kill all of us right there was nothing short of a miracle! How much time passed before the choppers finally showed, I really don't know. Maybe a half hour. But thank God! I could eventually hear their beautiful voices coming from far away. Just then Schriff pulled out a yellow smoke canister and popped it. The thick yellow smoke told the choppers where we were to keep us from being shot by them.

By the use of the radio Schriff directed the two gun ships to saturate the area about sixty yards down stream from our smoke and all around us. Man, the sound of those M-60's barking at Charley sounded like harps from Heaven. God! I thought. We are saved! The thick jungle ceiling overhead gave way to the enormous blast of air caused by the medi-evac chopper and the bright sun burned through the darkness of the jungle. Jackson came running back across the opposite side of the creek to where we were. He said, "It's just a scratch. I'll be okay!"

As I looked up I could see a cable with a seat hooked to it coming down through the thick jungle ceiling. Some of the small arms fire had stopped by then. All I could hear was the sound of the gun ship's rockets and guns, blowing Charley to bits. Soon Updike was up, loaded and on his way out. The chopper pilots said there was so much enemy fire they had to leave us until we could get to an open area. So Schriff told them we would try to get back to the area where we had met the Line Co. two days ago. They got the message and flew away.

All of us that were left re-grouped and headed back up stream. Fire started coming from everywhere! We ran as fast as we could, helping Jackson as much as we could. He was hurt worse than he thought. The bullet went right on through the side of his upper leg. The wound was not that deep but it was bleeding pretty bad. We made it back out into the clearing where I shot that V.C. the day before. We all crossed the creek and tried to set up a quick ambush. As the enemy came out of the thick jungle we zapped a few more but there were just too many. They were coming at us like bees.

Up the mountain we went. We nearly killed ourselves just trying to stay ahead of them. We were falling over high banks and rocks, sometimes stopping to rest and catch our breath. But Charley didn't have a wounded guy to carry or an eighty pound rut sack on his back. He could move much faster. We got back onto the path and headed back toward the V.C. base camp we had found, which helped us move faster. Every time we stopped there was Charley right on our heals! They just kept shooting and shooting. Sometimes I wondered if they would ever run out of ammo. But they never did.

Now the base camp was only a little ways away. From there it was mostly down hill, I thought. At least it would be easier going down a mountain than up one. But the base camp would be no refuge for us at all. During the night Charley had moved back in. As we got about fifty feet away from the camp we started getting a lot of gun fire from there. We weren't the only ones who could be rattled. Even that close, Charley missed us.

Schriff said, "Back off the path and in the bush. We have to go around the camp." We moved about one hundred yards to our left to try to go around the camp. I had the radio and was second in front. Lori was point man.

Just then Lori stopped and fired. A V.C. went flying. I saw another one coming from my right screaming like a mad man. I pulled up and shot him. I later found out from Schriff that the V.C. that came charging at us like that were a type of "Kamikaze" soldier like the Japanese had in WWII. He told me sometimes they were even ordered by the higher ups to do a charge like that or be shot by their own officers! Unlike a U.S. soldier they were not allowed to use their head, only to take orders like a nazi no-brain. The hard core V.C. even believed that a death charge like that could get them a one way ticket to V.C heaven. The way those crazy little dudes looked as they charged us, at times left me no doubt Schriff was El correcto!

On we went. All of us were just about dead from heat exhaustion, cuts and bangs. We couldn't see very far ahead because of the thick jungle. Not much light came in at all. But it was even darker than usual. It was getting late afternoon. We all knew we would have to make it back to the open flat lands before night or be caught and or surrounded by V.C. for sure by morning. Without light we couldn't read a compass. We could not turn a flash light on at night unless we wanted to become a target! Without the ability to read a compass, our stuff would be in the red….big time!

Suddenly Lori yelled out, "Jim look out!" Just then a V.C. came from no where!, right at me with a huge knife screaming like a total mad man. I was in shock for a second because I got freaked out so bad. I think that was the idea. On instinct alone I fired, killing him instantly with a chest and head shot. He fell face first right into my arms. I tossed him off of me like a limp doll. Lori looked at me and shook his head. He smiled, then he moved on ahead. We could still hear the enemy yelling all around us from every direction. We went on ahead.

By that time Jackson looked as wrung out as an old dish rag. I knew he must be beat. I fell back to give him a hand. He said, "Go on dude!…Man, I'm no pussy. I'll make it."

I replied, "Shut up! and move out!" I grabbed him under his arm to support him. His smile was so big. I almost laughed when I saw a gold capped tooth with the star cut out of it right in the middle of his right front tooth. There was no kidding me that man needed help.

Finally it got so dark we couldn't see anymore. We stopped to listen. The voices of the enemy were seemingly far away. Schriff said that we would stop for the night…but no one got much sleep that night. We just kept listening for sounds of Charley. I always wondered what all the endless running and physical workouts were for back in all the schools I went to. But then I thanked God….and my drill instructors for all of that. If I hadn't worked out that hard Charley would have had me long ago! No doubt in my mind!

The next morning we started to move as soon as we could see. We moved as slowly and as quietly as we could. On and on we went. Suddenly we heard enemy voices talking fairly close by. We all lay quietly down in the brush. The voices kept getting clearer and closer. Soon we could see them coming. No one made a sound or a move.

Little did we know that about fifteen or twenty feet away was a very clear foot path that V.C. used all the time. It was a main trail between two small base camps. We were smack in the middle of V.C. City once again. About three hundred yards from there was a very large full size N.V.A. base camp. The camp we stayed at two nights before was one of the smaller ones. No wonder there were so many V.C. A large N.V.A. base camp would sometimes hold two or three hundred V.C. and N.V.A. troops. Right at that time we didn't have any idea of what we were up against. We thought they were just a couple of V.C. squads we happened to run into again.

We had lain motionless for about fifteen minutes. During this time we saw a continuous flow of N.V.A. and V.C. troops. From where I laid the V.C. were only about ten or fifteen feet away. How they overlooked me I'll never know. I kept my head down most of the time. I was just frozen stiff! I don't think I looked up more than twice the whole time I heard them passing. No matter what, we were dead if we were spotted.

The ticks and leeches were really starting to itch and burn. Every night spent in the jungle was sheer torture between the bug bites and leaches. You didn't even have to be near water to have leaches all over you the next morning. The early morning dew would bring them out of the thick grass. Snakes and reptiles of every shape and size were a hazard also. It seemed everything in Nam wanted to kill us.

I didn't believe we could possibly make it back to that field to be picked up. There were V.C. everywhere. I thought, if I ever did make it back alive, would I ever be able to live with or forget what has happened to me in just two and a half days? I had a year to go and already I was this close to being killed or captured and possibly tortured to death. How would I ever cope with the rest of the time I had to spend there? These were the things that went through my mind as I lay there. I knew one thing for sure right then. Nothing! ever felt worse to me then the hot breath of Charley's AK-47 breathing into my face, nothing! And I would never, if I lived to be a hundred years old, forget it.

Some time had passed. I really don't know how much but the voices and sounds of V.C. moving stopped. Schriff slowly started to get up. He looked around at each one of us. Then with a high sign we all got up very slowly. He whispered, "According to the map the field is about six or eight hundred yards straight ahead."

We all started to move very slowly. First Lori then Jackson. I saw Jackson was all right so I picked up the radio and moved out. Schriff and Babbles followed. The jungle was thick so moving quietly was very difficult. There was no path to follow, just jungle. On we moved for about two hundred yards. Then we stopped so Schriff could call the Line Co. we were working with to find out if they were in the area yet. Uplift was supposed to send them back our way for support. He had no trouble contacting the Line Co. They were only about seven or eight hundred yards away at the bottom of the mountain. They said they would send two squads of men up the mountain to us. But as it turned out the two squads ran into a bunch of V.C. between us and them. The Line Co. instructed us to stay in our position and not to move for fear of being ambushed. We said we would stay in contact with them until the squads arrived.

About thirty minutes went by and all hell broke loose down in front of us. Bullets were whizzing past us like crazy from both sides. But right then there was no stopping them. We just hoped that the Line Co. had told their men to be watching out for us so we wouldn't end up killing each other. As luck would have it the squads drove the V.C. right up the mountain and into our lap! We could hear them coming a mile away.

Schriff said, "Get ready…something's coming. Make sure of your target."

Then almost point blank about ten V.C. came crashing through the brush right at us. We all jumped up and fired as fast as we could and they fell everywhere. Lori and I were the first into the very small clearing the V.C. came into. We saw no movement from any of them. But that didn't mean they were all dead. Charley liked to play opossum. When you flipped one over on his back, he would sometimes have a 9mm Chi-Com pistol waiting to surprise you or maybe a grenade or possibly even a knife, you never knew.

Very carefully we checked over the bodies one by one. During the fire fight when we started firing, the Line Co. squad heard all the shooting, but they didn't know who was doing the shooting. So they radioed back to the Line Co. and told them there was fire up ahead. Schriff then radioed the squad and told them about the ambush we just laid on Charley. So finally every one knew what was going on.

The Line Co. squad got up and moved ahead. It was a real slug festival for a while as they made their way up to us. As all that was going on Lori and I were still looking over the bodies. The V.C. were shot up and bloody…all except one.

Lori said, "Watch this one!" With that he kicked him so hard in the side I know he must have broken some ribs. That guy started to yell like a cat with a Doberman attached to his tail.

"No kill!….No kill!" He yelled. So I grabbed him by the back of the shirt collar and dragged him back to Schriff and the other guys.

Just as we got back to the rest of the team we could hear American voices. We started calling out to them, "Over here! You beautiful grunts!" I didn't believe I ever!…felt so good about seeing line grunts in my life. I could have won the million dollar lottery and it still wouldn't have felt as good as seeing those dudes. As they came closer they started joking and saying that no matter how bad Recondos were we still couldn't make it without a grunt's help. All we said was stuff like, you guys are all right, and let them have their fun. They could have called us anything they wanted to, it was all right with us!

The Line Co. squad leaders called back to the Co. A and said that the area was secure. They said they wanted a piece of the action and were instructed to go on ahead and see what they could find. We pointed the way to Charley, thanked them once again and said, see ya later!

We picked up our prisoner and left. Down the mountain we walked. Soon we were breaking through the jungle into the open plain. The rest of the Co. was down there so we all got a hot meal and rested. Jackson was given First Aid by one of their medics and the rest of us sat around picking ticks and leaches off ourselves. After a while, we could hear our chopper coming in to pick us up. It was one of the most beautiful sounds you could hear when you were out on a mission.

Headquarters said they wanted our V.C. prisoner as soon as we got back in. With his hands and feet tied and a blindfold over his eyes, Lori tossed him into the chopper as soon as it landed. Most G.I.s liked to play with or torment Charley. What I mean by that is they liked to scare the life out of him. They would love to kick, slap and poke at him. And often times if you didn't watch and guard him well you found your prisioner dead on the ground with his throat slit from ear to ear!

The helicopter ride back to Uplift almost turned into a heart attack for old Charley. The guy was about the same age as all of us, but very small and skinny. These men weren't very physically strong but very slippery and wiry. Getting him into the chopper was a real job. The guy kicked, twisted and screamed the whole time. At times I almost felt sorry for the poor little dude. But after thinking about him and his buddies on our tail for the past day or more I forgot all that soft-hearted bologna.

Soon after our chopper was airborne, the two intelligence men we saw inside the aircraft took hold of our V.C. guest and began asking him a few questions as the chopper climbed higher and higher. Then most of the way back those two guys had the V.C. dude hanging out the door of the chopper by his heals, just drilling him with questions about the amount of troops on that mountain and their location. They had his blind fold off, of course, so he could enjoy the scenery far below. Just watching this little dude going through contortions, truly believing he was about to start his first day of jump school without a parachute and all, gave me such a rush! I could just feel the fright the little dude was going through hanging out the door of the chopper by his toes up that high! Wow! What a rush he must have been having! Especially since he had never been on a chopper, or even in the air for that matter. And not knowing if the Intel. "buddies" he just got to meet had his best interests at heart. Well, I'll tell you, it was no time at all and that V.C. was singing the blues in stereo. I know I most likely would have been singin' myself! I'm not laughing at him one bit; I don't blame the guy for spilling the beans! The intelligence men could speak fluent Vietnamese and wrote down everything he cried out. The whole team got a kick out of the whole thing because we knew the guy was too valuable for thoes two Intel. jokers to let go of. So I guess we could see the humor in it…but for Charley….I never heard him laugh once!

After awhile the Intel. guys put his blind fold back on and let him sit down. He was shaking so bad I thought he was going to rattle apart. One Intel. man looked at us and said, "Man!….is this a big one!"

CHAPTER 11

Parrrty Time!

The chopper ride back was very enjoyable for all on board, except for old Charley, that is. But no one gave a hoot about him! It wasn't long and we could see black smoke and that circular dust bowl we called home. Dust bowl yes...but it looked a whole lot better than where we just came from. I felt glad to see that place again.

We were still up fairly high. I could see a good sized village off to the right about two miles down the mountain. I hadn't really noticed it on our way out a few days ago. But at that time I was so scared I looked like Charley over there, shaking apart at the seams. Like him I was in total shock the whole time. I wondered if that was the village of Bon Song I had heard about.

By that time we were almost down and no one on the team really said a word the whole way back. They just sat there laughing and watching the two Intel. dudes trying to kill Charley by way of fright. Myself, I was thankful it was over. My nerves were about shot watching them. It was so noisy on that chopper you could hardly think. I could hardly stand it much longer for wanting to scream and shout and jump up and down with sheer happiness that the mission was over and we were back safe and sound. Man I thought, we're home. I didn't really have to sweat old Charley that night. I bet he was wishing he didn't have to fear us...I thought yeeeeeahoo! Parrrrrrty time!

Just then I felt the chopper touch ground. In a flash we were out. The chopper turned its motor off to re-fuel. Schriff told us to go clean up or whatever we wanted and said he and the two intelligence men were going to take the prisoner to the interrogation station for a de-briefing. He said, "See you men later! Oh, by the way you animals were grrrrrrrreat! Badazz mother's to the bone!..Airborne!" We yelled out, "All the way to hell!" He smiled and walked off with the two Intel. men and the very soon to be sorry Mr. Viet Cong.

All at once the men in our team grabbed me and each other and we started jumping up and down yelling and screaming, "Yeeeeeeeeeea! hoo! Let's parrrrrty!" We all yelled "Airborne!....All!...the...way!"

We turned and started to walk away all talking at once about what we were going to do that night. Jackson said he was going to the small First Aid station we had on post to see if he could get some ghost time out of his wound. If we had any excuse to get out of the woods we would use it. And Jackson sure had a good excuse. We all wished him luck on how much ghost time he would get and we said see you later. "Love that mo' f*##**in' ghost time." He shouted as he walked away.

I took his rut sack with me. And off he went. So Lori, Babbles and I walked on. Lori asked me, "What are you doing tonight, Jim?"

I said, "I don't know. What do you guys do when you have time off?"

Lori said, "I get stoned out! And keep partying until our next mission." I said that I never was one to walk away from a good party and I said let's go!

Babbles said he was just going to clean up and relax and maybe make a tape to send home or something. He told me that if I ever wanted to make a tape to send home to feel free and use his tape recorder.

I said, "Thanks!….Maybe someday when I know what to say I may."

We all walked up the hill toward the hooches and rapped all the way. As we got to the hooch, Lori said in a little while when Schriff came up he would ask him to ask the old man about a couple of overnight passes for us. Maybe we could go down to the village and party that night.

I asked, "Yeah? Really? They let you do that?" Lori said that if Schriff thinks we deserve it he would be able to talk the old man into it no sweat.

He said, "We did a good job with getting a few kills and nabbin' a V.C. prisoner and all. It's in the bag dude!" He thought our chances were good.

I said, "Man! does that sound good!"

Lori said, "We should take a shower first before all the shower water is gone."

I said, "Yeeeah…you're right about the water."

Lori replied, "It's only about noon or so, there should be plenty."

All three of us unpacked and headed for the showers. Lori was right, there was plenty of just right shower water. While in the shower we all got to laugh at each other about the amount of ticks still stuck all over us. It sounds a little weird to think of picking them off each other, but sometimes they were in places you couldn't get to by yourself…if you know what I mean. You soon learn to live with the embarrassment rather than the pain and infection.

Soon we were all done and headed back down the hill toward our hooch. Just before going in, we saw Schriff coming up the hill. He waved and gave us a big high sign. We all smiled and went in.

When we were all about dressed Schriff came in and set his rut sack down. "Man, that's heavy." Then he sat down on his bunk and took a deep breath. He told us that the C.O. was very happy with the team and said we all did an excellent job. Then he reached into his shirt pocket and said, "Here! We all lucked out. The old man gave us all a 24 hour pass!"

Lori and I looked at each other and said, "Yeeeeah!!"

Schriff said, "Have fun…but don't bring anything back with you….Got it?"

We both said, "No sweat!"

Schriff started to hand Babbles his pass. By that time Babbles was on his cot out cold. Schriff said Jackson was all right and he got two weeks ghost time. We said, "Lucky dude!" Lori and I finished getting dressed. Then we told Schriff we would see him later and we headed down to the Vill. Schriff said he would see us down at Momma-son's in a little while.

It really felt strange to me to be dressed with clean clothes and ready to go party down to the Vill, still carrying my M-16 fully loaded and ready to fire. While we were on the post itself, except on bunker guard, we would have to keep the breach bolt pulled back and locked open, chamber empty so no one got shot by accident. But with an M-16 all you had to do to instantly lock and load a round with 19 behind it was to push the button. And the second we left Uplift, we would lock…and load! Nam to me always was half party and half war. Lock and load and then partying is a really weird combination.

Down the hill and out the gate we went. Lori said, "You got your pass?"
I said, "Yeah right here in my shirt pocket."

He said, "If an M.P. stops you and you don't have orders, they'll drag you back." So off we went. As we walked along the road there were people everywhere. Mostly Vietnamese people. But there were G.I.s walking along too, on both sides of the road, coming and going. There were carts pulled by hand and water buffalo. Water buffalo looked sort of like a black humped Brahma bull with huge horns. Mean looking but very gentle. They were a mountain of meat but the dumbbell's wouldn't eat them. They believed the animal might be a dead member of the family come back to life. I know one thing. If I was as hungry as these people looked...grandpappy would have landed on my Bar-B-Q in a flash!

Lori stuck out his thumb as a big deuce and a half approach us. This was a big army transport truck. They would usually stop to give a G.I. a ride. The truck stopped and the guys in back said, "Hop on!" There were a bunch of guys already in the back of the truck and they helped pull us on board. The box of the truck was about four feet off the ground and it was a bummer getting up in the back.

As the truck pulled away I could see a big open gate up ahead about fifty yards. It was about ten feet high, made of 2 x 10s with barbed wire woven all over it. On either side of the road were small lookout towers completely shielded with sand bags. At this road block there were M.P. guards. The guards were stopping Vietnamese people and checking their carts over real good. They let us right through.

On the other side of the gate which stretched about forty yards across, from one side of the road to the other, I could see a 50 cal. machine gun and an M-60 sticking out of each tower toward the road. There was a guy in each tower manning the guns. Each tower had handmade billboard-like signs plastered with all kinds of graffiti. Names of different states and names of guys that had passed through, I guessed. Everywhere there were Vietnamese people trying to sell us anything you could imagine. They even hung all over the truck we rode in and tried to sell us their stuff. The guys on the truck would just smash their fingers with the butts of their guns and punch their faces in and the people would fall off. There were so many people on the road that the truck had to move slowly and continuously. People would just move in a swarm around it as we went. The ride toward the village took a long time but it was only about three or four miles away.

After the endlessly slow ride, we finally got to the Vill, a.k.a. the village of Fu Mi. The houses or hooches were mostly composed of round grass. They were about ten to fifteen feet in diameter and about ten feet at the peak. Inside they were set up with a lot of curtained-off rooms. These rooms were constantly occupied by "ladies of the night," (and day as well) and the guys that were with them. In the main room, located in the middle of the hooch, was the living room, kitchen and dining room all in one. The stoves were made of rock, sort of like a cave man would use. How they cooked on them I'll never know. The floors were always dirt, I guess so that Momma-Son could spit out the juice of the red or black beetle nuts she always sucked on. We always had to watch out where we sat...Beetle nuts had some kind of numbing effect for the pain from their rotten teeth. Their teeth were in very bad shape and they must have needed the help, having a mouthful of chipped china. I never once saw a Dentist sign hung out anywhere in the country the whole time I was there.

Lori and I walked into the first big hooch we came to. I saw three girls about twelve or fourteen years old coming right up to greet us. Lori knew them all by name, which was easy…they were usually named Kimmy, Linda or Debbie. He tried to introduce me, half in Vietnamese, half in broken Spanish-American. It was as funny as it was embarrassing.

After he spit out a whole mouth full of bologna, we all laughed and sat down, (I looked around first to see if Momma son had been spitting out juice anywhere) on the big grass mats they had all over the floor.

Lori yelled, "Hey Pappa-son…bring out the good stuff." He told two of the girls to get something for us to drink as he laid back on the third one. "Man….now, we got the life, nothing but women and sex and fun for me for the next twenty four hours. Yeeeeeah!! hoo!!" he yelled. The girl he was laying back on kissed him all over the face. She looked a little young to me, but whatever. I looked over in the room off to my right and saw two more girls laughing softly and sort of pointing at me.

I looked at Lori and said, "What? Do I have something on my face or what?" The girl he was with said something in his ear, then giggled.

He said, "They like your blond hair and green eyes. They love things like that about you gringos." Then he snickered, "You'll make out all right my friend, you'll see."

Poppa-son, an older man about sixty or seventy years old came in. It was hard for me to tell these peoples' ages. To me they looked either real young or real old. It seemed hard to tell the ages of those in between. He carried a couple of small plastic bags in one hand and a black ball of something wrapped in plastic in the other. He sat down on a mat right in front of Lori and I. He gave Lori the two bags and nodded his head smiling.

Lori opened each bag and smelled inside each of them. I could see they were two bags of pot. Lori looked the pot over pinching and smelling it some more. Poppa-son took the plastic off the black ball he had in his hand. It was the size of a softball. Pure tar opium. He took out of his long sleeve a brass pipe about a foot and a half long with a very small funnel-shaped bowl on one end. He filled the bowl with a pea-size piece of opium. He handed it to Lori. Lori tossed back one of the bags of pot.

He said, "This one." It must have had about a quarter pound of pot inside from the size of the bag.

Old Poppa-son smiled and said, "5 p…5 p." That meant five dollars, the "P" meant "Piastres", or M.P.C. Piastres is what they called dollars. The exchange rate they used between their Piastre and M.P.C. was about the same. So Lori pulled out a ball of M.P.C. from his pocket and threw Poppa-son a five M.P.C. bill. Old poppa-son sat smiling with his mouth void of all but two or three black rotten stumps for teeth. He was kind of cute though, like some little detailed porcelain figure you might see in a knick knack shop some place. He sat there with this huge smile like he just made the big deal of the day or something, nodding his head as he put the five away in the sleeve of his long robe.

Lori lit the pipe, took a big hit and passed it to me. I took the pipe and did the same. We passed it back and forth until no more smoke came out. Thank God! By then I had a snoot full and I was totally stoned out!

Poppa-son said, "More?" starting to roll another ball in his fingers.

We both said, "No!"

Poppa-son took the bowl from me and emptied out the ashes. He refilled the pipe and set it down. Then said, "Maybe layta...layta G.I.?"

I said, "Yeah man...much layta."

Lori just laid there with the girl as she stroked his hair. Lori said, "Man, I'm starving."

I said, "Yeah me too." So he told the girl he was with to tell Momma-son to fix some goodies. She got up and walked out of the room. I asked Lori if they had a menu.

He rolled around laughing for awhile then said, "The munchies are good, Momma-son is a good munchie maker, don't worry."

In a short time Momma-son and two girls came in. They all worked at fixing things to eat. They made things like egg rolls and rice type pancakes with meat rolled up in them. They had all kinds of fruit and things for us to munch on. Lori was right, they didn't have much, but what they had was very tasty.

Lori was just about full and said he was thirsty. The two cold beers the girls first brought in were about gone. Most of the time you could get colder beer at the Vill than you could back on post. Army ice went to the big shots way back in the rear....Heaven forbid that their Martinis ever get warm. Lori said to Momma-son, "Hey, Momma-son make us a couple of your special lemon-lime drinks."

Momma-son smiled and said, "You likey G.I.?"

He said, "Boo-koo!" meaning a lot. Then Momma-son said something to one of the girls and she ran out of the room.

While Momma-son cleaned up, a young girl sat down with us. We both tried to make small talk with the girl while we waited for our drinks. Soon the girl that was sent out came back with six or eight very small limes and lemons she had just picked off a tree somewhere outside. Lori told me there were lemon and lime trees all over the place. He said they made a real good fresh drink from them. Also added to the drink, was some natural sweetener they had. Natural sugar cane juice and sugar beet juice was just like granulated sugar but was milder and had a slightly different taste. She would also add some of her homemade rice whiskey. About two or three of those and you could say nighty night for a while. But the drink itself was very tasty. Every time I came to the Vill from then on I would usually ask for one of those drinks instead of beer. In those days I only drank beer once in a while. I didn't really like the buzz from beer.

After a while Lori looked at me and said, "I don't know about you, but I'm 'bout horny."

I said, "Don't look at me and say that!" He laughed and said that he wouldn't want sex with me anyway! He told me my butt wasn't small enough. And he got up. He said all I had to do to get a girl was to grab the girl of my choice and walk her to one of the curtained-off rooms. Things were moving pretty fast for me at that point and I really wasn't horny for these girls anyway. They looked about the size of my little sister back home and that took the starch out of.....well, the whole idea....I told him I would pass for now. "Maybe layta...." I replied.

He said, "You don't know what you're missing." Then he walked off into room with his girl.

I thought about what he said about missing something. I felt I was missing something but it wasn't sex. More like what Schriff said not to bring back with me. A good dose of something I couldn't get rid of was what worried me. At R.V.N refresher school they told us and showed us movies about a type of bug that we could catch that there was no cure for. They may have been feeding us a bunch of bologna, but I didn't want to prove to myself if they were telling us the truth or not. Right then that worried me so much I don't think I could have had sex anyway.

The one remaining girl sat down with me and rubbed my back and shoulders. She kept saying boo-koo pretty G.I. She kept giggling and playing around with me. She loved to play with my hair and kept smelling it. I felt a bit strange but if she was having fun I wasn't going to spoil it for her. Besides, it felt good having someone pamper me to death for a change. For quite some time I was not sure that anyone gave a hoot if I was alive or dead. Anyway, she made me feel good. Maybe that meant something. Most likely all she wanted was my money. I tried to talk with her for a while but I was really getting nowhere so I closed my eyes to rest. From the drinks and opium, I was out in a flash.

I slept for awhile and was woken up to the sound of Schriff's voice. "We now...look at Casanova over here." I opened my eyes and saw Schriff smiling and looking down at me.

"It didn't take you long to get relaxed did it?" He asked.

I sat up smiling and said, "I or...we were just resting...you know."

He laughed and said. "Yeeeeah! tell me another one." With that he sat down and ordered up a cold drink. The girl that was lying there with me went over and hugged him, then she left.

Schriff said that it looked like I'd been into the good stuff already. My eyes felt sandy and puffy. I said, "Yeeeah, it was all Lori's fault. He made me do it."

Schriff laughed and said, "Yeah I can see your arm is all bent out of shape."

The girl with Schriff's drink came back in and sat down. I never could remember the girls' names. Everywhere I went in the Nam they were named the same but I could never remember who was who. So usually all I did was look at them and ask for something...that always worked.

Just about that time two more G.I.s came in and off with the girls they went. Schriff said to watch the places I went to...the cat houses that is. He said that some of them were clean because army medics would come in and give all the girls their shots from time to time. He said stay away from the other places. He said after while I would know which were which by the number of girls. Small places he said were fly by night operations. The larger ones with very young girls were usually okay.

He then went on and talked about the mission we had just come back from. He said all missions weren't as screwed up as that one was because most of the time we wouldn't run into as many V.C. as we did last time. He said at the briefing that morning, they learned from our prisoner that the mountain we were ambushed on was a major N.V.A.\V.C. base camp. He said it was a sheer miracle we made it out alive. From what the prisoner said, there were more than two hundred-fifty N.V.A.\V.C. soldiers tunneled into that mountain. The mountain was virtually a honey combed bee hive of enemy. He said we were real lucky. He also said the Line Co. that came to our aid was out there right now fighting their butts off. He said in a day or so our team and Moran's team were going back out to set up more ambushes for Charley. With just the thought of going back I could feel gut cramps coming on. He said that I handled myself like a pro. The whole time out there he felt as though his whole team was complete again. I found out a team member named Thomas was killed just a week before I landed in Uplift. Schriff said at first he felt as though he would have to babysit a cherry but said he found out he was wrong. He said that he also had a surprise for me when we got back to Uplift. I asked what it was. He said I would find out when we got back.

Off to our front, where Lori and his girlfriend were, Schriff and I could hear all kinds of moans and groans. Mostly words in Spanish neither of us could understand came out of a room. Schriff looked at me and said, "Lori seems to be having a good time. I was about to ask where Lori was. But I should have known. He's one horny little dude. I've never been here long with Lori before he had it whipped out,"

Scriff said to me. "Did you fall in love yet 'er what?"

I said I was set for now and was more interested in getting screwed up, than….He just laughed and said, "Well let's do it!"

I showed him the bag of pot that Lori bought and I asked, "Do you want me to fire up a bowl?" He said that it was too early for that stuff but some rice wine would suit him just fine for right now. With that he said he was going to look for Momma-son. Schriff was an older guy, to us anyway. We were all under twenty years old and he was pushing thirty-five. He had been in the army for going on ten years and was going to stay for at least ten more. So he planned, anyway. He was from Richmond, Virginia and he was a very nice guy until you ruffled his fur, then he would be all anyone could handle. For being nearly thirty-five years old he didn't have an ounce of fat on him anywhere. He was built like an ox. I wouldn't have wanted to mess with him and I was nineteen and full of fight.

Schriff came back in walking with a girl about his own age. She was very good looking and she had very long jet black hair. He introduced us. "Jim…this is Kimmy." (What did I tell you about their names?) She bowed her head and smiled and said, "You happ nice flend…"

Schriff replied, "Never mind him!…He! happ nicer flend…me!" They both sat down on the mat. Schriff had his bottle of rice wine in one hand and an egg roll in the other. The three of us rapped for a while about everything. Kimmy could speak English surprisingly well. She could hold her own in most any conversation. She was a little hard to understand but she could understand everything we talked about.

Soon Lori was done and came in. Lori said, "Well, look who finally made it." Schriff replied, "I'm not the only one that made it either, I see."

Lori smiled, "Duuuude…I had a throbber that wouldn't quit!"

Schriff said, "Don't you always?"

Lori said, "Cool it dude….Where's that good stuff Poppa-son sold me?"

Schriff replied, "Right here," handing over the bag to Lori.

Lori pulled out an old pipe made of good briar, but with the stem missing. He went on to explain, "This pipe looks beat, but it's had a lot of real good pot put through it. This bowl was brought over by a Ranger a long time ago. And whenever a guy that has it leaves or gets zapped, he always hands it down to someone else and so on. No one really knows who the first guy was."

Lori filled the bowl to the brim. He lit it with a long hard hit. "God!" he said "That's real good tasting weed duuuudes….want some?" He handed it to Schriff

"Yeeeeah, just a hit I guess." Schriff took a hit just to be…"one-a-the-guy's," I think, because he really didn't dig it, I could just tell. He then passed it to me.

The other two G.I.s that came in earlier came back in and sat down with us The two girls they were with were standing over in the corner of the rooms they were in, cleaning up, right in front of all of us. The drapes were open and everything I never saw anyone douche before, especially with a shook up bottle of Coke. started to laugh like mad. Lori, Schriff, and I started laughing like three fools The other guys just looked at us like we were nuts and just sat quietly passing the bowl of pot. They had a portable radio-tape player and asked if we wanted to hear some music. We said sure! They turned it on and we all got buzzed out.

After a while the three of us got tired of that first place and told the girls we would probably see them later. So Lori, Schriff and I walked out. As we walked out the back door, I could see old men and women outside, beating stalks of rice all over a big mat on the ground. This was the way they got the rice off the stalk There were young boys and girls sweeping up the rice as it fell on the mat. Over behind another hooch there were some kids doing the same thing with pot plants These plants were like small trees, not like I've seen before. Some were picking up the buds and leaves and grinding it down to the consistency of cigarette tobacco Pot in any country is like having gold….probably better. You can sell it easier.

On we went around the corner into the main street. Schriff said, "Let's go over to Joe-son's."

Lori said, "Cool." Joe-son's was the village bar. This bar was an old French styled stone and cement building. It was in pretty rough shape but looked fairly sturdy. They said it was an old French army base camp headquarters years ago Now it was used as a bar.

Inside, the place was packed with G.I.s. There were handmade wicker table and chairs everywhere, girls everywhere too. Some old stone steps led upstairs to many rooms. There were three fans overhead turning very slowly. The fans looked like the ones I saw in an old Humphrey Bogart movie one time. You could hardly see for the smoke. There was a small stage up front. Here local and out of town Vietnamese women would get up and try to sing songs like "Teen Angel" and "Blue Velvet" and other 60's–70's songs like that. It was more a comedy show than anything.

After we laughed long enough at these singers, we decided to move on. Back on the road again we were plagued by peddlers of every size and description. They were selling everything under the sun. There were even fathers trying to sell their wives and daughters for a few dollars worth of sex. That really blew me away to see that, just thinking about how good people at home lived. They had it so good and would never understand what it would be like to have to pimp your wife and daughter out each day to make a living and to stay alive. There were no jobs to speak of. They really had no other way of making a buck. It was and still is beyond my understanding how the man or father of his family could do that. If some dude ever came at my family like that, I would have turned him into fish food, "Now!"

In most Vietnamese homes the father was either in the S.V.N. army or working in the rice fields. Most were in the fields because they were too chicken to join the army. They figured why should they fight and die when we were dumb enough to be there doing it for them? The men would go off to work each day, whatever their work was, and the wives and daughters would stay in bed to make their living. If you were a half-way good looking woman you could make a good piece of change each day. The older ones worked in the rice fields.

On we walked, just looking at the people coming and going. What fascinated me was the way almost all the Vietnamese people walked together. Especially the young people would walk hand in hand down the road. Boys with boys, girls with girls, etc. As I got to know these people better, I could tell they were very affectionate people. You couldn't tell by just looking at them because most of the faces told a story of a very hard life with an uncertain future. They all looked sad and frightened to me for the most part. It was when I talked to them and they opened up and showed me what they had and held within them that I could see the warmth they had for one another and the appreciation they had for what little they had. Many times I saw a thing that looked a little weird or strange to me, though. It was the way they would groom each other. By grooming I mean they would pick fleas out of each other's hair and bite the flea, much like you would see monkeys do in the zoo.

The three of us just strolled around looking at and talking about everything. It was getting late afternoon and the army personnel and vehicles started numbering fewer and fewer on the road. As we made our way back to Momma-son's hooch, we stopped by Joe-son's once again.

Inside there were U.S. Army M.P.s telling everyone without a pass to get into the large truck they had parked out front. They asked to see our papers, then let us go. The place was about empty in a few short minutes, all except a couple of soldiers from the S.V.N. army. They were there waiting for their women who were still upstairs getting through work for the day.

All three of us sat down at the bar and ordered up some cold drinks. Joe-son was an Australian that lived there and owned the place. He said he used to be in the Australian army, which was over there too. But when he got out, he wanted to stay as long as the U.S. did and get rich, which no doubt he was doing. He asked us how long we were going to be in town. We said we had to be back by noon tomorrow. He then asked if we needed a room for the night. We said maybe later. He said thirty dollars each would get us a room with a girl and a good meal. He said he had real beds too. So we all decided to stay there. For me the real beds did it.

Joe was a very heavy-built guy, with a laugh you couldn't help enjoying. He said he only bought the place about nine months ago and had a very good business with the girls and all. He said we should think about doing the same after we got out of active duty. But we all said we wouldn't live there for all the money in Vietnam. He just laughed saying, "You Yanks never do know a good thing when you see it!"

I said, "It all depends on whose eyes you're looking through."

He said, "Could be my lad…could be. You gents hungry?" We said we were starved. So we sat down at a table.

Lori said, "I'll have some soup if you have it."

Joe replied, "Just made some chicken soup."

Lori said, "Yeah…that's good maybe some bread too."

Joe said, "O-kay-doke…How 'bout you two gents?"

Schriff asked, "You got any pork?…Like pork chops?"

"Yep…got a whole bunch of them."

Schriff said, "Yeah give me a pork chop dinner."

"Ooookay….How 'bout you mate?" I said that I would have the pork chops too. "Good then! Be right back. Help yourself to the beer and whiskey. It's right over behind the bar. It all comes with the night package."

So we all got a drink and sat back to relax. By that time the married girls were leaving with their men and some of the younger ones just hung around our table and the bar, talking to us. While we ate, the ladies were sizing us up and talking to each other, wondering who would get who for the night. The way they giggled and pointed I could just tell what they were talking about even though I couldn't understand a word.

After awhile we were all full to the brim and got another drink each. Then Lori pulled his pipe and bag of pot out of his lower leg pants pocket and filled the old bowl. After passing it around a couple of times the girls, five of them, came over and all sat down. They kept saying, "G.I.'s boo-koo dinky dow." And they kept shaking their heads at us. For some reason few Vietnamese people smoked pot. What they meant by boo-koo-dinky-dow was we were very crazy for smoking pot.

I said, "To each his own, baby. I think what you girls do is boo-koo-dinky-dow." They just shrugged their shoulders and giggled.

After awhile Joe came over with a cup of coffee and sat down. Lori offered him some pot. He said he never uses the stuff because it made him too sleepy. Out of his shirt pocket he pulled out a glass vile about two inches long. It was about as round as a pencil and looked just like a miniature glass bowling pin. Around the neck of the bowling pin shaped glass was a red ring painted on it.

Lori snickered and said, "He's a speed freak."

Joe said that this was his habit. He used speed to keep awake on busy nights.

He grabbed the top of the glass bottle and snapped the neck off right on the red line. Then he poured the clear liquid into his coffee. After stirring it up he put his finger into it and licked it off. "Yeah," he said, "It's good stuff." He said if it was bitter it was no good. The bitter stuff was a bad batch. He told us the speed was clinically made for the army and could be bought on the black market anywhere. The bottle would sell singly for one dollar. You could buy a pack of ten for six dollars and he sold the stuff right there if we wanted any. One of those small bottle's worth of liquid in a coke or coffee would wire you up for two days with no let up!

It wasn't long and Joe was talking our ears off. We looked at each other and rolled our eyes. "Well!" Lori said, as he got up from the table. "How about a room old dude." Schriff made the same motion.

"Sure!" Joe said, "Now about that thirty bucks each?" We all got out thirty M.P.C. and paid him. "Well! There are the girls…grab one!"

Joe laughed. He said, "$10.00 more for two…anyone want two?"

We all shook our heads no and started to walk toward the stairs. Lori turned around looking at the girls and said, "Well? Who's coming with me?" All five got up.

Schriff said, "Now hold on dude! You ain't that good!"

By the time we got to the top of the stairs we were about paired up. Lori all out grabbed one girl and Schriff was talking to another girl as he led her into a room. There I was by myself, standing out in the hall with the other three. I really didn't know what to say or do except just stand there looking stupid. That was my first time in a cat house with a decision like that to make. I said, "Well! Let's go…who's comin' with me?" I went to open the door, acting as though I had done this sort of thing a million times before. I figured as soon as one girl moved towards the door I would follow close behind and shut the door fast on the other two that would be left. For the life of me I couldn't figure out just what to do. I was starting to feel embarrassed and could feel my face starting to turn red. When I get embarrassed my face lights up like a light bulb. I could feel it coming on big time.

I moved for the door, pushing it open. At that time all three thought I wanted them all, I guess. Usually if a G.I. wanted a certain girl he would just all out say so. By not doing that they must have just thought I was a self-proclaimed super stud or something. As I opened the door they all rushed right in! Look at this, I thought. They all just started to undress and make themselves at home. Oh, man! Now what do I do? I thought. What was I going to tell them, when I couldn't even speak their language? I had no clue how I was going to get that mess ironed out. They were all sitting on the bed nude by then, patting the bed and saying Loa-dai, loa-dai. This means "Come here." My heart started to pump so hard, I couldn't tell if I would "come here" or "faint there." I just knew I would make an idiot out of myself…I felt that way anyhow. That night I was really too juiced-out to handle sex. Besides with everything going through my head like my chick back home, the mission coming up, well, just the whole place made me feel very edgy. Now I was going to have to perform like some X-rated porno star or be laughed out of the Nam.

Then it finally hit me. I had a plan. I would act totally out of it and just fall asleep like I was drunk. Maybe that will work, I thought. I fell about the place acting juiced. As I staggered around the room taking my clothes off, I acted as though I did this all the time. When I had everything off except my shorts, I walked over to the bed and sat down. The girl to my right put her finger on the waistband of my shorts and started to pull on it. "Off G.I.," she said pulling on the elastic band. With out a word I jumped under the sheets…I just acted like it was no big deal. Then they all jumped under the sheets and started pulling my shorts off. Laughing and giggling they lay all over me.

For a while we just played around like a bunch of kids. But that's all we were. As I lay there I started to put my escape plan into action. I just lay there for about ten minutes trying to act as though I was out cold. But as the girls kissed me all over my body and all I started to get turned on. It felt real good but…..Then I started to lose it, I had such a guilt trip going. I had such the notion to just run out of the room and down the road that it wasn't funny. Soon they all stopped kissing me and they just lay down holding me. Then I started to feel calmer. I was hoping my plan was starting to work. It felt real good to have women all over me. It had been a long time since I had felt the softness of a woman. It was very lonely in Vietnam even though there were buddies around me all the time. It was just no way near the same as having a woman hold you. Even for a few hours. There is a lot in the saying…reach out and touch someone. I believe we all need that from time to time.

The next morning came fast. I could hear Joe calling the girls downstairs saying, "Come, ladies….the doc's here," about three times. I could hear Lori coughing and Schriff laughing in the next rooms. I still lay there like I was asleep. The girls all got out of bed and got dressed. Then I could hear Schriff and Lori talking out in the hallway.

Lori said, "We'll see him downstairs," or something like that. I was still lying in my bed. The three girls walked out of the room. Right outside my door I could see Lori and Schriff standing out in the hall with their mouths open and eyes bugging out, looking at the three girls walk one at a time out of my room. As the last girl left, both of their heads turned toward me still lying in bed.

"Well! I'll be screwed…blued…and tattooed!" said Schriff. "Look at this bull! No wonder he has a tattoo of a bull on his arm."

They both came in and started pulling my sheets down and punching me. I laughed so hard I almost choked! When I stopped laughing I just said, "You never send a boy out to do a man's job."

Lori said, "Get the **#**! up! gringo, and let's go eat some breakfast."

All the way down the hall and stairs I had to listen to those guys saying, "Do you believe that!?" stuff like that. I got dressed and came down stairs. I saw a G.I. with a black doctor's bag sitting at the bar talking to Joe. Joe pulled out a roll of money and gave the guy some. The bar was still closed and the only people inside were Joe, the G.I., Schriff, Lori and the five girls and I. As I walked over to the table Lori and Schriff were sitting at I passed the women I stayed with that night. They all said, "Bye Jimmy, see you latta, Okay G. I.?"

I acted totally cool and said, "Yeah no sweat. I'll be back ladies….I'll catch ya later!" They all laughed. Right then I do believe I was having my rocks busted by the three girls big time! But with Lori and Schriff just staring at me and shaking their heads….I never had my stones busted like that before and still have it feel soooo good! I walked over to the ladies table and I put a twenty dollar M.P.C. note down and I winked as I gave it to them. That was payment for keeping our little secret if for nothing else. They said, "See you Jimmy!" Still giggling as they got up and went into the back room that lead to the kitchen.

I then walked over to the table with Lori and Schriff and I sat down and said, "It's a fine morning….What's for breakfast? I'm starved."

Lori said, "You should be…f@#*#ing gringo! You must have burned up more energy last night than you did in jump school."

Schriff said, "What do you have? an 18"…."

I interrupted, "Don't talk about stuff like that at the table…don't you have any manners?" I near popped a gut trying not to laugh. Joe was just about done rapping with the G.I. at the bar and they walked into the back room where the girls went. It was about 0700 and we had a few hours before we had to report back to Uplift. So we all had coffee and breakfast. I asked during our meal what that G.I. was doing out back. Schriff said he was a medic and was there to give the ladies their shots.

I said, "No sweat about any sickness or anything…..right guys?" They just grunted and kept eating.

After breakfast we said goodbye to Joe and the ladies. He said, "You blokes come back now…eh?"

We said, "Oh yeeeeah boy…bye now."

We walked out. Outside it was stifling hot. Traffic was jammed up as usual with people moving up and down the road. There were about five or six women that came in off the street and went into Joe's place. They were going to work, I thought. And off we went.

"Well," asked Schriff, "Want to head back?"

Lori and I said, "Yeah, might as well."

Schriff said, "Hey Jimmy…want to grab a couple of broads before we head back?"

Laughing softly I said, "Do we have enough time?"

He said, "After what I saw…I doubt it," Lori just started mumbling something in Spanish as we walked on.

"Want to walk or get a ride?" I asked.

Lori said, "We might as well walk, it would probably be quicker, with all this traffic." So we walked right out of town waving to Momma-son as we walked past her hooch. She just smiled and shook her fist at us, probably for not staying at her place. We walked slow but steady for about an hour before reaching the last check point gates. At the base of Uplift Mountain between the Vill and the gates, I had been suckered into buying all kinds of garbage from nearly every peddler on the road. I picked up a watch, three rings, two wrist bracelets and three or four neck chains. The peddlers just looked so needy to me I couldn't help it. All the way Lori and Schriff kept telling me I was nuts for buying stuff from these people and they probably had more money than all of us put together. Well, no matter. They still looked awful poor to me.

Joe Son's

CHAPTER 12

Letter From Home

After opening and locking the breach to our M-16s and ejecting the round in the chamber we walked on post. Up the mountain we went until we got to the top. We walked through the hill gate and up toward our hooch. Before we went into the hooch we all looked at the duty roster on the bulletin board up at the orderly room. That night Lori and I were assigned to bunker #2 and Schriff was on C.Q. duty in the C.O.'s office. All of us had an easy job that night. So we all went into the hooch to relax until then.

I went over to my cot and I saw a letter there. It was from my father. I opened it and it said, "Hi Jim, this is your old man. Just wondered how things were going with you. We all miss you real bad here at home. Ma and Debbie send their love and wonder why you don't write."

Oh no! I thought, this was going to be one of the few times the old man got mushy. I really wasn't ready for all that right then. I had to stop reading...I was about to start to sniffle so bad. I really missed them all so much...even that mean ol' disagreeable....I don't think I ever felt so lonely in my whole life.

Lori came over and said, "Hey man, everything okay?" I just walked out. I put the letter into my shirt pocket and sat down on the walkway outside.

Lori came out right behind me. I knew he was there but I said nothing.

"Letter from home?" He asked.

I nodded my head yes. He said, "When I got my first letter from home, I felt so far away and out of place I could have died. People like us shouldn't have anyone home to write to us because we both feel a lot inside. Some other guys don't care, but you and me, I think we're different. My life growing up in Spanish-Harlem was like growing up in hell. To make it, you had to be one tough mother. Until I got my first letter from home I thought I was the baddest dude around. After that, I felt like a weak punk. No matter where I am...here or home...I'm still only human...only a man. I know I have mucho feelings inside that just break me down sometimes from a bad azz to a weak punk. Being a Recondo is not only a job of being the strongest and baddest...but also a job of being just human....being only a man. Sometimes it's very hard being both even though we have to. Things will get better as time goes on. You'll see...."

I told Lori that he was a good friend and I appreciated what he was saying. I told him that I would see him inside and I took out the letter and I read on. The ol' man...my dad went on to say, "I know it's hard to find the time to sit and write a letter while in a war zone. I lived through the same type of thing during World War II and I know what it is like. I was a Ranger once just like you. And I've lived through combat just like you." It was the first time in my life he put me on the same level with him. He told me that if I found the time to write home, everyone would be very happy to hear from me. Especially my Mom and girl. He told me not to worry about writing to him because I had enough things to worry about right then.

I knew right there, right then, he was telling me he was missing me. I knew he was just too tough to say it because that was just the way he was. I also knew right then, my dad and I were now truly looking at each other eye to eye...I could see he knew that I had truly become a man. I was a combat soldier just like he once was and I saw he was telling me that he respected me for it. I believe every boy needs and has to walk that same road one day with their father to grow up and become a man. To me that's one big reason I believe every boy needs to have a father in his life, even if he has a father that was as tough and as hard to please as mine always was. There were many times I hated him...but I also loved him just because he was my dad. I also believe at times he hated me as well for the grief I brought to him... But I also believe he loved me in his own way, just because I was his son.

"Well soldier! Good-bye for now and take care. We will see ya soon. God bless you, Dad." I got back to my feet feeling as low as fifteen pounds of whale dung and I went inside the hooch. I almost started to write a letter home, but I just couldn't. I really didn't know just what to say. So I lay down to rest.

Then Lori and Schriff came and got me. They wanted to know if I wanted to go to chow with them. So I said, "Yeah, I'm starved."

"Let's go then," Schriff said.

After chow at the mess hall on the main post, we saw Moran's team walking towards the chopper pad. Schriff said that they were going out to where we went, on our last mission to do a little ambushing as we did.

I said, "I hope they have better luck than we did!" So we walked toward the chopper pad to say good luck to the other team. When we got there we all started to talk about our last mission and what we ran into.

Moran said, "Don't get too comfortable, you guys are coming out with us tomorrow. We were told that at the briefing just now!"

Oh nuts! I thought, here comes the gut cramps again. I was beginning to get a cold sweat just thinking about it. Schriff said, "Yeah! I already heard about the mission. I was talking to the old man about it this morning...!"

Just about then their chopper was all fueled up and started its motor. They all waved goodbye. We said, "good luck." And they jumped onboard. Up they went like a shot. Quickly they were out of sight. We walked away.

I asked, "We go out tomorrow?"

Schriff said, "Yeah...I guess so. I'll find out all about it tonight on C.Q. duty. As soon as I know something I'll come out to your bunker and tell you guys all about it."

As we walked up towards our hooch Schriff said, "It's about 1330 now. I'm going up to talk to the old man."

So we said, "See ya later."

Schriff turned back and yelled, "Be at the bunker around 1700." We said okay and walked on.

Lori and I were ready at 1700. He got his pot and handed down the special pipe out of his footlocker and he said, "I got my ammo how about you?" I laughed grabbing my M-16 and ammo belt and we walked out. Up at the bunker there were two guys sitting around getting high. We asked if they wanted any relief.

One guy said, "You guys are on time, how come?"

"Because we're such a couple of nice guys," I replied.

They said, "Bye now!" And they jumped down.

They were from a Line Co. down on the main post and they walked away. Every Line Co. soldier, Recon, and Ranger took a turn on guard duty while in the rear. No one was exempt except E-6 or higher. They pulled C.Q. duty in the offices just like Schriff. C.Q. duty was the job of sitting in the company office taking calls, etc. Mostly sleep time. So was bunker guard except the two hours that you were on watch.

Lori and I sat down and got all stoned out while we rapped about…well, you name it. We would like to talk about U.F.O.s, life after death, woman and every possible thing one could think of. After a while the rest of the guys on guard started to show up. Soon they were all there. No one really cared when we got there as long as the bunker was covered and everyone was there somewhere close to 1800. There were two guys from Recon, two guys from A Co. down below and Lori and I. We all had a good rap session and partied for quite a while that night.

Then it was time to crash. Lori and I didn't know what lay ahead for us the next day and we needed to get some sleep. During the night Schriff came over to our bunker and said that he didn't find out much except we were going out at 0800 for sure, and we would be briefed on the mission tomorrow at 0730. Here we go again, I thought. Back to Viet Cong City!

It seemed as though I just closed my eyes and I was up on the last shift of guard duty already. The watch I bought the day before on the road to Fu Mi was already water logged with sweat and stopped. I stood up and stretched. Naturally I was covered with bug bites from head to toe. The mosquito bites were something else! I looked around and saw guys coming out of hooches everywhere on the main post. Most were in green army shorts heading for the showers. Some were dressed and all ready for work. Ron, one of the guys from A. Co. was just sitting there half asleep, with his boony hat pulled over his face. The bright morning sun hitting him in the face was starting to wake him up. He was the guy I relieved the night before. The sun was half up over the mountain. It looked so big and red it seemed I could reach out and touch it. It really didn't hurt my eyes to look right at it right then. But you wouldn't want to do that about noon time. By then it looked white hot and it was. The air never had a pleasant coolness to it, even that early in the morning.

I could see guys starting to go into the chow hall down the hill about three hundred yards away. I thought, it must be about 0530 or shortly there after. Just another half hour or so and I could duff out of the detail I was on. Lori said, "Hey duuuude….what you dooooeeen'…?" He looked like an elephant sat on him all night he was so wrinkled up. His sunglasses half on half off cocked sideways and the same with his hat. He was a short, stocky Spanish Puerto Rican. Everything for some reason looked too big on him.

I said, "I'm on guard duty…that's what I'm dooeeen'….."

He laid back down and said, "Duuuude!…did I ever get a big f#@**#eeen' mosquito bite man."

I said, "Yeeeeah!? no kiddin'….I didn't get one bite." Which I didn't get just one…I had at least a million. I said that I had to go the head and I would catch him back at the hooch.

He said, "Okay man, see ya tee-tee," meaning a little while.

After jumping over the sand bags that were piled around us I almost left my best buddy. I jumped up, and grabbed it. After going to where my nose didn't want any part of, I headed for chow hall which smelled about the same. I figured I would get both jobs out of the way so I could relax a while and get a head start on packing for the mission. Just the word mission made my gut flip! After I left the john I walked down to chow and picked at my....well, the cooks called it "breakfast." I always called it something else. Nothing like powdered eggs and steamed toast. I looked at a guy's watch next to me; somehow it was still running. Maybe it was just a good one, or it had some parts inside and not just a face painted on it. It read ten of six. Although I hated to leave the rest of what was called "a good square meal," I just got tired of playing with it so I walked out the screen doors and I headed toward the hill.

As I started to cross the road, I could see all the local folks coming back on post for their day of work. Every day Vietnamese people were allowed to come on post and work menial jobs, such as work in the tailor shop, barber shop, burn detail and work in the mess halls cleaning up, jobs like that. For five bucks a week you could have a hooch maid come in and clean up your bunk area. That five bucks would also include your laundry cleaned, pressed and starched. If you wanted any extras, that would cost you more. The locals would love to get a job riding on a garbage truck. They would fight over that job. It was like the old Polish joke, ten bucks a week and all you could eat. Well, these people took it literally. Down at the dump they would flock all over the junk picking the garbage for anything.

When I was in training many times I had K.P. duty. At the day's end, the food garbage or anything edible, was put into 55 gallon drums. Pig farmers would buy the nasty looking stuff for next to nothing to feed their pigs. Well...in the Nam they gave it to the locals. They would pour this slop off a truck into the dump. Under the tail-gate of the truck would be many old Momma and Poppa-son's with buckets waiting to catch the stuff. But when you're starving, one man's "dump"...is another man's meal.

I was just about to the hooch area when I saw Lori coming out for formation. The only reason we went to formation that day was because we were going out that morning. We wanted to get any updated info. about the mission. Sometimes at the last second they would stop the mission. He said, "Ready to swoop?" I said, "Yep." So we walked the rest of the way up the hill.

Formation went as usual with the daily handing out of details and all the boring announcements. Sgt. Peppy said Schriff's team would be going out and for us to get our stuff ready by 0800 for a briefing. He also went on to say that three men from Schriff's team have been put in for a medal. Each by Schriff himself. I said to myself man, I wonder who those guys are? A medal, I thought. Peppy went on, "Also we have a promotion to give out today. PFC Gibbore...step forward please." I stood there dumbfounded....me? They want to promote me? I thought.

So I walked out of line and up to our company commander and stood at attention. He said, "PFC Gibbore, I am authorized by the U.S. Army to promote you to Sergeant E-5 as of this date. Also, you have been put in for a bronze star with gold leaf cluster for your outstanding performance against a hostile enemy force. And for possibly saving the life of a fellow soldier. Congratulations, Sergeant! You have done an excellent job." He also said that I was awarded two confirmed body counts. He then saluted me with a hearty, "Airborne!" I said, "All the way Sir!" and saluted him back.

I felt like a million bucks. I was glad I didn't have to make a speech or anything because I couldn't have said a word I was so shocked. I thought I was dreaming. A promotion two grades higher plus a medal. No way man, I'm dreaming I thought.

As I walked back to the formation, I looked at Schriff. He smiled then winked. He said, "Good job, Jimmy!" So that's what his surprise was. That big jerk, I thought. But he's all right in my book.

The C.O. said, "I am also authorized by the U.S. Army to announce that E-5's Jackson and Updike be given a purple heart each. E-5 Jackson will also receive a bronze star for the successful completion of his mission while wounded by enemy fire. These men are not here at this time…but are at the Ophu Cat M.A.S.H. unit for R&R. As soon as they get back, they will receive their awards. All three of these men have done an excellent job." He saluted the air and yelled, "Airborne!" The First Sgt. yelled out, "Companyyyyy!.....teeeeeeen-hut!...Dismissed…Fallout!"

Lori and most of the other men came right over to congratulate me. A couple of the older guys said, "Good job! Soldier!…We heard how you handled yourself. You can be on our team any time you want!" I only wished Moran had been there to see this one, I thought. His blood would have boiled.

As Lori, Schriff and I walked down to the hooch Schriff explained to me about the double jump in rank I got. He said that the old man thought for a new man, I really did a good job. And I was really an E-4 anyway. Because as soon as I landed in country I was automatically a Sp-4, just without official orders is all. He said he would make it official one step higher to E-5. He said that the old man told him he needed guys with brains to run a team, because team leaders were hard to come by. And he may need another team leader soon and he wanted me trained and ready a.s.a.p. In Nam, only E-5 or above could be a team leader. Except, in the case of a wiped out team, then the highest-ranking man would take over, even if he was a P.F.C.

I felt proud as a peacock in full bloom. Schriff said that around there everything you did counted at promotion time, everything! Even body counts. He said that the two body counts I got bought me my overnight pass. No kidding, I thought. That's what you have to do to get an overnight pass in this place!? Man, that's nuts! But that was that and it was all right with me. Screw it I thought, it don't mean nothin'! I hoped I got a few more the next time out. Man! I thought, what was I thinking? I didn't know it then, but the war was moving into my soul like a sickness.

It was about 0700 and time to finish packing for our next mission. I didn't know why, but that word mission didn't scare me anymore. It was more of a thrill than the scary feeling I just had felt that morning, only a couple of hours earlier. As time went on and the missions came and went, we all began to look at a mission like just another day's work and not the life-threatening nightmare that it really was.

Schriff said he was going up to supply to get our ammo and food for our mission. I said, "Bring lots of ammo!" Schriff, Babbles, Lori, myself and two other men were going out that morning. I didn't know who the other men were. I wondered who would be going in place of Jackson and Updike. Lori and I were about to rest a minute while we waited for Babbles and Schriff to come back from supply with our food and ammo.

Just then I saw the guy I met the first day down in the bunker shelling cigarettes. Westmore introduced him to me. The guy from Canada, O'Banyon they called him O.B. He walked in and set his rut sack down. He said, "Hi guys, my name is O'Banyon. They call me O.B."

Lori said, "Yeah man, I've seen you around before."

And then O.B. said, "Yeah, same here man."

He looked at me. "And you, didn't I meet you a few days ago down at the bunkers with Westmore?"

I said, " I remember you."

Lori asked, "What's up?"

He said that two months ago he put in for Recon and he finally got called. We said, "Congratulations man, welcome!" Lori asked, "You been out much?"

O.B. sat down and said, "I got 22 confirmed."

Lori looked at me and said, "Welcome duuude!" O.B. just smiled.

Lori said, "You must be replacing Updike, he just got hit the last mission we were on.

O.B. said, "Oh yeah?…I guess."

Just then Schriff came in with two boxes of supplies, Babbles right behind him with two more. Babbles yelled, " Man, that's a long way down that hill."

Schriff tossed his boxes to the floor saying, "Here is your Claymore mines and L.R.R.P.'s."

Babbles said, "I got M-16 rounds and baseballs." Baseballs were round hand grenades. Baseball fragmentation grenades or "Fraggs" as we called them. They had a high explosive called composition C-4 and ball bearings packed inside them. You could imagine what damage they would do, same thing as our Claymore mines.

Schriff asked, "Did you men meet O.B.?…There are only five of us going out on this mission. We're going to work with Moran's team when we get out there." We told Schriff we knew O.B. and it was soon time to go…we were all about ready. Schriff asked, "Everyone got everything?" We all double-checked and we said we were ready. He said, "Move out!"

We all put our packs on our backs and moved out. Down the hill we went, across the road and marched to the briefing bunker. We all dropped our rut sacks outside and went in.

After we sat down and started rapping for about ten minutes the C.O. and the two Intel. men came in and walked up front. One Intel. man unrolled a map he was carrying and hung it up on the wall, up front. Looking at us he said, "I hope you guys had a good rest. This mission could be up to two weeks long." Usually a mission would last between three and seven days. I've even heard of missions lasting up to a month. Most Line Co.'s would go out for at least a month at a time. So I guess we were lucky that way.

The intelligence man said that the prisoner we captured last mission gave them a lot of info. He said after the free introductory helicopter ride they gave him he was more than willing to tell them just what we had to know. Pointing up at the map on the wall he touched an area called the Annamitique Mountain Range. He said this is the area we got ambushed in and where we picked up our V.C. guest. He said that according to the info. that they extracted from Charley this area housed a very large N.V.A. and V.C. training and supply camp somewhere yet unknown to him. He said he didn't know just exactly how many V.C. were there or exactly where the main underground base camp was. But the prisoner told him that there were at least two hundred enemy troops and the underground camp was near the top of a mountain were we were going to be dropped. Our mission was to find the camp so they could clean them out. He said as far as V.C. base camps go, this was a very large one. He said Charley told them they had a hospital, many weapons and plenty of rice. The intelligence man went on to say that A. Co. was out there now working to back up Moran and another Recon team. He said both Recon teams had reported boo-koo enemy moving at night. Recon reported Charley moving every night since they have been out there. He said that day we were going to replace Recon team #2. He said Moran's team, Hunter #1, was going to be working their way around behind the two smaller enemy base camps one of which we stayed at the last time out to set up ambushes. And we were going in the front way to do the same. Both teams were to keep looking the area over to try to find the "door" to the underground camp. More or less in the same area we were chased out of.

No way, I thought. Right back down that tunnel leading to hell again. But in Nam, a job was a job. He said we would move in very quietly and cautiously to try and get the drop on Charley at night and do as much damage as we could. I thought, ambushing at night? This should be fun! How are we supposed to see to do it? I thought. Sooner than later, I would find out.

The Intel. man said we would ambush for a day or so to weed out as many enemy as we could and locate anything else we could find. The Line Co. would then be sent in to sweep the area and try to attack the V.C. on the mountain itself and clean out the cave if we could find it. He went on to say that before the attack of the Line Co. started they would shell and burn the mountain down to open it up and clean it off.

At the time I thought, how would they be able to flatten the mountain we were on? Right! I thought, they better bring an "A" bomb to level that big sucker, maybe two! Our Captain, the C.O. asked if we had any questions. He said, "If not, good luck on the mission and be very careful! This is no Sunday picnic! But I just want to say that it is very important that we find that hidden door.

CHAPTER 13

The Hidden Door

About ten minutes went by and Schriff came out of the briefing bunker. Schriff said that we all had a big job to do and to stay on our toes! He pointed at the man standing by the chopper, a crew chief I guessed. He twirled his hand over his head and the man jumped in.

Just then, the chopper started its motor. "Let's go, men!" Schriff yelled and we ran to the thundering air ship. In just a couple of minutes we were all in and lifting off. As I looked down at home, I could see people getting smaller and smaller. We banked to our left harder and harder and over the mountain we flew.

Uplift went quickly out of sight. Far off in the distance I could see the town of Phu Mi where Lori, Schriff and I had partied just yesterday. We'll be back Momma-son, we'll be back, I thought to myself.

Higher and higher we climbed. Soon my ears were plugged tight. We flew for about twenty minutes and I could see the mountain we had to hump. Far below in the valley was the open area we would land in. I just hoped that Charley's welcoming committee stayed home that day.

Schriff must have been reading my mind. He said, "This time the L.Z. is secured. No V.C. Jim."

I smiled back and said, "Sounds good to me!" My ears were starting to pop open again and I felt the old butterflies on the move in my guts again. It was only a couple of minutes circling the L.Z. once and we were down.

As soon as the chopper hit ground we all jumped out and ran toward the jungle edge. There was a Line Co. Captain on his way over to us with Recon team #2 team leader. The Captain asked, "How you men doing?" Then he said, "You guys really stirred Charley up last time." He wanted us to sit down and hear what Sgt. Morris of Recon team #2 had to say. So we all got rid of our rut sacks and sat down.

Morris said that he and his team had been out there for over a week and saw enemy coming and going from more than just one base camp. He said they had been watching Charley from different positions at night with a starlight scope. He said that they had made every effort not to let the V.C. know they had been observing them. He said he thought that they had been successful. They hadn't made any contact with Charley at all. He said Charley had been seen watching the Line Co. but they hadn't really let it bother his activity. Morris told us that they had found a second base camp and he felt that there was an underground base camp still undiscovered somewhere on the mountain. He said that the enemy just seemed to disappear after they followed V.C. into the very dense jungle area on the other side of the mountain.

Morris said, "Let's walk out in the open and I can show you where I am talking about. I can also show you approximately where you found the camp you stayed at." So we took a few steps out and looked up. It was like looking up at a life size map. Morris pointed up and said, "Do you see that tallest tree line up at the top just a few hundred yards to the right of that very steep rock face?" We all saw just where he pointed and said we did. He said, "We followed V.C. on both sides of that clear rock face area and when we get to the peak of the face, they vanish. From that peak come back down to the right about half way down the face. Now to the right about three hundred yards and that is where you guys spent the night in V.C. land...Straight up from there, right near the top...is the second camp. From the other side you can look down at the creek and waterfalls. That is the area that they had you guys pinned down. Anyone below them would be sittin' ducks! Some place near that mountaintop is an entrance to a cave. Just where...I don't know...I just feel it. That is where they vanish into thin air". He said that it was the perfect ambush point for Charley to use on our side of the mountain. And that the top of the face in back, on the other side would be a good vantage point for Charley too. From either side it would be hell trying to get at him. He said that his team was going back to Uplift and for us to use their starlight scope for night observation.

Schriff said, "'Thanks! I hope our observations won't be a point blank ambush." Schriff thanked Morris for the info. He said that we were going to move out just as soon as we contacted Moran's team to let them know we were on our way up.

"Hunter 1, This is Hunter 2, Do you copy over?" No answer. The same message went out again.

Then, "This is Hunter 1, we copy, Over."

Schriff said, "Okay we got them!...Hunter 1, this is Hunter 2, stand by for message. Over."

"Hunter 2, 10-4 we copy stand by for message. Over!"

"Hunter 1, Hunter 2 requests present location, over!" Moran's team, using the code book, gave us their approximate location. Schriff located it on the map easily. Schriff sent the message, "Hunter 1....Hunter 2 request pow-wow a.s.a.p....over." Meaning we'll get together as soon as possible.

They were about three-quarters of the way up the front of the mountain. Just before we left the Line Co. their Captain said that every day they set Charley up for an ambush using small squads of men. He said he wanted to keep Charley busy and harass him enough to keep him off track on what was going on. He said that he didn't think the V.C. were going to expect any night ambushes and it would blow Charley's mind. Charley was not going to expect night ambushes, because the Line Co. squads only hit the V.C. during the day. He thought we would have the element of surprise on them enough to nail them good, especially when they were doing most of their movement at night.

Schriff asked, "You guys ready to swoop?" We told him let's do it! So up on our backs went the rut sacks. The rut sacks were so heavy we would have to sit on the ground and get into the straps of the sack then adjust them tight. Then with ninety pounds in them try to get up. What a ball! It was totally funny watching a new guy.

The Line Captain bid us farewell and up the mountain we went. Even going very slowly it was a bummer! We got snagged on everything we came near. Those rut sacks were a real ball to hump with. As we walked, we kept trying to stay on target with Moran's team, using a map and compass all the way. It was about a two-hour steady walk until we stopped. Everyone was soaked with sweat and bushed. Each of our backs were white with the salt from the sweat out of our bodies. It had to be one hundred degrees in the shade. Although we were completely shaded by the jungle roof, it was like a steam bath with no ventilation. Very little air would penetrate that thick hair-like jungle. We all took out our water and sipped it.

After we caught our breath Schriff wanted to contact Moran's team. Schriff took the mic. off me and began calling. "Hunter 1, this is Hunter 2. Come in, over!" He whispered as quietly as he could. Out in the woods we never spoke above a whisper. We never knew when Charley was around. After a few days of that, our throat was so sore that it wasn't even funny! Schriff called again. "Hunter 1, Hunter 1, this is Hunter 2. Do you copy? Come back. Over!"

"Hunter 2, This is Hunter 1, we read you. Over!" They hashed out on the map by radio where each of us was. We were approximately an hour's walk from each other. Schriff told them we would be there A.S.A.P.

After we were rested up we moved on. A little more than an hour of walking and I heard the mic. "Hunter 2, this is Hunter 1, do you copy? Over." I stopped everyone and gave the mic. to Schriff.

"Hunter 1, Hunter 1. This is Hunter 2, we copy? Over." Hunter one said we should each send out one scout to meet the other. There would be much less movement and sound that way. They agreed our man would follow a course of due north and they would come south. Lori asked if he could go and thought he could find their man no sweat.

Schriff said, "Go easy." Lori nodded yes and he was gone.

We all sat back to relax while we could. I pulled out a cigarette and Schriff shook his head no! He pulled back his eyes at the corners and pointed to his nose, sniffing slightly. I understood that Charley might smell it and put it away.

About twenty five or thirty minutes went by and we could hear someone coming. Schriff said, "Watch." Pointing to our front left. Just then Lori appeared. He waved us toward him. So we got up and followed. We walked for a little ways until we could see an American Indian named Brown Mountain. He was on Moran's team. He waved us over and we followed.

Soon we were there. We sat down in a ten-foot circle around Moran and Schriff as they made plans for that night. After a while Schriff pointed at me and put his hand up to his ear. So I moved over to him and Moran. Schriff called the Line Co. and told them of our set up location or Night Logger.

Moran moved over close to me and said. "So I hear you're a f#**#in' hero already!"

I replied, "That hero stuff's for dopes like you!"

He said, "Don't get all bent out-a-shape dude! I'm just busting your rocks. From what I hear you done good! I guess maybe I'll get to see for myself how good you really are."

I replied, "Moran…just stay away from me, you make me sick!"

After Schriff got off the radio both teams got to talk over our plans. Moran said the second base camp was just about four hundred fifty yards straight ahead. He said there were big foot path trails about one hundred yards up that led right into the camp…a whole bunch of trails. That afternoon our team planned to move in the front as close to the camp as we could before dark and set up a bunch of booby traps with our Claymore mines. Moran's team was going around back to do the same thing. Then we were to meet back at this position later.

So our teams took off every unnecessary piece of gear. I still humped the radio so I didn't have to plant mines. It would be too hard to work quietly with that on my back. All I had to do was follow Schriff fairly close behind and keep watch. Schriff left one man behind to guard our packs and we took off.

After we just about crawled on our bellies those four hundred fifty yards we could see the small hooches…and the big one we stayed in last mission out.   I started to feel the cramps coming on again. There was a little clearing on the jungle floor where the camp was located. We could see V.C. moving around. We were really close, but we got away with doing our job anyway.

When everyone was done with their work we came back together. Schriff motioned to pull back and we did very carefully. When we got back to the place both teams said we would meet at our night logger. Schriff told us that he felt we had caught Charley with his pants down big time. He said, "I think we are really going to kick his butt this time!" He said if Moran's men made out as well as we did, we would probably screw up Charley's moonlight stroll but good!

About an hour and a half went by and Moran's team radioed back to us to warn us of their approach. After they came in, we all got in a twenty-foot circle and waited until about dark. We were all starved but we couldn't risk making any noise from a canteen cup ringing out, so no one ate. We munched on a granola-like bar we called "gorilla bars." I guess they called them that either because we were guerilla fighters or you had to be a gorilla to eat the dried out stuff, I don't know which. They tasted like sweet ground up cardboard to me and looked like it too.

Soon it was dark and we all got ready. It wasn't long until we heard one loud blast and soon another one. They sounded a-ways away. Must be Moran's goodies, I thought. All night long we heard blasts from close and far. Moran was having a ball with himself just knowing how bad old Charley was killing himself with the gifts we left him. All night we passed the radio on to the next guy, while on radio watch. Two hours on, four hours off. Each hour we would have to report everything was okay to the Line Co. below.

By morning old Charley was still stepping on our tricks. We could still hear explosions from time to time. I couldn't believe Charley was dumb enough to still be trying to move around in the dark. Was he dumb or just determined? I wondered.

As the blackness of night slowly turned into daylight, the sounds of the blasts finally stopped. Every time a blast went off we counted it to make sure that all mines went off. All but two were confirmed. We were going to have to check them and pick them up so Charley wouldn't take them and use them on us. Every one had to be accounted for.

We were all fairly close together and I could hear a guy named Doc that hung out with Moran whispering to him about Moran's birthday. Doc said, "Hey Moran! I'll get you a couple of V.C. for your birthday today if I get the chance."

"When is your birthday?" asked Schriff.

Moran said, "I'm twenty today. Maybe I'll get to go in, so I can go in front of the Board. That's supposed to be coming up soon, isn't it?"

Schriff whispered, "Tomorrow they are supposed to meet. And you were on the list I saw in the old man's office. I was going to tell you about it, but I forgot."

Moran replied, "I'm getting so short it's not even funny. Only two more days to go and I'm going home for thirty days leave. But I'll be back. After the next six month extension, I am gonna' call it quits. But I want one more trip to make it two whole years here. That will make my re-up bonus a lot bigger next time."

The N.C.O. board only got together once in a while to promote anyone with enough time in whatever grade. They would grade you on your past record, and ask you some questions about all kinds of things. They would then decide whether or not to promote you to the next grade higher, whatever grade you were, E-4 to E-5-6-7, etc. If I remember right, the board was made up of two higher non-commissioned officers and your commanding officer. If they vote to give it to you, you got it. If not, forget it. You would only have to go in front of this board to get E-5 up. The only other way to get promoted, was to get it like I did. An officer is the only one allowed to promote on the spot. My post commander authorized my promotion to E-5. He was a Colonel. Moran was an E-5 going for E-6 so he had to go in front of the board.

Schriff said, "I'll find out today if you can go back in for the board, when I call Uplift in a little while."

Moran said, "My record is good so I should make E-6 no sweat! As for the leave, even if I have to walk back in, I'm going in! I need a day to pack so I can swoop the day after tomorrow."

How lucky that dope was to have made it that far without a scratch. He had two days to go to end this nightmare for good. But he still wanted six more months of this after a year and a half. I wondered just how long he would make it back in the world before he flipped out and started murdering people. This guy shouldn't be let loose in a civilized society. He loved to kill, you could see it all over him.

Somehow he seemed a little more docile that day. He spoke very smoothly and was quieter than usual about everything. He just acted different for some reason. I just couldn't put my finger on it. Maybe he was happy about his birthday, or leave, I thought. Oh well, who gives a hoot anyway? I thought.

It was daylight and Moran's team started making plans to check out the area where they set up their mines yesterday afternoon and to look for the two that didn't go off. They also wanted to see what damage we did if any. Look for blood or bodies, that sort of thing.

Schriff motioned me over. He wanted the radio. Schriff tuned in the radio and called Uplift…"Hunter 2, calling Big Momma, Come in Big Momma, over!" Schriff told Uplift that we were all going in to look over the camp to see if we could find anything. Uplift said that was okay and to report back any findings right away, especially the hidden door if we could find it. He also asked about Moran's going in for the board. They said if everything was quiet out there that day, he could hump down to the Line Co. area in the valley and jump on a re-supply bird that was coming in late that afternoon. Schriff said he copied that transmission and said he was out. Schriff told Moran what was said on the radio and Moran got his team up on their feet. Moran said, "We'll contact you in three hours at the most and we will plan where to meet you later on."

Schriff said, "Let's move out." We all got up and moved ahead quietly. That time we took our packs and all with us because we were going to keep moving that day to another location.

Moran was pulling point for his team and Lori pulled point on our team. The first man, or point man, had a very dangerous job. They were usually the first ones to get hit during an ambush. With Moran so short I couldn't believe he would take the chance. But he always pulled point because that's where all the action started first. I had to admit the guy had a lot of guts! No brains, just guts.

We all stayed together until we got to the trails that separated the two small camps near the mountaintop. We all stopped and let Moran's team move out ahead towards the second small camp where he went the day before. His team was once again going sweep around the back behind both camps as they did yesterday. Everyone on my team started to move out, to check the traps they laid all over the numerous trails we found. It was a slow job because we had to be careful that Charley didn't re-booby trap them to use against us. He would do that if he found them before they blew him up.

We were soon only about one hundred yards from the base camp. We found no un-detonated mines. Moran's team was gone about thirty minutes. All of a sudden we heard gun fire just a little ways away. It was AK-47 fire. I could tell the difference between the sounds. M-16 fire was a very fast high pitched crack, where an AK-47, Charley's weapon, was lower in tone and sounded slower when fired on full auto. Then I heard a gun shot that was almost like a .50 caliber machine gun. They were in an ambush, I just knew it!

Right then all hell broke loose. It was an all out fire-fight, just a short distance away. The radio came on with a loud, "Hunter 2!.. Hunter 2!...Come in, over!"

Schriff grabbed the mic. "Hunter 1, hunter 1! This is Hunter 2, come back over!"

"Hunter 2! we have boo-koo contact over!"

Schriff replied, "Hunter 1, can we move to assist you? Over!" They said Moran was hit bad and they were getting fire from everywhere. Schriff told them that we would move into the first camp to flush the enemy to them…but watch out for us. He said to just stay down and only try to keep them off. He thought we could catch the enemy between us and knock them out. Hunter 1 told us to go for it.

Schriff said, "Move out." He quickly ran up front to the point position. I was shaking like a dog poopin' a peach pit, but I still tried to keep my head. I was the fourth man back and kept a sharp eye out. The gunfire was almost constant as we moved in slow. I was so shook up I could hardly breathe, and at times I knew that I wasn't breathing I was so freaked out.

I could see the clearing just ahead where we found all the spider holes the last time in center of the camp. There were V.C. standing behind trees shooting out to our left and front. They were shooting at Moran's team as the team was trying to sneak around the camp to their rear.

Schriff said, "Hit as many as you can on my signal." We all got down on one knee and drew down on Charley…each man picking out a good target. He whispered, "Ready…Fire!!" We all cut loose and five V.C. went flipping. There was so much gunfire going off you couldn't hear yourself think. Most of the V.C. shooting at Hunter 1 never even saw us at first because they were fixed on Hunter 1 and because of all the noise of the gun fire. But soon they knew we were at their rear flank somewhere as we began to pick them off one by one. Every time one would start to move we nailed him.

Soon there were only about five or six V.C. still in sight in the main camp area. But we had to be careful of the spider holes. They were everywhere. Each time we spotted a spider hole as we advanced, we would toss a hand grenade into it. Three out of five revealed V.C. in them. They would stay motionless in the hole and let you pass then as you went by they would shoot you in the back.

As we moved in I could see a stone and dirt bunker with a large barrel pointing out the front firing like mad. Schriff said, "Lori, Babbles, see if you can work your way around and get that bunker cleared out." They moved out like a shot. I could hear AK-47 fire from the direction they ran off in. Suddenly two V.C. ran out into the camp clearing shooting in Lori's direction. Schriff and I opened up and hit both of them. Then two more ran out screaming like mad men as they fired. I threw a fragg out. Baaaboom! The hand grenade went off right between them throwing one V.C. up about six feet in the air.

Schriff yelled, "Good shot! Jim! You got 'um both." I thought, no way! Talk about horseshoes and hand grenades. I guess close really does count with a fragg. I didn't think I came that close to them.

The firing suddenly stopped. Schriff, O.B. and I got up. We were about twenty or thirty yards inside the base camp and I could see Lori and Babbles coming back into the camp from our left front after they took out the heavy gun. I waved my arm at them to let them see us. Lori waved his M-16 back. We all moved in slowly towards each other. Be very careful, I thought.

I felt that I was beginning to breathe once again. I thought to myself, not only watch the spider holes in the ground, but also watch for guns popping out of the thick trees above us as well. Lori was the first one to the large main hooch where we all stayed the last time out. Slowly he looked inside….very slowly. Suddenly he jumped back. "Watch it!" He yelled. I dropped to my knees and I ducked. An AK-47 barked right into our face through the open door way in the hooch, blowing it's hot breath right at Lori and I, but no one was hit. I couldn't see the V.C. soldier but I saw the muzzle of the AK flash around the corner, in the far-left corner of the room. Many times that happened and each time I wondered how could a weapon go off so close to me and not hit me? How could the guy ever have missed me?

Lori popped a grenade and held it for a couple of seconds while Babbles and I stood guard. "'Throw it!" Babbles said. Lori still held on. Babbles yelled again, "Throw it!" Just then he tossed it inside. We all dove. As soon as it cleared the door just inside it went off. Baaaboom! The side wall blew out and I could see one screwed up V.C. inside. He was still trying to crawl out through the back of the hooch and get away. Lori ran in and shot him in the back of the head. He was one blown up bloody mess.

All at once bullets were coming from behind us like rain. I could hear them popping over and to the side of my head like popcorn. I ran over to Schriff a few feet away and then I got down with him. He grabbed the mic. and called Hunter 1. He told them that we were being hit from behind and we were going to move toward them. He told them to watch what they shot at. They said that they understood to be careful and to watch out for us. They told Schriff to keep a sharp eye out because they still saw some V.C. in front of them in between us and them moving around. Schriff told them that half of us would move around them to the left and half to the right to see if we could come up around the enemy and push them to Hunter 1.

Lori and Babbles were told to go around to the left side. Schriff said that O.B. and I would go in a circle to the right side and he would be coming up the middle close to my side in case he needed to get to the radio quickly. Behind us V.C. were moving all over the place and firing every chance they got.

We moved out to try to keep the enemy back behind us for as long as we could. But it was no use. We kept firing, but for every one we hit two more rushed toward us. They were true Kamikazes in every sense of the word. The whole thing was terrifying so we just kept moving out fast! We were almost in a state of panic as I ran around towards Hunter 1 to the right. O.B. and I bumped into V.C. from every direction. O.B. yelled, "Where the hell are they all coming from?" At times we were shooting V.C. almost at point blank range. Either they ran into us or vice versa. I just kept stopping from time to time along side of a wide tree and used it as cover to shield myself from bullets. Every few yards I fired at V.C. as we moved ahead.

Not far ahead we found Hunter 1. Quickly we ran over to them and Schriff said, "Let's go!…move back down the mountain! Where's Moran?"

Just then Doc, Moran's friend dragged his dead limp body over to us. Doc said, "He got zapped! I'll carry him! Someone take my pack." O.B. grabbed it and put one strap over his shoulder. Just then Lori and Babbles came out of the brush right next to us.

Schriff said, "Move it!"

I looked down at Moran's cold lifeless face with his eyes bugging out and his tongue sticking out about two inches. He had huge bullet holes in his chest that layed him open like Jack the ripper attacked him. First of all, it really didn't even look like him except I knew it was. I knew somehow that it would happen. I almost felt sorry for him…almost. For some reason I just couldn't feel any sorrow for the guy…like I would feel for a friend or even a guy I really didn't know even a little bit. And I know it wasn't just because we hated each others' guts! I think it was because to me the dude just all out asked for it. See, when most men extended their tour in the Nam it was to get an early out of the army. Or the "lifer" would extend to get away from a cheating wife, or a girlfriend with his bun in the oven. Or he may have a good easy job, far back in the rear or whatever, out of harm's way. With Moran, all he wanted to extend for is for one reason….to kill more people and add a few more ears to the hideous collection that he wore around his neck…his very dead neck.

As we moved on down the mountain we kept running into V.C. everywhere. There was no place to run or hide. We all got down and formed a fifteen foot circle, and guarded all of our sides the best we could. We were totally surrounded with no way out. The Line Co. had been trying to contact us as we ran but we never stopped long enough for me to tell Schriff until then. I handed the mic. to Schriff as I tried to catch my breath.

I said, "I think big brother has been trying to call us."

He said, "Big brother! Big brother!, this is Hunter 2, do you copy over!" Then A. Co. answered.

"Hunter 2, this is Big brother, we copy! Over!" Schriff told them of our predicament and asked for a back up squad. They said they were on their way already. They said they called in a gun ship and it was on its way from Uplift to help as well. Alpha Company said to hold our 10-10, (our position) as long as we could and keep popping smoke to show our position.

We popped smoke when we heard the chopper coming. Two gun ships hovered over head and let Charley have a snoot full. As the gun ships were holding off large groups of enemy, we kept trying to get as many as would show their faces. Man, they were everywhere!

Soon we were told by radio that the squad was very near us and to keep popping smoke. Soon we could hear M-16 fire from just down below us. The Line Co. was chasing the enemy right back at us. As they came at us we shot them.

Just then I heard Lori screaming all kinds of stuff in Spanish. "He's hit!" Babbles yelled.

"Help him get back over here!" Schriff yelled back.

Just then the Line Co. broke through the jungle and crawled up to us. Gunfire was all around us. The Line Co. medic went to Lori's aid. He had been shot just below the kneecap. It was a nasty hit. It was a compound bone fracture. His leg looked like a piece of splintered wood. He was in so much pain they had to give him two shots of morphine before he stopped thrashing around.

There were just too many V.C., even for all of us to handle. Doc picked up Moran's body and I took off the radio and gave it to Babbles. I then put that little Spanish buddy of mine over my shoulder and I moved out quickly! Down the mountain we ran with the V.C. hot after us. Even with the help of the squad from A. Co. we were still just barely keeping Charley off us enough to stay alive. With Lori's leg so shot up the run through the jungle was harder on him than it was on me. Once in a while I would stumble and fall down, smashing Lori's leg against a tree or the ground. Man, that little dude must have been in so much pain, it was incredible!

Down we went and still no let up from Charley. The Line Co. was starting to lose men left and right. They kept trying to stop and hold the V.C. back. But they kept getting shot themselves. They were one super tough, super bad azz bunch of soldiers. I'll always hold the memory of those men in my heart as long as I live.

Suddenly I heard someone screaming. Then one of the Line Co.'s men yelled, "Recon's been hit!..Medic!" I could hear a man screaming from over to my left. "Medic!!" It sounded like that Indian on Moran's team named Brown Mountain. "Med!..." then quiet. The guys that were near him said they found him but he didn't need a medic anymore. They dragged his body over toward us and I could see he was hit in the chest and his head was almost blown in half.

There was gunfire from everywhere! Some M-16, some AK-47. I could hear the two choppers leaving the area overhead. There was just too much enemy gun fire coming up at them. Schriff screamed, "Get up and move down the hill! Move! Move! Let's go!" We all got up and duffed again. We dragged the dead and wounded as fast as we could down the mountain. With Lori still screaming on my back I remember I kept apologizing to him for bumping his leg on everything but he kept saying, "Just get me the f#*&#! out of here gringo!...Get me out alive!"

It seemed like we ran forever going down that mountain. But after a while we could see fresh troops coming up our way to try to help hold Charley back. As we passed them they relieved the guys dragging the dead and wounded and helped us down to the bottom. I just kept running with Lori on my back until I reached the small aid station they had set up at the bottom of the hill, and then I collapsed.

After we were all down to the bottom of that evil mountain we got to rest and get our stuff together. The Line Co. Captain wanted Schriff to tell the whole story. He briefed the Captain on everything.

Once he was patched up enough to move I helped carry Lori out to a medievac chopper on the ground in the open field area on a stretcher. Lori said, "Jim…I'll never forget you! You saved my life! You saved my life! You…you gringo!…"

As he tried to get up to hug me, I pushed him down and said, "Relax, you Spanish peanut! I'll come see you down at Ophu Cat hospital in a few days." Lori just kept thanking me as they loaded him and three other guys onto the chopper. Soon the chopper was full and another one was on its way in. I grabbed Lori's hand and squeezed it hard.

"Come see me at the hospital gringo!" I just smiled as the chopper lifted off the ground. I stood there waving to him as the chopper quickly flew away. That was the last time I ever saw Lori. I never got to see my little buddy again.

Just then I saw three gun ships swooping in and I could hear jets overhead. I ran back to Schriff who was still talking to the Line Co. Captain. Schriff said that the Captain called in a jet air strike with rockets and napalm. But first the chopper gun ships would go in and shoot it out with Charley. The Line Co. Captain called his men back off the mountain because they were getting fire from everywhere up there.

The pilot of the first gun ship that came in to help said he saw V.C. pouring out of the top of the rock face area on the other side of the mountain. We could hear his voice on the radio. He said it was a cave or opening and probably the way into an underground base camp. Schriff and I looked at each other and we both said at the same time… "The hidden door!" The pilot said that he couldn't even begin to count how many V.C. there really were.

After all of A. Co. was back off the hill the jets went in. They hit that mountain with everything they had. Rockets bursting and napalm burning. All day they kept it up. When the jets went back to the Air force base for more bombs, a few two prop helicopter cargo ships came in with nets full of fifty five gallon drums of gasoline. They just kept dumping and dumping net full after net full of gas on Charley.

Soon the mountain was a solid ball of flame. It looked like hell itself! I wondered in the beginning of the mission how they would do it. Now I could see. But what I saw was more than I could believe.

All the dead and wounded were counted, fifteen wounded counting Lori and nine dead counting Moran and Brown Mountain. We all just helped load the wounded on choppers and watched the fire works show on the mountain. Soon it turned late afternoon and the chopper pilots said it was too late to come back for the dead. They said they would be back for them in the morning. In Nam choppers would not fly at night for fear of being shot down.

The jet air strikes continued right up until just about dark. We all made camp right next to the Line Company. We put Moran and Brown Mountain's bodies right in our area. Then we all sat down for chow and a good rest. Schriff called Uplift to find out what they wanted us to do. Either come in, or whatever. They asked if he had sent his list of K.I.A. and W.I.A. back with the last chopper. He said he did. They asked if he still had a complete team. He said counting Moran's men he did. They asked us to stand by and they would get back with us A.S.A.P. Schriff told us to just relax and wait.

The mountain behind us was so hot and smoky we could hardly stand it. But it was too risky to move out into the open, so we just put up with it. The whole mountain was a solid ball of flame. If there was a hell on earth that mountain was a perfect picture of it, I thought. All you could see above the flames was pitch-black smoke. The flames were hundreds of feet high, lashing and curling in every direction. I thought that no living thing could withstand heat and smoke like that. I never saw a real volcano. But it looked like what I saw on a TV show of an active volcano once. Kabbatt said that it was real close to what it looked like. He said he had seen a volcano at home in Hawaii.

There was only Kabbatt, Doc, Prat, and James left on Moran's team. And all but Lori left on ours. Eight men all together out of eleven. That wasn't really bad for what we just ran into. Alpha Co. lost a whole lot more. That's why I was glad I was not a line grunt.

It was dark by then but you could see just as good as day because of the hell that burned away behind us. We all walked around fairly free at mind, not too worried about Charley, who was the "main course" at our barbecue that night. So we all sat around rapping about how close that one was and we ate real good chow made by the Line Co. mess people.

We finally got our call from Uplift. They said we were going to be sent back up the mountain, but around to the other side. They said when the mountain had stopped burning and it was safe to go back on the mountain the Line Co. would sweep up one side and down the other pushing any enemy left down into our ambushes in the valley below. They thought any V.C. left would make a run for the creek to get away because it was clear walking and they could move out of the area fast that way, and we would be there to stop them. It might not sound like a job for eight men but when we had the time we could set up a very effective ambush. We were to try to get around the flame even if the mountain was still burning to get the element of surprise working for us. They thought Charley would never think we would do a crazy move like that and wouldn't be expecting it.

Schriff said that he understood the plan. We received the plan in code. Schriff said we would contact them before leaving in the morning. We had all just become Hunter 1; the mission would continue.

Just before Uplift signed off they said the E-5 that we had going in front of the board could come in on the first chopper in the morning.

Schriff asked, "Did you guys get my "hit" list yet?"

They said, "Negative."

He said, "The E-5 will be coming in alright! But not for the Board!.. Hunter 1!.... Out." Everyone looked at Schriff when he talked about a man going in for the board. He said, "The jerks didn't even get my killed in action list yet!"

Doc, Moran's buddy, got up and walked away saying, "On his Birthday! The guy had to get zapped on his birthday! Damn this place anyway."

No matter what Moran was we all knew what Doc meant. It just wasn't fair. So close….yet so infinitely far away.

We were all tired so we lay down to rest. The Line Co. Captain said his men would stand guard that night so we all could rest up good for tomorrow. We all thanked him immensely and got out our hammocks and sleeping gear and slept. Well, I did anyway!

To stand at last on that unknown ground,
Is a thing that soldiers can understand,
When the battle is over and friends are down,
He knows—I can cry, I am a man.

D. J. —

CHAPTER 14

Death Valley

Soon the morning sun burned through the very thick black smoke that filled the whole valley, waking me up. I got out of my thin but very strong nylon hammock. It was very comfortable and it kept me off the ground away from insects and snakes. The day before one of the Line Co. men must have lost it out of his pack near the bottom of the hill where I found it. Possession was the law there and it was mine now.

I jumped out and looked around. The hill was still burning like mad up near the top. But a couple hundred yards from the bottom up, it was just charred and smoking. We could go around the mountain easy. All the vegetation was burned off except huge roots from very large trees that still stuck out of the ground. This was a tropical forest. The trees did not have very deep roots. The roots would grow down, then back up and out then down and so forth. Some of the arches made by these tree roots were ten to fifteen feet over my head and very large!

I sat relaxing and just looking around. I saw Doc lying on the ground sleeping with his head on Moran's gut. Must be he needed a pillow, I thought. Schriff was talking with the Line Co. Captain looking at a map. Kabbatt was burning a tic off his belly and everyone else was still asleep.

I walked over to Kabbatt and said, "What a bummer those ticks are."

He said, "Man I hate them suckers." He said that he had to get himself another hammock from supply back in the rear someday if they ever got any more.

I said, "Yeah man, that's the only way to sleep out here. You hungry?"

He said, "Yeah!" So he got up. We went over to the Line Co. mess tent to eat. I guess last night's meal was something special that they didn't do very often because we were right back to soggy bread and powdered eggs again. So we went back to our rut sacks and made a L.R.R.P. meal. Nothing like chili in the morning to get you poppin'.

It was about 0730 or so before Schriff called Uplift to tell them of our departure. After contact we got ready to go. We all got packed with more food and ammo from the re-supply ship that took Doc's pillow away with the rest of the dead that morning.

Soon after we got packed we started our climb around the back of the mountain. The ground was about one foot, and sometimes as much as three feet deep with ashes. The earth was very hot. The hot earth even made the rubber soles of our boots gummy. The smoke where we were was bad enough to give us a headache. There was napalm hanging on sticks and limbs in big globs. It looked like dried model airplane glue. This was napalm that spattered but didn't fully burn. Everything was just black, charred and very dirty. It was a scene from hell.

By the time we got half way to the top we were all covered with and gagging up black soot. We were covered from head to toe. I could feel streams of black mud oozing down my shorts. It was gritty and gave us all a bad a rash. The people at Uplift told us not to worry about breathing the stuff. They said, "The stuff won't harm you." Years later we found out that the "stuff" not only killed Charley but was doing a job on us as well!

About noon that day we were at the top of the mountain and we stopped to rest. The ground was too hot and dirty to sit on and the boulders that stuck out of the ground radiated heat like an oven. We were all totally disgusted with the way we looked and felt and decided to go the rest of the way down to a stream to wash up.

After another two hours or so of breathing that black dirt we started to run into thick vegetation again near the stream that lay six hundred yards ahead. We were about to break into a dead run for the water. Just listening to the sound of the water falls just ahead drove us on. Soon we were there and took turns cleaning up while others watched in every direction.

After we were all cleaned and refreshed, Schriff said that we would go back into the valley where we had been ambushed during my first mission out. He thought the big boulders and high cliffs on the mountain would be a good spot for our base and ambush points. From there we could see Charley's hill clearly, now that all there was left was ash and smoke. So we moved out.

After moving downstream very slowly and watching for any possible ambush area, we started to move into the heavily covered jungle area down through the valley. We were going to go in just about where we were ambushed and move up the mountainside to a large rocky open area to set up our logger.

As we started into the darkness of the shaded area of the jungle we stopped dead because of the horror we saw. We couldn't believe our eyes. There were dead V.C. lying out all over the creek bed. Dead V.C. hung from tree branches above our heads and they were lying all over the ground and really just everywhere. Some burned black, some without a burn mark on them. Schriff motioned us to squat down and huddle around. He whispered, "Watch yourselves! This could be some kind of weird trap. Maybe the body's are booby trapped…don't touch a thing!" We all stayed motionless for about five minutes looking around and kept our ears open for any sound, then we got up slowly.

As we moved I lost count of dead bodies. I wasn't really looking that hard for dead ones. It was the possibility of live ones that may be lying among them that gave me the creeps. We all assumed they were V.C. that just panicked and jumped from above when the air strike started. Or maybe because of so much heat, smoke, and high explosives going off they couldn't breath and jumped from the very high rock cliffs above to get away from it all. Panic makes people do drastic things. I looked up the side of the mountain trying to spot some place they could have come from, but I spotted nothing like a cave or whatever anywhere! It was all burned black and cleared off bare and I could see a long ways up, but nothing could be seen. Talk about mass hysteric suicide, this was definitely it. But where could they have come from? kept going through my head. There were dead enemy everywhere!

As we walked very carefully we noticed no movement among the bodies. We then started up the opposite mountainside across the creek to an ambush point about three hundred feet up another high mountain on that side. We walked up about two hundred feet and stopped to rest, while Schriff reported our findings to Uplift. We were instructed by Uplift to move into a night logger and they would get back with us. They said they would be standing by in case of any emergency. It was only a short walk from there to a good night logger area.

As I walked out of the thicker jungle into the rocky area I could sense a warm breeze blowing. It was warm, but nonetheless, it was moving air. We started up the rocky area, which was fairly straight up. Not so steep that we needed ropes, but you really had to watch your step. In between the enormous boulders there were large hallway-like cracks or openings. The rock walls were very high and about four to eight feet wide. There were places we could hide around those rocks everywhere! The area was fairly safe. In case of attack, we could duck down under rocks and ledges. When we got to the logger spot we all got our rut sacks off and we sat down to relax.

Then I began to wonder about the V.C. that were strewn all over down below. I wondered just what kind of horror they must of have had to cope with. I wondered if I was in their place, would I have jumped too? Just remembering the mass explosions and fire from the air strike, it must have been unreal!

Schriff sent Kabbatt and O.B. out a short distance from our position as lookouts. The rest of us just sat back and watched everything below....and above. I looked up at the charred face of Charley's mountain and watched for anything that might move or emerge from a spider hole or escape hole but I saw nothing.

I heard Uplift on the horn so I gave the mic. to Schriff. We were instructed to just sit tight for the rest of the day and night and keep an eye out for any movement. They said the other side of the mountain was still burning and the Line Co.'s assault wouldn't happen until the next day. They said to use the night scope and watch very carefully that night. That's when Charley was doing most of his movement. They said to try to avoid any contact and to stay out of sight. Uplift said they would be standing by all day and night in case we needed help.

Schriff said that he wanted all of us in two-man teams to go below and set up booby traps for the ambush tomorrow. He told us not to make them so they would go off with any movement from Charley, but to set them so we could set them off at our own discretion. Schriff carried the hand-operated detonator that would send the electric shock out and set off our booby traps when needed. Schriff sent Doc out to get Kabbatt and O.B. back to tell them of his plan.

When they returned Schriff paired us up and we got ready to move out. We left all unnecessary gear so we could move fast and quietly. We each had four Claymore mines, two belts of M-16 ammo and four hand grenades. I left the radio with Schriff and James, who that stayed in our night position to guard it. Schriff said he would call for help if anything started with us below. He also said, "If you see any dinks, let them go by. Just hide and try not to make any contact unless you have no other choice."

We got all ready and moved out. Babbles and I were together as a team, as did O.B. and Kabbatt and Doc and Pratt. We all stayed together until we hit the creek bed. With all the dead V.C. lying all over, it was real spooky and the area was beginning to smell really bad.

At the creek bed we decided to split up and move in different directions. Babbles and I went downstream deeper into the jungle, O.B. and Kabbatt went back upstream, to where the creek flowed from the more open valley into the jungle where we first came in. Doc and Pratt went up Charley's mountain across from the mountain where we were making our camp. That way Charley's side of the mountain would be covered with booby traps in case any enemy came directly down towards the creek to get a clear run downstream and away.

The work took about two hours. We moved very slowly and cautiously. We took our time setting up our Claymore mines so that they would be as effective as possible. The slowest part of the job was stringing and hiding the detonation cord or det. cord as we called it. This was a white plastic fuse cord that burned thousands of feet per second and was used to set off explosives. Babbles and I took turns setting ours up. First Babbles set one up and I watched for V.C., then vice versa.

After we placed our Claymores facing up and down the creek bed we were done. We checked everything over to make sure the detonator cords and mines were all set and armed right. We also made sure they were out of sight so Charley couldn't find them and use them on us. Most of the mines we set were out of sight from our spot above, but there were a few open spaces.

With Claymore mines you only had to be fairly close to have them work effectively. They were about ten to twelve inches long, about two inches thick and six inches wide. They had the words "Front Toward Enemy" embossed on the front so you wouldn't place them backwards by mistake and blow yourself up if you were right behind them. They would only send the blast and ball bearings one way. There were hundreds of ball bearings and about a pound or so of composition C-4 packed into them. C-4 was a white putty-like substance that could be molded around just about anything. And it was very powerful! C-4 was a very fast burning propellant, that worked like an explosive compound. It was a propellant, not an explosive….there is a difference. It would send those ball bearings flying like hundreds of little bullets. The outside shell was very strong plastic. You could also snap the back off and take out the C-4 for use in any other demolition job you wanted as long as you had det. cord and/or blasting caps. The C-4 was only explosive when used with a blasting cap or det. cord. If you ran out of heat tabs for cooking your L.R.R.P. meals, you could just light a small piece of C-4 for heat. But you couldn't hit it, because it would explode, just as heat would detonate the stuff. C-4 really worked very well.

After Babbles and I double-checked everything we moved out to meet up with the rest of the men. We were the first ones back to our meeting place. We both sat down to rest.

Not long after, everyone else came sneaking back to where Babbles and I were and we all started back up toward our logger, placing det. cord as we went up and into our night log position. We climbed back up the steep incline of the mountain to where Schriff and James were waiting. Everything was set. As we moved into our camp Schriff asked each team how they made out. We all said okay and we sat down to catch our breath.

It was sometime in the late afternoon when we got back. So we got ready to eat. Schriff sent out two lookouts while the rest of us ate. After I ate I went out to relieve Doc who was on watch to our right side.

As I sat there on guard I started thinking about all the stuff I ran into while I

Vietnam and how lucky I had been so far. I just prayed my luck wouldn't run out. So far both times I was out, I had been in the area I was in right then. Each time it turned into a total nightmare. I just hoped that place stayed as dead and quiet as it seemed. That just turned out to be wishful thinking.

We all took our turn on watch. None of us had anything to report, other than the usual animal sights and sounds. There were rock apes all over this area. They looked like a chimpanzee you might see in a circus, but a lighter shade of brown. Every once in a while, we could see one or more trying to sneak a peek at us, but they were usually shy and didn't stay around long.

I remember one time a guy back at Uplift had a small young rock ape he got from somewhere and made a pet out of the thing. It would go around bumming food, candy or just about anything you would give it. Guys even got the ape high on pot by blowing smoke into his face. Then they would sit back and goof on how loofy the thing acted. Maybe that's the way Vietnamese people looked at us when we smoked pot. Anyway, the ape would like to sneak up on the roof on the mess hall and stand above the guys standing in the chow line below and pee on them. Well, one day the dude that got wet didn't think it was so cute and he locked and loaded right there and blew the ape right off the roof. That guy was Moran. The guy that owned the ape yelled and screamed about Moran killing his ape but Moran told him if he didn't shut up he would be shot next. The dude shut up on the spot and walked away. Moran cut the ape's head off, skinned and dried the skull, and wore that along with all the dead V.C. ears around his neck like a string of jewelry when he was in the rear. And you may wonder why I didn't "bemoan" the dude's death all that much!

It started to get toward dark as I sat there looking up Charley's mountain relaxing on guard and I was called back to the team. We all picked out the most comfortable spot we could find among the rocks to bed down in. There weren't any trees close enough to us to string my hammock so I made my bed on the ground. As it got darker we all stayed together so no one would be lost in case of any ambush during the night. You could never tell when the enemy would run right into you by accident, even at night. We still had to pull guard duty with the radio two on, four hours off all night. During the night we used the night scope but we saw and heard nothing.

In the morning, I woke up to a beautiful sunny day. That's how the days were every day except during the Monsoon season. Then we never saw the sun, just rain and clouds. It was very early, maybe about 0500 or 0530. The sun hadn't heated up the air too bad yet and you could still breathe. So I got up slowly to stretch and get some of that clean morning air. As I sat there looking up at Charley's mountain I could see very little smoke coming from the top of the mountain in front of us. I felt this would be the day the Line Co. would begin their assault on the hill.

Soon everyone was up and starting to make breakfast. My breakfast of beef stew was about gone when I heard the radio. "Hunter one, Hunter one, This is Big Momma, Do you copy, over?" I handed the mic. to Schriff who was sitting right behind me.

He said, "This is Hunter one! We copy, over."

"Hunter one, how's everything out there?" they asked.

Schriff said, "Quiet here and we're standing by for instruction, over." Uplift said that at 0800 Big brother was going to start his morning walk up the mountain and down the other side to us.

Schriff said, "Roger that, we copy, over."

Uplift said if we could handle the flow of enemy, if any, to do so at our discretion. If not to call for help at anytime and they would send a gun ship right over the mountain to us for support. Schriff said he understood the message and he signed off.

The sun was up over our mountain by then and it was very hot. I was all sweat just sitting around waiting for the shooting to start on the mountain across from us. Babbles was right next to me and pointed at his watch. Schriff shook his head okay. Then he told us to pair off again and move down a little to a good ambush point. He told us not to fire at the V.C. across from us until they were far enough down the mountainside or about half way down. That way they wouldn't really have enough time to get back up and away or have any place to run to. That way we could lock our ambush right in on them before they could escape or get re-set up. He said that he would be watching the bottom for any V.C. that made it that far. If any did he would zap them with our Claymore mines and M-16 fire.

We all understood and moved a short ways down into position. Before we even got set we could hear gunfire from far over the mountain on the other side. really found it hard to believe that the Line Co. found anything still left alive to shoot at. But they were running into a lot of contact.

Schriff heard over the radio that the Line Co. was running into all kinds of deep hidden bunkers and deep spider holes. Some spider holes and bunkers were built in an "L" or upside down "T" type shape so the enemy could avoid being killed or cooked alive during an air strike. They would duck down into the bottom of the "L" or "T" shape. At the bottom of the hole or bunker they would dig sideways into the earth at the bottom and crawl into that nook, and the explosives and heat couldn't get at them.

The fighting went on all the way up the mountain to the top. As the Line Co. advanced up the hill they shot V.C. in spider holes and bunkers non-stop! How the enemy could have survived I'll never know. At the top they found a cave entrance the "door" that we all had been looking for. The opening led way down into the mountain itself.

As all this was going on, our side of the mountain was still quiet. We contacted the Line Co. to report nothing had come our way yet, but we were still on guard and watching. The Line Co. said they were sending five South Korean Tiger down into the cave to push out anything inside. Tigers were the South Korean Special Forces, like us. These guys were well trained for that sort of fighting and were very small so they could explore caves easily. They were small, but bad dudes. They knew and could do their job very well. It took a special type of soldier or man to crawl into a pitch dark cave or crawl space after enemy soldiers See, if you enter a dark cave, (which is usually booby trapped), with a light of any kind to locate them and the enemy you instantly become a lit up target. It's still pitch-dark way back in the hole where the enemy is. The enemy can see you with

94

a light in your hand long before you spot them.

The one and only time I ever went into a hole before it was totally cleared and checked out I was nearly killed! I had no idea what it looked like inside, or how it was set up. As I crawled down into the hole I had only a .45 automatic pistol for a weapon because it was easy to swing around into action, unlike a three-foot long rifle. It was a good thing that is what I had. I didn't know it but about thirty feet into the passageway, two feet above my head, off to my right side and back up just out of sight was a hidden "nook." It was just large enough for a small enemy soldier to fit into so he could look down and guard the crawl space. Suddenly, the pitch-dark passageway lit up bright from the semi-automatic gun fire muzzle flash of a sniper just above my right arm and head. The bullets Charley fired failed to hit me point blank, because he could not get the weapon pointed down far enough to hit me. All the bullets he fired flew just inches over my head and back but never touched me. The butt stock or the bottom of the AK-47's stock was pinned against the top of the "nook" and the side of the gun was pinned against the ledge he was laying on. Charley's gun blasts were so close to my ears I about went deaf. I just quickly rolled over on my left side, pointed the small pistol up at Charley at point blank range and I tried to get a bead on him. He kept firing, trying to get the weapon down enough to hit me and in just seconds he quickly ran out of rounds. That is why I never used full auto. The weapons of today just eat ammo too quickly. All you need to kill someone is one well-placed shot.

I think we were both in shock. Me for not being killed and Charley for not being able to hit and kill me. Charley and I looked at each other face to face for a second or so until the flashes and the light of his AK came to an end. It was like watching a very old, very flashy black and white movie you might see on the late show. It seemed almost like everything was moving in slow motion. It was weird because the split second before I fired the passageway went pitch dark because Charley's AK quit firing and I really could only guess where he was. I just instinctively pointed the pistol and I fired twice.

The passageway lit up brightly as my pistol went off. I saw Charley's face light up as a round hit him smack in the face! Instantly the passageway went pitch black again. Like I said, that was the one and only time I ever tried crawling into a pitch-black passageway before it was totally checked and cleared out of all enemy and booby traps.

Not more than fifteen or twenty minutes after the Tigers went in, Schriff was the first one to see a large boulder on our side of the mountain in front of us move. Schriff whispered, "Look at that. See that big round rock over there? Watch it." Sure enough the rock moved and started rolling down the mountain. We could see a two or so foot hole right in the side of the hill. He said, "So, that's where they came from. Here they come! Get ready. But wait until they get far enough from the hole and down the mountainside before you fire, or they will just go back into the hole."

We all said okay and watched. First two or three came out. Then six or eight more, then a steady flow one right after the other. Schriff told Babbles and I to get down even closer to the creek and open up when he did. We both took off like a shot. Then when we got half way down near the bottom we heard Schriff and the team begin to cut loose. We could see the creek bed just a short way down below us. We could see no enemy yet down there…but not for long. Soon I could see V.C. running, falling, rolling and even flying down from above us in a state of panic on the other side.

Babbles nodded at me and we started shooting every V.C. we could. Some were hit but kept right on running. More and more started to jump into the creek bed. As they did we shot them. Soon there were so many coming down into the creek bed area we couldn't shoot them fast enough. My M-16 was red hot and smoking. I believe I was looking at just about the same thing that had happened the day before. They were killing themselves trying to get off that mountain.

Suddenly a bunch of them spotted us firing at them from our side and they opened up on us. So Babbles yelled, "To hell with this….move back up fast…go!..go." So I turned around and ran as fast as I could back up the mountain. As we moved back up we would stop from time to time to catch our breath and at those times we would turn and fire, trying to nail a few more V.C. across from us when we could see them, as they shot back up at us. Their rounds were coming at us like rain hitting rocks and trees all around us. We got up and ran into the rocky area where the team was positioned.

Babbles told Schriff to blow the Claymores. He said the creek bed was crawling with V.C. by then. Schriff, not saying a word took the detonator and squeezed the lever. "Baaaaboom!" All we could see down below was white gray smoke curling into the air. There were voices yelling and screaming from below like I never heard before! Schriff said that he figured we were being swamped with enemy, but he was afraid of killing us with all the Claymores going off at once. So he figured he would wait until he got word from us or saw us coming before touching them off. We were happy he did. The thick area below was about blown open after all those Claymore mines went off. From the looks and sound of that blast Charley's mom and dad must have heard it all the way up in North Vietnam!

Soon the team was starting to run low on ammo. So we all tried to slow down our rate of fire and we took careful aim, so as not to waste any. Schriff said the Line Co. was on its way over the mountain towards us in hot pursuit of Charley He said that an air strike was about to make its way over to our side as well. He soon ordered a cease fire to conserve our ammo. He said, "Let the Line Co. mop up. Save your ammo in case we have to defend our 10-10." Soon we could see the gun ships coming over the mountain and heading down toward the creek and hillside across from us. Talk about mass slaughter! What a sight. Rockets, mini-gun fire, you name it! Munitions rained down on Charley as he tried in vain to get away. There was just no place to hide, the side of the mountain across from us was burned off almost bare. The only place for Charley to hide was behind a large rock or burned up log. For him it was just stand and fight. But there was no way he could win.

Soon the Line Co. was swarming all over the top of the mountain and pushing their way down. We popped two canisters of yellow smoke to warn the choppers and the Line Co. of our location on our side of the mountain across from them No friendly fire came our way, just complete success. We kicked Charley's butt that time.

We all sat back, watched and listened for any V.C. that tried to make it up our side of the mountain. But not a one made it out of the creek bed alive, not one. Eventually all the firing stopped and the gun ships flew back over the mountain from where they came from. They would come and go...just like the Angel of Death. They would appear out of nowhere, then leave the same way. But what a toll would be paid for their presence. Gun ships saved many U.S. soldiers over there. I thank God we had them.

About an hour or so went by and Alpha Co. was most of the way down the mountain. We could see a squad of men talking to the Tigers that were just starting to emerge from the hole in the side of the mountain. They all started down toward the creek bed. Soon everyone from the Line Co. was down in the creek or out into the open area near the water falls. Schriff radioed to A. Co. that we were on our way down to them. They said the area near the falls was secure. We were told to move into that area. Schriff said he understood and we headed down.

Mountain of Death

By the time we got down off our side of the mountain, the Tigers were dragging out P.O.W.s and wounded V.C. from the caves above. The team sat down in the creek to cool off and rest awhile. There were loads of wounded V.C to be extracted and piles of dead ones.

The wounded ones were in very rough shape. Arms, legs blown off, gut shots and shots every place you could think of. Many were real bad off because they were hurt bad during the first assault on the hill a couple days earlier and were not getting the right medical help they needed. If a V.C. was hurt bad enough to where he was most likely going to die, his people wouldn't even help that man. He was thought of as dead anyway, and to use rare and valuable medical supplies on him was thought to be a waste. It was up to him, the soldier, to do the "right thing" and save the medical supplies for someone that could be patched up and sent right back into action to fight. The "right thing" was to put a bullet in his own head, or just sit there and suffer until he died. We learned that from P.O.W.s. Many V.C. died from shock or a loss of blood long before they made it to a hospital. Many were burned real bad and full of infection because of their burns as well.

When I stood back to look at all the death and suffering around me, it totally overtook me. The reality of it all it was so...unreal. My mind just couldn't imagine or comprehend that degree of suffering, especially because of the numbers...all at once like that. As I stood there looking at all the dead and soon to be dead people around me, the screaming, crying, the all out agony I felt faint...My mind just couldn't take it all in and deal with it all at once like that. It was too much for all of us. I could see it in every face I looked at. The frenzy, the madness of all out pitch battle. When it's happening around you it becomes other worldly...unreal. You become brain dead and just move by instinct. The smell of gun smoke...the deafing sounds of gun fire and explosives going off all around you, the screaming...Even the smell of blood in the air.

Then, when the battle's are over, you think Lord God! as you look around. You have to look around and see what you've done. You have to try to gather what strength you have left, after the exausting, terrifying, real-life nightmare hits you. You have to get to your feet....And drive on soldier...Somehow, you have to drive on.

I remember a time a friend of mine took a round in the head as we lay very close next to each other. When he got hit the bullet burst his head like a melon. A mist, a vapor of blood and brain filled the air around my face and head. The shot and the sight of what happened startled me. I breathed in deeply and quickly from fright like you would before you scream from fright, filling my lungs with my friend's vaporized blood and brain. I could taste my friend in my throat and lungs for two days....Somehow you recover from these things, somehow you accept them as part of your reality and strive on. After a while you realize the battles don't always end in the bush. You have to keep fighting, that's the soldier's duty.

The Line Co. had medi-evac choppers coming and going constantly the rest of that day, taking out our men first, then the hurt V.C. The next day the Tigers found many underground tunnels and many rooms filled with guns, ammo, explosives, medical supplies, tons of food, more bodies and all kinds of other supplies and a small make shift "operating room" if you could call it that, as well. They captured many V.C., N.C.O.s and even two officers.

When the whole tunnel system was checked out by the Rocks I went down into the tunnels just to see how the other side lived. I really wish I hadn't. What I saw was almost unbelievable. How human beings could live like the V.C. lived was really something unbelievable to most people today. The tunnels led in all different directions down under the ground and would just suddenly drop off into rooms of various sizes. The main crawl spaces were very confining with really just enough room to keep going on ahead further into the system. Turning around would really be quite hard to do unless you were built very small. The air was cold, damp and stale. The smell of dead or rotting flesh and urine permeated the tunnels, especially the farther down we went. The many passage ways led to many small, medium and sometimes fairly large rooms. There were small oil lamps, torches and cans of wax-like large candles that gave the only light once down inside the rooms.

The rooms were filled with all kinds of goods. Bags of rice, ammo, oil and all kinds of things. I saw some sewer pits and trenches that stunk so bad that you could hardly breathe. In what was supposed to be their operating room I was shocked to see maggots living in and feeding on the blood soaked dirt floor and the two dead bodies lying in there. It was too much to believe. I saw a large bag hanging by a stick stuck into the dirt wall full of body parts. Inside the bag too were large blood soaked cotton-like balls that the V.C. got from some type of plant, like milkweed, that had been used to soak up blood and clean wounds. There was a foot long blood clot hanging from the bottom of the the bag all the way to the floor. The operating table was made up of bamboo poles for a frame with a piece of canvas stretched across it. That too was blood soaked and in no way free from germs! It looked more like a medievil torture chamber than anything else. The filth and stench of rotted flesh along with the blood-soaked floor was just unbelievable, to say the least. It seemed impossible to me that anyone could possibly survive in that place.

We also found boxes of U.S. medical supplies like penicillin, and a few first aid kits that they had picked up at the black market in a vill somewhere. Not all that much material to do any real life saving with, though. But they did survive down there and that's only because they were so tough and so determined to win. Until you've seen what I saw no one could ever know what "having it tough" really means. Until I saw that hell hole for myself I never really knew or understood just how tough those little guys were or just what conditions they had to live in. I know no one I ever knew could have hacked living like that for very long, no doubt in my mind! It really was quite a jackpot of goods and enemy soldiers, though.

Most of the kills went to the chopper gun ships, but we each got three or so. It took the rest of that second day to collect all the bodies out of the tunnels and the Rocks still found more bodies the next day. For two days we all stayed together to help out with the mess we made and then we got to relax for an extra day. The nights were nice because the Line Co. had enough guards posted so we could ghost.

After the two more days of clean up, we found twenty-six dead V.C. and another forty or fifty wounded. There were five G.I.s dead and twenty-one hurt. As I said before, we kicked the tar out of Charley that time, for sure. I just hoped our luck wouldn't run out.

The third morning we were there Uplift called us back in. I was told by Schriff that the Line Co. was going to stay around the area for awhile, to scout it out to see if we might have missed anything. This made all of us pray they would find no more camps. Right then all I could think of was that pass I was going to get for all the enemy we got. They only gave us a confirmed body count of three each because most every time gun ships were called in, there were so many V.C. that could have been hit by the ships that it was very hard to tell who got who. So they would usually be recorded as gun ship kills.

CHAPTER 16
Jar Head Brother

About 1400 that third day A. Co. had some choppers coming in for re-supply. So we all got ready to go in. As the ships came in I got that old deep down going-in feeling, it just felt so good!

In just a short time we were off on our magic carpet ride out of that place. I nicknamed the place, "Death Valley" because it just fit the place so well.

Soon we could see signs of being close to home, by the black smoke that wrapped itself all around the top of Uplift mountain. Closer and closer we got. Soon I could see the dusty, dirty, smelly, depressing dung pile we called home. But, I quickly learned to love the place.

When we got on the ground and out of the chopper the first thing I had on my mind was a shower. Schriff said he had to report to the briefing room as usual and we could do what we wanted to until 1800 hours formation that afternoon. So we walked back up on Recon Hill. I got some clean clothes out and headed up toward the showers. There was plenty of water for a change so I soaked for a long time. To heck with the next guy. After I got clean, I walked back down to my hooch to unpack and relax. Inside, I saw Kabbatt working out on the floor with his homemade barbell set. Babbles was unpacking his rut sack and James, who once told me his uncle played in a '30's or '40's big band was making a tape to send home. James also told me he was going to write a book about the mad house called Nam. He wanted all the tapes he made every mission out as a record of the stories to help keep all of it fresh in his mind so he wouldn't forget anything. Personally, I couldn't see how anyone could ever forget one second of the Vietnam nightmare. Our story was almost unbelievable. The story of Hunter 1 would be quite some book, I thought.

I walked over to my cot and sat down. I was thinking about the letter my old man had sent me. So I took it out and read it again. After I read it, I felt I had been away from home long enough. So I borrowed some paper from Babbles and started to write to my girl. I started the letter off sounding as if I was on vacation. I told everyone back home not to worry about me because although I was assigned to a Recondo Co., I told them I was only in the motor pool. I just couldn't see making anyone worry about me going out on these crazy missions. Although my girl did find out the truth one day when Babbles slipped telling her about a mission we were on. He said it on a tape I sent to her about what a hero I was when I got put in for a medal, and I never knew about it until it was too late. He saw the tape lying on my cot just before I sent it out and he added his extra little story. Wow!...Did I have some explaining to do. I also said I missed everyone very much and always thought about them. I wrote about some of the parties and fun times I'd had and stuff like that.

I got an envelope from Babbles and sent it out. We all got envelopes with the postage already paid by the army. So it never cost a cent for anything we sent home. Most days back in the rear were boring except bunker guard at night, which was just a big party. So I lay back to relax and I fell asleep until I heard Schriff come in yelling, "Mail call!" He handed a fist full of letters to Babbles and Kabbatt. He said, "Here Jim! You got one too!"

I grabbed it and saw the return address. I saw on the letter....Pvt. Tom Gibbore!...Camp LaJune!...S.C. I yelled, "Oh No!"... I tore the letter open and began to read. The letter was from my younger brother Tom, telling me he had just joined the jar head Marines! I couldn't believe my eyes! Then I thought when I got my hands on him, I would kill him! In the Nam all Marines were was moving targets! I felt the next thing I was going to be reading was his obituary. He never got into hunting or really killing anything before. So I knew his butt was grass, if he made it over to Nam. Man I was mad!

The first sentence said, "Hi Jim, this is your brother Tom. I know you'll kill me for this, but I'm a Marine now." Kill wasn't the word I thought.

He went on to say, "Don't be mad...but I just had to do it. Everyone back home is being drafted for Nam. So I decided to get the jump on that by enlisting for the job I wanted." Well, I thought, he was right about the draft, but what job did he get?

I read on, "I'm training for the job of crew chief on a gun ship." When I saw that I was so mad I tore the letter up. Everyone around me looked up.

Schriff asked, "What's wrong?"

I said, "My duuuuumb younger brother just joined the jar heads!"

They all shook their heads and said things like, "Oh brother!...Lots of luck dude!"

"Yeeeeah !" I replied.

Now that he just screwed up the rest of my day, I figured it was time for a buzz! I thought, if only that little sucker would have written me sooner...but it's too late now. It was just too bad he didn't know what he was in for. Just then I thought of what my old man said to me, just before I left home...about not knowing what I was in for. I guess no matter who you are, you have to do things your own way. It's like they say....live and learn! That is if we live long enough to learn.

At that time it was 1969 or 1970. Most young men just out of high school like my brother and I were brought up with the idea that whenever our country needed us we would just have to come up with the guts and honor enough to see it through. But there were also a lot of men that didn't believe that. There were some that would actually leave our beautiful country and give up their home and family just to get out of service. But for the most part guys my age wanted to go and do what had to be done. They knew it was the only decent thing to do.

Even though I was so disruptive in school and the community, I did not then believe we should be in Vietnam, dying and all that. But, if my country thought it was right, I still would have volunteered for Nam.

I could also see the other guy's side, wanting to run and all. They listened to those who told them that it was right to do so. Now I also realize that the enemy was as active at home as he was in Vietnam.

Even some of the people over there didn't want us around except for the times we liberated whole towns and villages from slaughter by their own people, the

V.C. and the N.V.A. troops. That disclosed the real struggle in Vietnam, the struggle between good and evil.

Until I saw these people that had been butchered by the V.C. and the N.V.A. troops, I did not know just why we were there. I remember five or six times our team ran into a small village that had been terrorized by the animals called Charley Cong. There were two instances in particular.

In 1970, the army had a new plan to win the people over to our side called "Pacification." This was a plan to work with the local people to help them in any way we could. We gave them food, clothing, medicine, protection, you name it. In general, just be their big buddies type of deal. Once when we were the only team out there in this particular area and we heard gunfire and we went to check it out.

It took about an hour to hump through the jungle to the village where the shots came from and when we arrived we saw that the villagers were all in a state of panic and all shook up. Schriff asked the village big shot what had happened and what all the gunfire was about. This guy led us to a large hooch and showed us five young men that had been shot dead on the spot for not joining the V.C. squad that had just left the village on a recruiting mission. The villagers told us the V.C. shot them dead on the spot as a lesson to the other local villages where they would soon be recruiting.

The other time I remember I will never get out of my mind! We came through a small village and we saw a young man hanging from a tree by a piece of wire cable. His body was decaying. He was about sixteen years old and he was hanging by his neck, his arms bound behind him with wire. He hung by that wire with his toes just touching the ground. He must have died a horribly long and agonizingly slow death. His toes kept him just high enough to keep him from choking until his strength gave out. His crime was spitting in the face of a V.C. that tried to recruit him with a kick in the "rocks". The villagers were told that if they ever cut his body down the V.C. would come back and burn the village and kill everyone there. Men, women, and children!

Many times I saw things like this in Vietnam. It was most inhumane and unforgettable! We were fighting an evil force that abused its own people, like evil always does.

That's what made our job and our presence there worth our weight in gold, even though we wanted out of it. I may be wrong….but you ask some Vietnamese mother that has had her two year old boy or girl split in half by some heartless animal named Charley just because her older son wouldn't join their army, she would tell you they really needed and wanted our help very badly. Even with all my anger and fear and mistrust of them, somehow I could just feel their cries for mercy and help every time I looked at these villagers.

I worked harder and stronger at that than any job I had ever done before. But the longer I was there the more I began to enjoy killing. That started to worry me a lot. After awhile most every mission I was sent out on would turn out about the same as the first two. They all started to seem the same. We ambushed Charley…he ambushed us. I was in country pulling mission after mission for five months.

CHAPTER 17

Sniper School and Ghost Time

It was about a month or so into the Monsoon season and the whole place was a big mud hole. Rain just poured down everyday. Each time I would go out on a mission I would end up with jungle rot...chafing and sores of all kinds. The weather was always so warm and wet you would just about rot alive. It would kick every G.I.s butt real bad. A lot of G.I.s luck ran out during the Monsoons, because you were so wet, sore and fed up with living like a mud turtle you would not be thinking very straight. Charley grew up with that type of climate every year of his life. He was used to it. Usually Charley loved it. It was his favorite time to attack!

Early one morning after a mission was over we had to walk back in from the mission. Sometimes it rained so hard choppers wouldn't fly. After we got back in I got all cleaned up and I was called up to my commanding officer's hooch. After I walked up the moving mudslide called Recon Hill I knocked on his door. He said, "Come in!" I walked up to him and saluted, "Airborne!" He saluted me back.

He said, "At ease...Sit down Jim....I want to talk to you. I've been looking at your record and I see you have done an outstanding job!"

I replied. "Thank you sir."

He went on, "You have been here less than six months and you have been put in for a medal, you've been promoted from E-3 to E-5 and have many confirmed body counts. To me that shows something special." He told me that there were openings for various schools that the army had to offer. He said the schools were Recondo/Ranger, Pathfinder and Sniper school. He said these schools would offer a lot of in-country travel and a lot of ghost time. He said that Recondo/Ranger school combined was a month long in Nha Trang. Pathfinder school was a three week deal...almost all vacation in Quy Nhon and Sniper school was another three to four weeks in An Khe. He said the only physically hard one was Recondo/Ranger school. Lots of hikes and running, that sort of thing. He asked, "Would you be interested?" My mouth started to water to just think of getting out of the boonies for two months or more.

I said, "Yes! Sir!...I'm interested in all of them Sir!"

He said, "Well then, I'll get your papers all set and get you started."

I said, "Yes Sir! Thank you Sir! May I speak freely Sir!?"

He replied, "Go ahead."

"Sir!, I just want to thank you for offering me the chance to go to these schools. I will do well! And I will not let you down, Sir!"

He said, "I'm sure you won't. You're a very good soldier that is why I thought of you first. And when you get out of these schools you will be a real butt kicker! Smarter, tougher, and meaner then you are now!"

"Yes, Sir!" I said and saluted him. "Airborne!...All the way! Sir!"

He said, "Jim I'm going to need a good team leader soon! Just remember, for you E-6 will go along with that. You're dismissed."

I started to turn around to leave and the C.O. said, "Hey Jim....off the books...Tell me why didn't you go into the Green Beret part of Special Forces? You've been too darn near every combat school the army has to offer. You could have made it easy."

I replied, "Sir! To me green beanies are teachers. Recondos are killers! That is what I am Sir!" He just smiled.

As I left the old man's hooch I felt so happy I could have flipped. I laughed thinking about all that bad guy stuff I had layed on the C.O. I wasn't full of bad! I was full of bologna and that dope fell for all I had to feed him. All I wanted to do was get out of the boonies as long as possible.

I ran back down to the hooch to tell Babbles and Schriff. As I walked in soaked from head to toe, I saw only Babbles inside. So I sat down and told him what had happened up at the C.O.'s hooch.

He said, "No way....ghost time? Good for you. At least one of us will get out of the mud for a while."

I said, "Yeah you should ask about the schools maybe you could get one or two of them." Babbles said that he was too short for having a good chance at that and he could pull the thirty two more days he had left anywhere, he didn't care where. He was too short to give a hoot.

I was so happy I could hardly sleep all that night. The next day Schriff gave me some papers just after morning formation. Schriff said, "Hey Jim, the old man just gave me your orders for Recondo and Pathfinder school." He said that I would first go to Recondo/Ranger school in Nha Trang. He said my papers included my flight papers for both schools. First I would go to Quy Nhon U.S. Air Force Base and catch a plane for Nha Trang. It was quite a ways south from Uplift and Quy Nhon was the closest A.F.B. Then after Recondo school I would go directly to Pathfinder school back at Quy Nhon. Quy Nhon was a very large Air Force Base. Next to the A.F.B. was a small army post. That was where I would spend three weeks learning Pathfinder or advanced Scout training. He said after that I would come back to Uplift, then I would eventually go to Sniper school a little later when another sniper class started at Camp Radkey in An Khe up north.

Everyone in the hooch busted my rocks about how lucky I was for getting over a month of ghost time and all. All I did was smile. Schriff said I would have to hitch a ride from Uplift to Quy Nhon A.F. Base, unless a chopper was headed that way out of Uplift. Or I could hitch a ride all the way to Nha Trang, which was a real long hall. He said to check down at the chopper pad in the morning, maybe I would luck out and catch a ride one way or the other. He said the trip was about forty miles to Quy Nhon, which was shorter. They gave me more than enough time to get there. In those days I was young and strong enough to walk thirty miles. I didn't really care how I got there just thinking about saying bye-bye to the jungle made me so happy it didn't matter if I did have to walk or low crawl.

That night I sat in my hooch making tapes to send home and to help pass the time. Babbles came in and said, "Hey Jim, why don't you put that stuff away for a while and come to the club with me. I'll buy you a beer." He said that this would probably be our last night together because he would probably be home in the world when I got back, he was so short.

I said, "Good idea, let's go."

As we walked down the wooden walkway leading out in front of the hooch and around the corner, I could see the whole place was lit up. As we walked inside, I saw James, Doc, Kabbatt, O.B., Pratt and Schriff. Babbles and I walked in.

Schriff came up and said, "This will be the last time we are all together as the team Hunter 1. Some of us are very short now and will be gone when you get back from school. I know we'll never forget the scared cherry that first came here six months ago. The brand new cherry, that shook in his new jungle boots. And now he has Charley shaking in his. We'll miss you a lot, Jim. You've helped everyone in this room time after time. As we've helped you. We are all a team. We are all brothers.....We are Hunter 1...and we always will be. We just hope you will never forget any of us."

With tears in both our eyes we hugged each other. I felt my steel heart melt right there on the spot. There really were people around me that cared that I was alive. It took me almost six months to see that...I guess it's like they say....the best place to hide something is within. There were always people that cared about me but I didn't want to know it.

At first I didn't know just what to say, then..."Forget you jerks!? How could I ever? You have all burned an everlasting impression on my mind. I will never forget Hunter One...Never!"

O.B. yelled out, "It's parrrrrrty time!!" And did we ever. All night we partied. Telling jokes and laughing about each other's stupid actions and mistakes while in combat. All night we partied and laughed.

After 0300 the only ones awake were Kabbatt and I. I was drunk but not completely gone. Kabbatt didn't drink he just smoked a little bit. But only during a special occasion like that. He said he still had five months left in country and was going to try for Sniper school. In the next few days he said he was going to talk to the old man about it.

The next morning I was up early, so I could pack some things for the trip and eat breakfast. While I was down on the main post, I stopped to ask the guys at the chopper pad if any choppers were flying out toward Quy Nhon or Nha Trang that morning. They said if the rain let up there were a couple flights going towards Quy Nhon - if it stopped raining. So I said to heck with it and I walked back up to my hooch.

The whole team was just about ready for formation about then and they started up the hill. I didn't have to go that day because they already knew I was packing to head out. As they all passed me I said goodbye one by one. The guys that were short said to be careful and make it back to the world so we could have a reunion party some day. All of us knew it would never happen but that's what everyone used to say. What else could you say? You live, work, eat, sleep, sometimes put your very life in the hands of these guys everyday. How could one say goodbye forever? How could you? That's one thing I never found the answer to.

I walked inside and finished all my packing. When I was ready I walked outside and down towards the road. Just before I got onto the road I could hear Schriff yelling to me from the formation area. I turned around and saw him waving his hand at me from way up on Recon Hill. He yelled, "See you back in the world, Jimmy!"

CHAPTER 18

Travelin' and Ghostin'

It was only sprinkling that morning, slow but steady. It was so warm and humid you had to breathe hard to get any air. The road leading north and south was already swarming with vehicles and people. I had a lot of time to get to Nha Trang so I figured I would take the flight out of Quy Nhon; I had heard it was a real nice place.

I saw a G.I. hitching a ride on the other side of the road so I asked him, "Which way to Quy Nhon A.F.B.?"

He said, "About twenty five or thirty miles that way." He pointed north and he said that's the way he was going. So I came across the road with my duffel bag and stood with him. We only stood there for a few minutes before a truck pulled up.

"Where you boys headed?" the driver yelled out.

"Quy Nhon," I replied.

"Jump on in, I'm going right past it," he said. So we both jumped in and got seated on the bench that was built in the truck's box.

That was really the first long distance travel that I'd been on since I got there. I'd been to Fu Mi, just a short distance away on that road, but never twenty five or thirty miles from Uplift. I was excited and very interested in the sights and sounds of the people and places I passed. We passed very small hamlets and some fairly large sized villages. Mostly all the Vills looked the same, houses made of reeds and mud. There were many people walking and slipping in the mud and water holes, it was really funny. Although it rained just about constantly, the people still worked very hard in the rice patties with their water buffaloes pulling and straining behind their plows, it was such a mud hole.

I wouldn't work in a rice patty for all the rice in that whole country! Every once in a while I would see some rice patty worker just drop their pants and go to the bathroom right where they stood in the patties. They went right on the roadside as well. The Vietnamese outhouse was where they stood at the time. Even their dead would sometimes go right into the rice patty mud to help fertilize the soil. We found many V.C. like that…just stuffed into the mud. The patties always had a bad smell to them. I couldn't even imagine working and wading in that scummy hole all day, every day.

I remember one mission I was on when Schriff was the first one to jump into a rice patty we had to cross. As he took his first couple of steps he got his feet tangled up when he stepped into the chest of a badly decomposed body that was buried in the rice patty. He fell forward right on his face in that dirty, greasy, sloppy, smelly muck. We were on the outskirts of a very small Vill in the middle of nowhere and we had to be very quiet. Most guys would have yelled and sworn for two hours non-stop because of the smell and being so wet and filthy from rotted flesh plastered all over them. But Schriff just looked at the rest of us and opened his mouth like he was screaming, "f##***!" But no sound came out of his muck oozing mouth. That was control in my book. He just kept walking and never let it bother him a bit. The team near died laughing…quietly that is. Man did he stink! We still had three days to go before we came in. But that nasty way of life got to be everyday life. We just had to get used to it.

That morning the people on the roads made travelling very slow, as usual, especially in all the rain and mud. As we rode along I kept a poncho liner over me just so the rain didn't do that Chinese water torture thing to me. Forget trying to keep dry. So I curled up and tried to rest a while. The ride was so bumpy I just about had to tie myself down so I wouldn't fly out of the truck bed! The driver of the truck drove like a guy in a dare devil stunt show and nearly ran people over the whole way.

I was sitting there half-asleep and I could feel someone nudging my leg. I looked up ahead. About fifty yards ahead was the town of Quy Nhon. There was a right turn off the main road we were on with a sign stretched all the way across the road. It said, "Welcome to Quy Nhon Air Force Base."

The driver pulled over and said, "Here you go, dude, Quy Nhon! Have fun!" So I jumped off the truck and thanked the driver. He said goodbye and he drove away.

I looked back and forth, up and down the road I started to cross. Quickly I walked toward the other side. Women started to hit on me like a trout on a minnow. All I could do was push them away and I kept saying get lost or no way. It wouldn't have been so bad if they would just take no for an answer. Not only that, but they would get belligerent and mad about it. So I just had to try to pretend they weren't even there.

When I got on the Air Force base side of the road I walked up the street toward the A.F.B. There I could find out about a flight out to Nha Trang for Recondo school. There were choppers and planes taking off all the time on the base.

CHAPTER 19

It Must Be Nice!

As I got closer to the front gate of the A.F.B. I could see into the post really well. I thought I was dreaming. Just inside the gate to the right, there was a large bulletin board with a map of the whole post on it. The post area was so beautiful I thought I was back in the world. There were paved roads and very well kept lawns everywhere. There were A.F.B. Air Police at the gate checking out all locals and their belongings. I just walked right through the gate and past them. I walked up to the bulletin board and looked the map over. I could see the air field was all the way across on the other side of the post. It looked like it was two miles away at least.

As I looked at the map I saw a golf course, tennis courts, pool areas, N.C.O. and E.M. clubs. The place was a resort, not an Air Force base. I had to turn around and look back out the gate to see if I was still in Vietnam. I said to myself, sure enough, I'm still in Nam. I could see grass shacks and Orientals walking everywhere up and down the road outside the gate. I turned and looked back at the post. Man! I must be dreaming! The place looked like an A.F. base you might see in Florida or something. Banana trees, palm and coconut trees. It was just beautiful! I thought, Man! I wish Schriff and the boys were here to see this. We could really party hearty in this place. I doubted if this place was ready for us crazies, though.

As I stood there looking in disbelief at the map, I saw that it stopped raining and I took off my poncho liner and put it into my duffel bag. A truck pulled up and the driver asked, "Where you headed?"

I said, "The Air Field."

"Come on!" He said, "That's where I'm headed." So I got my bag and hopped in. He was an E-4 in the Air Force and about the same age as me.

He said, "Where are you coming from?"

I replied, "Uplift."

He gasped, "I've heard of that place before. A lot of combat out that way, no?"

I said, "A lot of combat out that way…yes!"

He said, "I don't know how you guys could put up with that stuff!"

I said, "Well, if that's your job, it's your job."

He said, "We never see any of that combat stuff here. We're well protected by the army that guards this A.F.B. They do all that for us."

He asked where I was from back in the world. I said, "New York State, upstate New York that is."

"Nice country out there." He replied. He was from Tampa Florida, but his grandmother lived in a small town named Ithaca, a short distance from the town I was from. I told him that was only about an hour's drive from my house. "No way." He said, "It's a small world."

"Yeah, sometimes it is," I replied.

He said, "By the looks of you….you must have seen lots of dead gooks and stuff being an Airborne Recondo and all!"

I said, "I've seen enough for a life time already. I've only been here about six months now!"

He said, "Did you kill anyone yet?"

I said, "I have twenty confirmed."

"No way…!" He gasped. "Twenty?"

I said, "Yeah, that's when I stopped counting."

"Man….how do you guys do that?"

I said, "Just aim and squeeze the trigger." He just laughed and shook his head. I asked, "What's your job here?"

He said, "I truck napalm and high explosive rockets and bombs to the air field, to be put on F-4 Phantom Jets."

I replied, "What?….Man you got to be out-a-yer-mind!"

See to me, his job sounded just as dangerously interesting as my job sounded to him. I started asking him all about the jet. He said, "You should ride in one of those mothers if you want a rush! Do they ever fly!"

I said, "I can just imagine, I've seen them in combat before during air strikes and they are so fast you just wouldn't believe it! The only time you can see them is when they swoop back up after they drop their stuff. You see them shoot back up like a bullet and vanish, just that quick!"

He replied, "That's why they're called Phantoms." He said he had never seen them in combat but when a new pilot comes in country he has to get some flight practice before he is allowed to fly a combat mission. He said, "It's some kind of rule the Air Force has. So I get to ride with them from time to time. The pilots really ain't supposed to do that sort of thing. But, you know how it is, some let me do it anyway just to scare the snot out of me and act cool, know what I mean?"

"No kiddin'?!" I said, "I think that would be a total riot!"

He said, "It's a riot all right."

Just ahead I could see the air field. There were planes and helicopters flying in and out all over the place. He said, "If you want, I can set up your chopper flight for you no sweat. I know all the chopper pilots and jet pilots around here. I work with them every day. I should be able to get you on a flight to just about anywhere you want!"

I replied, "Really? Man! Would that be a help. I don't even know where to go to find out about a flight."

He asked, "When do you have to report to…where?"

"Nha Trang. On Saturday before 1200." I replied.

He said, "Oh yeah!…that's no sweat. Today is only Thursday so you got the rest of today and tomorrow, right?"

I said, "Yeah!"

He replied, "Well man! There it is! No hurry then, right?"

I said, "Yeah? I guess so. Just so long as I'm in Nah Trang on Saturday by noon."

He said, "No problemo dude! If you want you could stay in my hooch tonight and party out with me tonight. Tomorrow I'll get your flight set up and you can be on your way. How's that?"

I said, "Great! You can really do all that?"

He smiled and said. "Are you kiddin'? I got pull around here pal!"

Then he asked if I was hungry and I told him that I could always eat. He said, "Right over there is the air field mess hall. Just go in and grab something to eat. I'll be back for you after I dump my load on an F-4. I'll be right back in twenty or so."

I looked into the back of the truck through the rear window. There were napalm and high explosive bombs stacked into the back of the truck like bowling pins. I asked, "You mean I have been riding with that load of high explosives all the way across this post?"

He snickered, "Yeah man! No sweat! They only go off when you smack them on the nose with something!" Then he smiled.

As I jumped out of the truck I said, "Why you... See ya in a little while!" I waved as I shut the door and he drove away. What a nut!, I thought. I wouldn't jockey that bomb on wheels for nothing!

I walked into the A.F.B. mess hall. It was a brand new concrete building. It was very nice with shrubs and flowers all around. No kiddin' I thought, this place was just like the world! I walked in and signed the personnel register. The next thing I saw was that I was the only man in the place carrying a weapon. The meals on post never cost any money, all you had to do was sign for them. There were beautiful flower arrangements on each long table set up just like a very large restaurant, with waiters and clean up boys.

I set my stuff down at the sign in desk and asked the guy there to watch my stuff for me. He said I couldn't carry a weapon inside with me anyway and to just leave my things there. I asked him if he knew that a war was going on outside the gate. He asked, "What's a war?" I just smiled and got into the chow line.

I stuck out like a sore thumb! They were all dressed in Air force blue or green. There I was with a nasty looking boony hat and Tiger fatigues covered with combat patches. Airborne, Recon unit patches, looking like something straight out of the boonies, which I was. As I walked through the line I could see everyone staring at my uniform and my combat patches. Guys were letting me ahead of them and treating me like a king. They helped me find my silverware, tray and everything I needed.

As I came up to the cook that was flipping real eggs he said, "Yes sir! Sarge, how do you want your eggs today?"

I replied, "I thought they only came one way... powdered!"

He laughed and said, "We have the real thing here! Over easy, scrambled, how 'bout a ham and cheese omelette?:

I smiled, "If it's possible, I'll have the omelette!"

He asked, "Home fries and bacon?"

"Yeah!" I replied.

He said, "Coming right up."

Man, I thought, I know I'm dreaming now. Home fries, bacon, omelettes! Must be real rough around here, it must be nice! I thought. And at 0900. The army stops breakfast at 0800 at the latest. If Babbles and the boys could see me now, I thought.

By the time I got to the end of the line, I had an eight inch long omelette, four strips of bacon, two fist fulls of home fries, four pieces of good (dry!) buttered toast, one glass of orange juice and a half a grapefruit. I hate grapefruit, but I had to eat one anyway. Just knowing this was the best meal I've had since I came to Nam over five and a half months ago. As a matter of fact, it was the only breakfast I could get down my throat since I'd been there. They had real coffee too, not reboiled chickory.

I sat down by myself and started to stuff myself full. I could feel everyone staring at me, eating as though I had never seen food before. But right then it tasted so good I could not have cared less whether I acted like a pig or not. I just kept stuffing it in anyway. I think I only came up to breathe once or twice.

When I was all done I burped and lit a cigarette. I drank the rest of my coffee and saw the guy that cooked eggs telling a local boy something as he pointed at me. The boy came right over and asked, "More coffee?"

I said, "Yes, please!" He filled the cup and I said thanks! I waved to the cook and he threw me the A-okay sign and he went back into the kitchen.

Just then I saw the truck driver that gave me a ride walk into the dining room. He walked over and sat down. Then he pointed at the boy with the pitcher of coffee and waved him over. He asked, "Have enough to eat?"

I said, "Oh, yeah! How about you? Are you going to eat?"

He said, "No way. The food sucks here. Besides I'm not hungry anyway." He said he was speeding so bad he couldn't see straight. I thought no wonder this guy talked my ear off on the ride over here. That would also explain why he wasn't hungry. He was as skinny as a pin. I thought, man this guy should eat something before he turns sideways and disappears.

He said, "I never got your name. Mine is Ted, Ted Springer."

"My name is Jim Gibbore" I replied.

"Glad to meet you, Jim!" He said with his hand out. I shook his hand and said it was nice to meet him.

He looked at my name tag and said, "Gibbore...I once knew a Gibb...Gibbons. Do you have any relatives over here?"

I replied. "No! Just me."

Ted went on, "'This guy is about your same build, with blond hair too."

I said, "Nope! I don't know him."

He said, "He used to be here but did his fifteen month tour and went home." •

I raised my voice because I thought me didn't hear me, "Ted!...I don't know him...Fifteen months?" I asked.

He said, "Yeah!...We pull fifteen months here, you army guys only have to pull twelve or thirteen months, right?"

I said, "Yeah....just thirteen months."

He said, "I still wouldn't want your job for a million bucks! Even if we had to pull twenty months it's better than getting shot at."

I said, "You're sure right about that! Getting your butt shot off is about as bad a situation as you could get." He agreed.

"Jim, you about done?" He asked.

I replied, "All set." So we got up and walked towards the door. On the way out I picked up my M-16 and duffel bag and we left.

Ted said, "I have to work another five hours loading bombs..... So why not just go to my hooch and leave your stuff? Then you can buzz around and check out the clubs or walk around post and check it out until I get off work. Then I'll meet you back at the hooch."

I said, "Great! Let's go!" We jumped into his truck and drove off.

We rode for about five minutes and we were there. They had brand new buildings with rooms and everything, even indoor plumbing and showers. Everything I could want. Ted told me no one was staying in his room for now except him. His roommate left country two days ago and I could use that bunk and locker. I thought it was great! Ted said he would see me later and to make myself at home. He said his name was on the door. I thanked him and he left.

Once I found the room I looked around and couldn't believe it. A real bunk bed with a mattress and sheets. Must be rough, I thought. So I took my things and put them into a locker and locked it. Then I laid down to rest. That bed was so soft and comfortable. I never wanted to leave that place. But I knew all good things for me always had to come to an end. I shut my eyes and I was out cold.

It seemed as though I had only shut my eyes for a few moments and I could hear men yelling and laughing. I looked up and I could see Ted's legs hanging down in front of my face. He was sitting on top of his bunk above me writing a letter. He looked down and said, "Well...Look who's back from the dead."

I sat up with a head full of fog. Shaking my head I said, "Ohhhhh!....I was out cold!"

He snickered, "No kiddin'....I thought you would never wake up! With all the racket in the place I don't know how you could sleep."

I replied, "That's was the most restful sleep I've gotten since I've been here! What time is it?" He said about 1800. "No way....six hours I was out. Man I must have been beat," I replied.

"I guess so! Hey.....do you drink?" He asked.

I replied, "Not since I bought a funnel."

He put his letter away and said, "Let's boogy!" I went for my M-16 but he said I wouldn't be allowed into any bars with that sucker. So reluctantly I put it in the locker. I guess my old buddy had to stay home that night, I thought.

As we walked down the long barracks hallway, I could see many men walking back and forth from room to room. All you could smell was pot smoke. As we walked past each room they all had to come out and look. I guess they had to see what an Airborne Recondo looked like. At the end of the hallway there were about twenty wooden steps leading down to the ground from the second floor where we were. Ted pulled out a joint and lit it. "Want some?" he asked.

"Sure, I smoke that stuff!" There were men walking everywhere because there was so many places to go. Bowling alley, pool hall, bars, just about anything you wanted to do. Even a hobby shop with all kinds of model airplanes and things.

We were just about to the club as we finished the joint. We both had a good buzz on and walked in. The place was beautiful - all paneled and painted up, nice tables and even fairly good looking Korean waitresses. The place was packed. On stage was a live Korean band that was very good. G.I.s danced up a storm all over the place.

We grabbed a table and ordered two cold Manhattans on ice. They were fifty cents each. "Not bad," I said, as I leaned back to enjoy the show and the girls. The chicks were all dressed up in nice dresses and everything.

I asked Ted, "Why do you fly boys get treated so good?" He said that forty percent of all the men on post were pilots. And pilots were officers and officers are like big ball babies. If they didn't have it that good they would never stop raising heck about it.

"No wonder....so that's it. A post full of officers!" I said. Ted told me not only that, but when Air Force people got there they couldn't ever leave the post for the whole fifteen months they were there. So they had to make things good for the men or they would go nuts.

He said, "Like you...you get to have passes for R&R downtown in the Vills, right?"

I replied, "Yeah! But who would ever want to go downtown when you have such a beautiful place here?"

He said, "After a while you get really sick of the same old stuff....I'll tell ya!"

I said, "I would trade places with you at Uplift, anytime!"

Ted laughed, "I'm not that sick of this stuff!"

By the end of the night or about 0230 we were out there! How we got back to the barracks, I don't know! Ted said he was on auto-pilot. When we got back, there were guys up playing cards and getting high. I just about fell all the way down the long hallway to Ted's room. When we got inside Ted pulled out another joint and lit it.

Two more guys came in and sat down on my bunk. Ted introduced me to them as we passed the joint around. The guys I met had only been in country less than a month. I guess I intrigued them by being a Recondo. For an hour I explained what all my army patches were and they wanted to know all about combat. As I whipped off a few war stories they all sat around, including Ted with their eyes and mouths wide open. They looked like three Boy Scouts on an overnight camping trip during a ghost story. They all loved it! More stories....they kept wanting to hear more. I told them that to me they were all the same. And they were lucky never to have to worry about such stories coming to life.

After a while Ted and I chased the two cherries out and we crashed. We both got up about 0700 and Ted got ready for work. Ted told me to relax and maybe later we could do something. He said he only had to drive the truck until 1100 that day. He said he could get off about then and maybe we could do something.

So I said, "I'll see you back here later. And don't forget about my flight, okay?"

He said, "No sweat! It's all set up for tomorrow at 0700." He told me I would get to Nha Trang in fifteen to twenty minutes from there by jet.

"By jet!?" I asked.

He smiled and said, "You wanted to ride in a Phantom didn't you?"

I said, "Say what?..Yeah but!..But this…!"

He said, "You got your ticket now pal! All you have to do is hang on to your butt! I talked a cherry Captain into giving you a ride to Recondo school tomorrow. So don't worry you'll get there in time all right."

"You aren't kiddin' me?" I asked.

He just smiled and said, "You asked for it."

I thought, this guy isn't kiddin', I think he means it.

I was already loaded up with butterflies just to think of it. I had to smoke a roach that Ted left behind just to calm down after I heard that one. I sat around for a couple of hours and talked with some of the guys in the barracks. Then I sat outside for a while waiting for Ted to get back.

Soon I saw him coming across the big open baseball field, next to the barracks. As he got closer to me he said, "Man, I'm glad that's it for today. I've had it after last night."

I replied, "We did cop quite the buzz, didn't we?" Ted said he was going to clean up and see if he could talk one of the A.P.'s at the gate into selling him a carton of joints later.

I said, "Man…I can go get them for ya if you want. Hey dude….let's both go downtown today!"

He said, "No way man….How can I get out of the gate with this uniform on?"

I said, "How would you like to become an Airborne Recondo/Ranger for a day?"

With a big goofy smile he said, "What?"

I said, "If You got the guts!…You could put on one of my extra sets of camo's. All you have to do is change my name tag with yours. How would anyone know?"

He smiled and said, "You might have something there." He said he had been living there for going on a year and had never seen the Vill of Quy Nhon.

I said, "Well then….It's time you did."

He yelled out, "Yeeeah! hooo!" And he ran upstairs to clean up and to change. He was so excited he couldn't get showered up fast enough.

While he got cleaned up, I took my name tag off one of my extra shirts and I asked a guy next door for a needle and thread to sew Ted's name tag to my uniform. When he came back into the room, I had the camo uniform of mine laid out on his bed. He just looked at it and smiled. "God!…..That looks tougher than!…Just think, I can be an Airborne Ranger today. I can't believe it!"

So he put the uniform on and grabbed an old boony hat that he bought from some Line Co. grunt and strutted around the room like John Wayne or something. He said, "Now…How about an M-16? Where can I get one of those?"

I reached into the locker and took out my old buddy. "Here!" I said, handing him my M-16. His eyes bugged out two inches.

"Hot diggity!" He yelled. "Now I am a real bad dude, just like you!"

I said, "Let's not get carried away! We'll just say we're traveling together. Both of us don't need a weapon. You bikh?"

"Whatever you say, dude! Whatever you say. I bikh, man, I bikh!" Bikh meant understand in Vietnamese.

He stood there looking at, and holding my M-16 like it was a piece of gold. We walked out into the hall and as we passed the last room a guy came out and said, "Hey Ted, what are you up to? They'll hang you if they catch you looking like that!"

Ted said, "If you don't tell them, I sure won't!"

The guy just smiled shaking his head and said, "Have fun!"

Ted said, "Airborne ...all the way!" I just laughed and shook my head.

All the way to the gate he had to strut around like he was real bad. It made me laugh to see this guy having so much fun with just a uniform. As we walked toward the gate I said, "Just act normal...if that's possible. Walk straight through and don't stop or look at anyone! We'll make it no sweat."

"Do I look alright?" He asked. His voice quivered a bit.

"No sweat, you look real bad!" I chuckled to myself.

He walked right past the guards like he just bought the place. On the other side he said, "See! those A.P.'s know better than to mess with a bad dude like me."

I said, "Yeeeeah man! You're real bad!" I thought I would pop a gut laughing.

As we walked down the street that led to the main road called Highway #1, he had to stop at every hooch and talk to nearly every girl. I didn't say anything, I just let him have his fun. Finally we got off the slum block and on the main road. "So...What do you want to do first?"

I asked. "I've never been to the Vill so your guess is as good as mine."

He said the army guys had told him that the big white stone cat house was supposed to be the best one. So we walked across the street and went in. As soon as we got inside he went ape....laughing and grabbing girls everywhere. I sat down and bought a pack of Bong Son bombers. I lit one and passed it to Ted. He took a long hard hit and passed it back. "Boy!" he said, "Those suckers are tasty ain't they?"

"They are at that!" I replied.

Within the first five minutes we were stoned out and he started telling me about all the chicks he was going to make. I said, "Knock yourself out, man. That's what you came here for......Right?"

He said, "You got that el correcto dude!"

He jumped up and grabbed a little honey that was just sitting around smiling a lot and that's the last I saw of him for an hour or so. I just sat around smoking and drinking lemonade and rice whiskey drinks. I asked a chick for a carton of joints and paid her $20.00 M.P.C.

Soon I could see Ted coming back out to the main room where I was sitting around with two chicks. I guess business was slow for the girls that day. As he came into the room I handed the carton of joints to him. "Here are your joints, keep track of them."

He said, "Thanks man." He took out forty dollars and handed it to me.

"Forty dollars." I said. "They're only twenty dollars."

He asked. "What?"

I replied, "Yeah! $20.00."

He asked, "That's all they cost? Why those A.P. f#*#*!ers!"

"What's wrong?" I asked.

"Them dudes always charge everyone $40.00 a carton."

"Well," I said. "From now on when I come to Quy Nhon I'll bring them for you so you don't get ripped off anymore."

"Great! To heck with them rip offs," he said as we sat back and got wiped out.

We spent most of the day messing around at the Vill, checking everything out and staying high. Ted must have blown thirty dollars on different girls that day, at five dollars a shot. He said he was horny....I believed him.

As we walked back to the road leading back to the A.F.B. we noticed the workers, the locals, starting to leave post. "We better get back soon," I said. Ted agreed and we headed back to the gate. As we got closer to the gate he started the 'do I look okay?' stuff again. I said just relax and walk through.

As we passed through, he saw the A.P. that he usually gets his pot from. Ted said, "That A.P. over there....I hope he don't see me and start something." Sure enough the A.P. started to walk over to us.

He came up to us and said to Ted, "Don't I know you from somewhere?"

Ted said, "You sucker! Don't mess with me now, you'll get me locked up but fast."

The A.P. said, "Man!...I don't believe you. You must be crazy!"

Ted said, "This uniform makes you do strange things."

The A.P. replied, "Move out!" then laughed.

Before we got to the barracks I took a detour to his company's mess hall which was only a short distance away. He said he was going back to change before the wrong person saw him. So I said I would wait for him at the mess hall. I walked over to a bench out in front of the mess hall and waited for Ted.

Soon he came walking up and said, "Let's pig out!"

"Sounds good to me," I replied as I walked into the mess hall. I just knew I smelled real beef cooking. For a while, I thought I'd forgotten what it smelled like.

I said, "Boy, does this place smell good."

"Yeah! I've got a bad case of the munchies," Ted replied. So we signed the register and got in line.

As we stood there waiting to move Ted looked up at the menu on the wall. He said, "Man!...Prime rib again?"

I looked at him and shook my head. "So what's wrong with that?" He said he didn't like prime rib because they always cooked it too rare.

So I said, "Man, you have to be nuts! Prime rib and you're bitching about it."

He asked, "Could you eat mine if I get it?"

I said, "You just watch me."

So as we got up to the guy cutting the meat, we both asked for big pieces. The piece we each got was about two inches thick, five inches wide and six inches long. It was the most beautiful piece of prime rib I ever saw. I could just about taste that sucker right then.

Ted said, "If you eat all of this meat I'll faint."

I said, "You best lay down on the floor right now so you don't have as far to fall!"

He just laughed and shook his head, saying, "No way!"

We sat down and before he put in sugar and milk and stirred his coffee my piece of meat was history. He looked up from his coffee cup and saw my mouth full and my steak gone. He said, "Man, you have got to be kiddin' me! You must be three quarters pig."

I said, "Oink...Oink!" I stabbed his steak with my fork dragging it across his plate, tray, and the table onto my plate.

He just shook his head. "I never saw such an animal, where do you put it?" He asked. "In my belly," I replied as I let out an enormous burp! He jumped up and said I was also embarrassing and said, "I'll meet you outside."

I said, "I may go back for seconds so don't hold your breath."

He said, "Good enough then.... I'll see ya back at the hooch."

I replied, "See ya!" I shook my head wondering how this guy kept alive with as little as he ate. Or maybe I was a pig and didn't know it. Oink!..Oink! I thought when I got up for seconds.

After my belly was stuffed full of prime rib, I walked out of the chow hall and headed back to Ted's barracks. We were both about beat from all the partying we did that day. So I said I was going to crash to get rested up for tomorrow. He asked, "When are you coming back this way?" I told him Recondo/Ranger school was supposed to be about three weeks long. Then I was coming back to the army post at Quy Nhon for Pathfinder school. He said, "The Pathfinders are over on the army post next door to the Air force base. Did you see the road to the army post today when we were coming through the gate out front?"

I said, "No."

He replied, "Well yeah you could miss it. It's kind of hidden. Just take the road left, next to the A.P. guard shack straight ahead about two hundred yards and you can't miss it." He said that it looks like part of the A.F.B. but if I just kept on that road I would come to the army post. He told me it would be great when I got back, then we could party out again. I told him maybe someday he could come to Uplift for a weekend if he could ever get the time and see how I live. He said he probably could get the time but he said he didn't think he would ever have the guts to do a trip like that. Especially out where V.C. and like that was. I said all he would have to do is set up a chopper ride to and from Uplift and he would have no sweat about getting ambushed on the road between here and Uplift. He said it sounded exciting but he would have to see. So I told him goodnight, see you in the morning. He said, "I'll get you up in plenty of time to eat breakfast. So don't lose any sleep worrying about not getting your bottomless pit filled up."

"Goodnight!" I replied. And I started to drift off to sleep.

As I lay there I thought how strange the situation was. We meet someone so suddenly in the service and grow to be very good friends so quickly. I guess we just had to grab onto each friend we could. Because they all go, just as quickly as they come to us. They never seem to last very long...

CHAPTER 20

Wooooooh Momma!

In the morning I heard Ted calling me, "Jim! Get your dead butt up!" So I sat up.

"Man!...that was one short night." I said as I sat up.

He replied, "I never was much of a sack hound. I always get up early and get my shower out of the way before the others get up." I was next to hit the showers and boy did that hot water feel good! It also felt good not to have to worry about the next guy.

After I got all cleaned up and dressed Ted and I walked to the mess hall to eat. I took all my stuff with me because right after chow I had to be at the air field to meet the Captain who was flying me to Nha Trang. We got into the chow line and as I got up to my old buddy the egg cooker he said, "What will it be today Sarge.?"

I said, "I guess the usual." He smiled and filled my plate with a monster ham and cheese omelette, home fires, bacon, and toast. I took two oranges and stuffed them into my lower pants pocket and walked over to a table.

I immediately stuffed down the last good meal I knew I would have for three weeks at least and waited for Ted to finish. Ted said that I was nuts for eating so much because if I got sick on the jet ride I would be a real mess. I just laughed and told him I came from a long line of cast iron guts. He smiled and told me it was about time to meet Nelson. He said that Captain Nelson was the guy that was going to fly me to Nha Trang. I said that I was so excited about the flight I could just flip! Ted said if I had to go the john go then, or I would be cleaning out my pants in Nha Trang. That made sense to me, so I took his advice.

After we both got outside we headed toward the air field. As we got closer to the jet hangars I could see they were all housed in very large dome-shaped concrete buildings. They looked like very large sewer pipes cut length wise and laid flat-side on the ground. Inside these billets were men getting the beautiful birds fueled up and checked out.

The F-4 Phantom jets were two jet engines with wings attached to them. They were beautiful! They must have some kind of power, I thought. Darn near as far as could see, all I could see, were these billets with jets inside. I just stood there with my mouth open staring at those beautiful jet planes. They were camouflage in color, very dull brown and tan. There was no shine to them at all. That just made them look all that much meaner, which they were!

Then I heard Ted's voice. "Captain Nelson, I want you to meet your passenger." turned around and saw a Captain that looked to me to be about thirty years old r so. Not very tall or built very big but kind of husky. I saluted him.

He said, "I'm glad to meet you. My name is Jim Nelson."

I said, "It is a pleasure to meet you, Sir! Jim is my name."

"Jim," he said, "Welcome aboard." He told me the crew would be rolling his rd out in just a couple of minutes and they would put my things on board. He ld me to give my things to one of the men so I did.

I relaxed a few minutes and looked around outside. I saw the clouds were all puffed up like big cotton balls in the sky. I revelled, knowing I would be among them very shortly.

"I guess we're going to get a nice day." Captain Nelson said.

I replied, "It's a beautiful day! Just right for flying."

"Have you flown much?" He asked.

I said, "Oh, yeah! I've even jumped out of perfectly good air planes. But I never flew in a rocket like these babies." He told me not to worry, flying was all the same really.

Then he asked me about combat and things that I did there. I said after a while I got used to combat and all, it's really all just the same. He laughed and said, "I guess we all have our different and unusual jobs to do. Sometimes we don't really think they're very exciting. Some of us really do have a very extraordinary job but soon we just get used to it, making it all the same."

"For sure," I said, "You're right there!"

He said he wasn't supposed to be doing this sort of thing, taxiing people around with Air Force equipment. But he said what they don't know won't hurt them. I just laughed and said, "I'm just glad I don't have to buy the gas for this baby!"

He said, "The only way you could afford the gas for this bird, is if your name was Uncle Sam!" He said the M.P.G. rating was real bad! I laughed and said I could imagine.

He said, "Over here in this locker is a flight suit you can put on so we can get ready to go." He said not to forget the helmet. So I took off my camos and I put on the flight suit while Nelson checked out the F-4.

It was not long before they started rolling the jet out of the billet. There was one crewman sitting in the front seat getting things ready to go as they pulled the jet out. Nelson said, "When the crew man gets out of the front seat he will instruct you on how to get yourself all buckled in. But most of all make sure you don't bump or touch anything! Okay?"

"Yes sir!" I said, "You're the boss."

The jet was pulled out onto a yellow line that led out onto the air field. The crew man got out of the cockpit and waved me over. He told me to climb up the five step ladder that went down the side of the air craft and told me to get in the front cockpit very carefully. He said he would come up the ladder and help me get all secured.

Just then Ted ran over to me and said, "Well sucker! You asked for it. Now you got it!"

I said, "Man....I still don't know how you did it. But I see you do have pull around here and you do just what you say you'll do! Thanks a lot buddy! I'll see you in about three weeks okay?"

He replied, "Hurry back! We still have a lot of partying to do."

I said, "You know it dude!" He patted my back and I went up the ladder, just after I slid my helmet on.

I started into the cockpit very cautiously, so as not to bump or touch anything

I shouldn't. Inside was a very comfortable looking seat. I slid into it slowly. As I looked around all I could see were lights and switches everywhere. I couldn't believe my eyes, looking at all the things around me a pilot would have to know about. Mounted in the middle of the console between my legs was a foot high stick. It had red, yellow, and green buttons all over it. In the middle of the console, just in front of the stick was a three inch radar screen. It was green in color and had lines etched all over it.

Once the crew man had me seated in, I felt as though I just slipped my body into a perfectly fitting glove. The ship was engineered absolutely perfectly. What a beautiful machine! I thought. The crew man hooked up some wires and stuff to my helmet and tapped me on the head, giving me the A-okay sign. He went back down the ladder. Holy moly! I thought. I still couldn't believe I was sitting in the cockpit of a Phantom jet about to blast off. I felt as though I wasn't really there. I could hardly breathe with all the excitement that was building up inside of me.

Out of the corner of my eye I saw Nelson coming up the ladder to the cockpit just behind me. Ted still stood down below on the ground. He had the smile of the Cheshire Cat.

Just then I heard Nelson's voice coming into my helmet. "Hey Ranger, you all set?" I nodded my head yes. He said, "Let's go!" I could hear a very high-pitched jet engine noise and feel a very slight vibration. The high-pitched sound got louder and louder, then I felt the F-4 start to roll forward. As I looked up, to an almost full blue sky, I saw the clear dome of the cockpit start to close down. As it shut, I could feel my ears start to plug up.

As we taxied out of the hangar area, I could see the long air strip to my left and right. We moved very slowly out to the far left side of the runway area. I could see two other Phantoms sitting on the runway. One starting to move out and one moving into position. Suddenly, I could see a big blast of black and orange smoke, then fire flew out of the back of the jet taking off in front of us. It moved out like a bullet! I never saw anything leave the earth that fast before.

We started to move forward. As we did I counted to seventeen and the jet that just took off was out of sight except for the jet-black stream of smoke he left looking like a huge black marker line in the sky behind him. The second F-4 was in line with the runway and in a moment he too was gone! God, I thought. I was next. I think if I had time to jump out I would have done it. I heard Nelson, "Hey Ranger, grab on! We're out-a-here!"

Just then I heard a big explosion behind us. I thought we blew up. But with the "G" forces pushing me back into my seat, I knew we were going airborne one way or another. The broken yellow line in the middle of the runway was one solid blur. The end of the runway was coming up very fast. For a second I thought we would run out of airstrip. Just then we shot almost straight up. I yelled out, "Wooooooh-momma!" We climbed straight up like a bullet! It was so very different than I could have ever dreamed flying could be. The feeling of moving that fast was so overwhelming I couldn't even speak.

I heard Nelson, "You okay Ranger? Hey buddy! You okay in there?"

I yelled, "Yeeeeeeeahaaaaaaa! I can't believe this! I love it!" I heard him laugh and with that I could feel us start to accelerate three times faster! "Oh! Momma!" I yelled.

Nelson replied, "Hang on Ranger! Now we're gonna fly! We've got a lot of miles to cover." It seemed as though we would run out of air space we moved from horizon to horizon so quickly.

Nelson said, "Let's see what the South China Sea looks like today."

I yelled back, "Man! I can't believe how fast this rocket is!"

He started to bank slightly to the right and far off in the distance I could see a thin blue line that stretched from left to right as far as the eye could see. In less then a minute there it was, the South China Sea. We flew out about five miles and started a left bank and down we went like a rocket to the sea far below. It felt like I left my gut ten miles behind in one second as we dove. What a rush! He started to bring the jet down closer and closer to the sea. Off to my right far off in the distance I could see the very edge of Vietnam. Soon he had that F-4 no more than one hundred fifty feet off the ocean. As I looked behind us I could see the water gushing up like a tornado was hooked to our tail.

Suddenly we shot straight up and I was looking up at a pure blue sky as we did a roll. The sky looked just like the sea below, except much lighter blue. In just seconds we were thousands of feet above the sea. He turned the jet slowly back toward the land and then he dove the jet down once again. He said, "We are moving past the speed of sound right….about…..Now!"

Suddenly I could feel a funny thump and a slight shake to the air craft and the sound of thunder just behind us. Nelson said, "And I don't have it floored all the way."

I said, "This is fast enough for me." By the time I said that, we shot back over the land once again. I couldn't see how that plane could hold together without bursting into pieces. It felt like I was riding inside a bullet. Nelson said "During combat with an enemy aircraft not only can we go this fast, but twice as fast as we are now. This aircraft will still handle and maneuver just as well as it does now."

That jet was a piece of engineering that was too much for me to comprehend! We started to descend toward the earth again. My guts were doing flip flops by then just like Ted warned me about. Nelson said we only had about ten more minutes to go before we would be headed down the landing strip.

As we got closer to the ground I could start to make out villages and a fairly large city. He told me we were just about to Nha Trang, near the air field. "It's jus' about below us now." He said. I looked out to my left. I could see the long black runway with a yellow line strip. Down and down we went. Headed straight for us was the long black runway. It looked as though we were going to crash. But jus' seconds before we hit he brought the nose slightly up. Suddenly I could feel us touch the ground.

As I looked out the dome over our heads, I could see the terrain was similar to Uplift area, but there was a much fuller looking jungle and lower mountains mor' like hills. There was really little difference, Nam was Nam.

Captain Nelson taxied the jet across the air field toward the same type c' billets that housed the jets back in Quy Nhon A.F.B. Soon he killed the jet engine and we stopped. The Plexiglas dome above our heads slowly opened and a crew man helped us out. I climbed down and walked over to the four lockers in the hangar. I then took off my flight suit and helmet and put them inside one of the lockers.

Captain Nelson came over and he looked at me and smiled, "Well!" he asked, "How did you like the ride?"

I said, "I loved it and if I was to start my military life all over again, I would love to become a pilot just like you. It was the most exciting ride I've ever had."

He said, "I'm glad you liked it. Most people would have been all upset after that ride because I was a little bit rough on you. For the first flight and all you did very well by not getting sick."

I thanked him a lot for the ride and said, "I hope I will see you around Quy Nhon some time." He said he would be happy if I stopped at his hooch and had a drink with him if I ever got back to Quy Nhon again. I said that I would be looking forward to that. He said goodbye and walked away.

I stood there shaking in my boots. An Airman who had my bag with my camos in it, along with my M-16, came up to me and handed them to me. I took them, got dressed, and told him thanks. I walked out of the air field area and headed for the gate leading outside the airfield fence. There I could see an army post just a short ways ahead. I walked into the army post guard station and I asked a guy where Recondo/Ranger School was. He told me it was on the other side of the P.X. over there, pointing to our front. He said, "You'll find the Recondo hooches just beyond that water tower over there."

I replied, "Thanks," as I walked away.

CHAPTER 21

Just Like the Real Thing?

Nha Trang was down south near a beach of the South China Sea. There was sand everywhere. As I got closer to the Recondo/Ranger barracks I could see rut sacks laid out on the ground in front of the barracks and the C.O.'s office. I figured I would go and report in to the office the first thing.

I walked in and spoke to the E-4 clerk. I told him who I was and gave him my written orders and said I was reporting for Recondo school. The Sp-4 told me most of the men had already reported and were at an orientation meeting in the day room. He said I should go attend the meeting and he would get my bunk squared away when the meeting was over. So I left my duffel bag with him and walked out to where he told me the day room was. I walked all the way to the other end of the building and saw the sign that said Day Room.

I walked in and saw twenty men seated in chairs listening to a Captain at the front of the room. I found a seat and sat down. The Captain stopped what he was saying and asked my name and where I was coming from. I told him what he wanted to know and he said he would go over the things quickly that he had already told everyone else.

He said most of the people that were there had already been in combat but not everyone. He asked the guys that had to tell the rest of the class any helpful tips that we might have learned by our experiences. He said anytime we had anything to say to raise our hand and say it, anytime we wanted. He said during our stay at Recondo/Ranger school we would be learning about Recondo/Ranger missions and guerilla warfare tactics. He told the already combat-experienced men that they would still get some new knowledge and helpful tips above what they might already know. Most of the guys were already in Recon back at their post. But some of the men were from various Line Companies around Vietnam.

He looked over at me and said, "I see Sgt. Gibbore is in an Airborne Recon Unit already. And I'm sure he has spent a lot of time studying camo, cover and deception. The right combination of these things can give a Ranger/Recondo, or anyone else, the edge that it takes to stay alive and to complete a mission. Sergeant, you have probably learned most of what we teach here, so if you have anything to add it would be helpful to guide the rest of these men onto the right path.

He started out by telling us what a Recondo/Ranger was and what they were used for. "Recondos and Rangers pull much the same type of missions. A Recondo or Recon mission is used to gather as much info. on the enemy as possible, without the enemy knowing you are in the area. They are sent out to study and report any enemy movement, keeping away from contact as much as possible.

"A Ranger mission is usually a mission for ambushing the enemy – a hunter-killer type mission. Rangers go in, viciously kick butt, gather info., and then vanish as soon as they're seen."

He then described the logistics of the course itself. He said the course was two weeks long and we would be Recondo qualified if we finished the course. Every morning we had to do extensive physical training. He said the P.T. would help us if we were ever chased or had to get out of an area fast. The uniform every morning for P.T. would be boots, pants and T- shirt. After P.T. each morning we would fall back into the barracks to get our shirts and hats, then head for our classroom instructions. He said that on the last two days there would be no P.T. We would be dropped off by chopper out in the boonies. We would then be hunted and tracked by other Recondo students.

The Captain said, "To many, this course is consdidered the course from hell. But the real hell is in the bush. These are war games...But it will be just like the real thing. You will learn things here that may save your life some day!" I thought, Basic Training City. Yeah! Just like the real thing? Here we go again!

Soon we were dismissed and told to get ready for P.T. We went outside and the men headed for the barracks. I went to get my stuff in the orderly room and then went to the barracks.

I had no locker so I asked a Marine that was also taking the course if I could put my stuff in his locker until I got one of my own. He said, "Sure, Sarge!" So I put my bag, hat, outer shirt and M-16 into his locker.

He asked, "How long have you been in country?"' I said that this was my fifth, almost sixth month. He said he had only been there twenty-one days.

I said, "I remember when I used to count days but I soon lost track of them."

He said, "Yeah I can imagine it gets hard after a few months."

I told him I had a younger brother that just screwed up and joined the Marines, too.

The guy said, "He sure screwed up alright." Suddenly I wanted to see my brother so I could choke him. But I thought, what good would that do?

I asked, "What's your name?"

He said, "Al Parks, what's yours?"

"Jim....just call me that."

He said, "Okay Jim you about ready for P.T.?"

I said, "I guess so."

We walked outside to the P.T. area out front where I saw all the rut sacks earlier. We all got lined up and started our work out. First sit ups, then pushups and all the rest of that kind of stuff. Then our drill Sgt. told us to get to a rut sack and put it on.

Watching the cherries was fun! The rut sacks were filled with sand and weighed a ton. So from my experience with them, I sat down in front of mine and got into it. Getting up was another job, but no harder than usual. The Sgt. said, "For those of you who have little experience with this task, check out the Sarge over there." They all looked at me sitting on the ground. Then as I got to my feet, the instructor went on, "This is the only way you could ever get that sucker on your back unless you happen to be Mr. America himself, and I don't think he could do it either! Now, do it right." All the guys that didn't know what they were doing learned fast. Then everyone got all set and stood on their feet in formation again.

Our drill instructor said, "We only run a mile today, but every day I will increase the distance more and more. For you pussies that can't finish today's run, or any other day's run, you will be on your way back to wherever you came from the next day! Now, get in line and double tiiiiime, hut!"

We all started running down toward the sandy beach. Talk about punishment! One hundred degrees in the shade with the sun beating down on us and sand to run in, plus the rut sacks filled with sand! Brother! That was tough. There were twenty of us that started that day. After that first run there were only seventeen left. Three quit. They went back to their units the next day. The school was very strict about P.T., even near the end of the two weeks guys were still being sent back, or quit because there was so much hard P.T. Some men just couldn't hack it. That course was the roughest thing I ever went through. It kicked my butt at times pretty bad but I just kept mentally singing an old Ranger song I learned in jump school. It usually would keep my mind busy and keep me from thinking about how bad my rear was being kicked. It was a school right out of hell. Later this training saved my life, though.

The classroom work was usually pretty boring except for the map and compass lessons we had. I really got into that because in the boonies that was the only thing that could guide you home if you were lost. Our lives depended on knowing where we were in the jungle and how to get back out again. The map and compass lessons were very thorough and in-depth. The time I spent there for the most part was very helpful and informative. But classroom study always was a bore to me.

Soon the day came to show how much we really did learn while we were there. Nha Trang was a fairly large military post and there was plenty of jungle area for our training exercise. The second to the last day we were split into two groups. The Red Army and the Blue Army. At that time there were only fourteen men left out of the twenty that first started the course, and each team had seven men.

The Red Army was supposed to be Charley and the Blue was Recondo. The Red Army was flown into a jungle area first, then the Blue Army about one hour later. That was enough time for the Reds to get set, to try to follow and or capture the blue guys, of which I was one. The Blue Army had to land, work as a team, and try to avoid being caught.

There were only two cherries left. Each team had one. The one that we had was the Marine I first met there my first day, Al Parks. As we waited for our turn to go out he asked if he could follow me back in. I asked, "What makes you think I'll make it?"

He just smiled and said, "Recon are supposed to be good, and you're Recon already."

I said, "I guess, but to me good is what attitude you have in the field. If you think you're dead you're dead!" He said he just hoped he didn't give Recon a bad name by getting us caught. I replied, "What did I just tell you about attitude?"

He smiled and said, "Yeah! Yeah, now I see!"

I replied, "Jar heads!" and I shook my head.

It finally came our time to go. So we put our sand filled rut sacks on our back and got up. We were loaded into a chopper and it lifted off. It was really only a two or three minute ride from the L.Z. so we were there in no time. It was all a bunch of make believe war. It was not the real thing.

After we landed the team got out the map and compass. We split up in a staggered line and I let the team move on as I hung back a ways. As I moved through the jungle I could see Parks far behind me trying to keep up. The distance back to base was only about two miles or less. On the way out by chopper I kept watching the ground to keep my directions in one neat pile. I never had to use my map or compass even once. It was super easy compared to the real thing.

I stopped for a couple of minutes to wait for Parks to find me again and as I did I could hear two or three men talking. So I lay down and got all set to ambush them. I could see it was two of the Red army coming very close to me. I made no movement. They saw Parks coming right behind me. They hid and waited until Parks was right next to them. Then they jumped right out and captured him. The two Red army dudes still never knew I was right behind them the whole time.

They went to tie Park's hands as we would do to a prisoner. That's when I stood up fifteen feet behind them. With a big smile I said, "What's up, Charley?" The two men in the Red army knew they were had.

"Oh man!" One of them said. Parks relieved them of their weapons. He then tied up their hands and we all moved out.

It only took about an hour and we were back. We were way ahead of all the other guys. We sat down and hung out relaxing until everyone else got back. Our two prisoners were embarrassed and swore they would have our butts tied up tomorrow when it was their turn to be the Blue army. I reminded them if this was the real thing, there would be no tomorrow for either of them…they would be quite dead! I asked, "Is that a bet? Or are you just blowin' smoke again?"

They just sat there saying, "You suckers, you just wait."

Soon I could see our drill Sgt. walking up to where we all were supposed to meet. He asked, "What do we have here?" looking at the two guys we had tied up.

I said, "They just felt like playing Cowboys and Indians. They're the Indians So we tied um' up."

He just laughed as he untied them. "Did you two boneheads learn anything?" he asked.

The one guy said, "Yeah!"

The Sgt. asked, "What?"

He said, "Never turn your back on Recon." Parks just laughed and poked me.

The Sgt. said, "This time it's only an exercise, next time you two might not be so lucky. Sarge, when every one gets back tell them to go clean up. I'll see you guys later." As he walked past Parks and I he said, "Nice job Sarge! A live prisoner is much more informative than a dead one." He smiled and walked away.

Soon we saw both the Red and Blue teams coming back toward the barracks. Everyone had their share of simulated killed or captured. As they came toward us I told them what our drill Sgt. had told me.

After chow we all had a meeting in the day room about how everything went that day. We were quizzed about what we learned and we talked about our mistakes.

The drill Sgt. told us the same thing was going to happen the next day, except we would change sides. Reds would be blues and vice versa. After our meeting we were all dismissed and could do as we wanted.

The first thing I did was go catch a buzz. I asked Parks if he wanted to get high and he said yes. So we walked out the door toward the club just down the street. By the time we got there we finished a joint and walked in. There were three guys sitting at the bar talking with the guy tending bar. We walked up to the bar and got a shot of Jack Daniel's on ice and a can of Budweiser each. We joked about catching those two dopes that day and talked about how we would get through the next day without getting caught. We drank awhile and soon it got late so we headed back. When we got to our barracks we got ready for bed. Inside the hooch most everyone was sleeping already. I guess everyone was tired out from all the P.T. all week and the walk through the boonies that day.

Morning came quickly as usual. After breakfast we watched the Blue team put their sand-filled rut sacks on their backs as they got ready to move out. Then we put our Red armbands on and jumped into our chopper. Just before we lifted off, Parks poked me and pointed out the door. I saw the two guys we captured the day before, smiling and shaking their fists at us. I just looked at them and smiled. Then I turned to Parks and asked, "Want to screw up their whole act?"

He said, "I'm with you all the way! You lead the way, Sarge." I smiled.

We flew back to just about the same area we were let off in the day before. When we landed it was just about three to four hundred yards farther off to the west from the day before. Parks kept asking me what I was up to. I just told him don't worry. I told him and the whole team, "I guess what we should do, if you men want, is catch them in the middle of an ambush." They all said it was a good idea. I told them to quickly go on ahead about five or six hundred yards and set up. I said Parks and I would stay behind and follow the Blue team until they ran into the men on our team. That way they would be caught between us and would be dead meat. They all loved my plan and they took off.

As soon as they were out of sight, I took off running the other way about one hundred yards. Parks followed. As we ran Parks asked, "Where the Sam hill you going? The barracks is the other way!"

I said, "Shut up or go with the other guys."

He said, "You're the boss." I jumped into the bushes, just off the open landing area to wait.

Parks said, "If we stay here, they will see us when they land for sure!"

I said, "Just keep quiet and very still! Like you're not even here. Don't move a muscle till I do!"

He said, "I hear ya!"

Soon we could hear the Blue army's chopper coming. I said to Parks, "Now lay down and stay motionless for a while, don't move!" We both lay flat down on the ground. The chopper landed and the Blue team jumped out.

As soon as the chopper left the area got dead quiet. We could hear everything that those guys said. Parks just kept slowly shaking his head wondering what we were going to do next. The Blue army said they would stay together because they figured it would be better in a larger bunch. That's just what I hoped and thought they would do. They all came from a line company. After they got done checking their map and compass, they slowly headed into the bush to our front and out of sight.

About three or four minutes went by. Parks asked, "Now what?"

I said, "It's time to go." With that we got up and we ran back across the open L.Z. area. Once we got to where the Blue army went in the jungle I stopped and told Parks to stay right on my heels. I said we would sneak up from behind them and nab them unexpectedly. The path that the seven men left through the jungle a blind man could follow. So I moved very quickly.

Soon I could see men just about twenty to thirty yards in front. I stopped to listen. Those guys were really not taking this very seriously. I could hear them a mile away. They complained because it was hot, they were already tired, thirsty, you name it. They had already stopped to rest. So did Parks and I. I whispered to Parks, "These guys are cream puff. We're going to catch 'um all at once no sweat!"

He whispered, "Cream puff! How are we going to catch all seven of those dudes?"

I replied, "Look, you go around and grab their attention. But don't let them see you right away. Just stay moving along to their left awhile. Be real quiet when you move around them. Then when they stop for another rest, move in closer. Hopefully they will see or hear you and take their attention off me coming up from behind them! Ya got me?"

He said, "Sounds good! But I just hope it works! We're gonna look real stupid tied up if you know what I mean!"

I replied, "What did I tell you about attitude?" Parks quickly took off.

I watched the Blue army until they started to move, then Parks and I followed. We all walked for about two hundred yards. It was slow going because the jungle was thick. Soon the Blue army stopped for another rest, just as I thought they would. I saw Parks slowly moving in from their left out just far enough. He was doing just what I wanted.

About ten minutes went by and I could see that they still hadn't spotted Parks. I thought they would just get up and leave. But finally, I could hear a guy say, "Hey! You guys, hear that? Out front listen! Watch up in front." I started to move in. Very slowly I crept in toward them on my hands and knees. I could see they all had their backs right towards me, just like I wanted.

Closer and closer I came. I couldn't believe they never assigned a rear guard. I was only about fifteen feet behind them when I got up very slowly. One guy said, "I know there is someone just up in front of us about twenty yards. Did you guys hear that?"

As I stood up right behind them I said, "What's up, G.I.? Me have AK-47 on full auto. Not to move please."

"No way....!" I heard one of them say as they slowly turned to see me standing right behind them.

Parks stood up in front of them and said, "Drop the weapons, boys!" Parks had a smile from ear to ear!

About one hundred yards ahead we ran into the rest of our Red team who totally busted the Blue teams rocks all the way back. As we went we talked about how they screwed up and how they could have prevented their whole team from being captured. We all really had a good laugh and joked about it all. There it was funny, but in real life it would have been a whole different story. I just hoped they had learned something.

As we all came walking out of the jungle together, we saw our drill Sergeant. The Red team kept busting the Blue team about how they got nabbed and all. The drill Sgt. asked, "What the heck happened? How could a whole team get captured at once?" All of us looked at each other and started laughing.

I replied, "I think we all learned a real good lesson today." Parks enthusiastically told the drill Sgt. the story about how he nearly captured the whole Blue army single handedly and all. I just about busted a gut trying not to laugh. But he finally did say, with my help of course!

The Sgt. knew he wasn't going to get anywhere with us right then and said, "We will discuss this further at the meeting tonight. But for now clean up and get ready for chow." We all laughed and moved out.

All that day I had to hear over and over from Parks how good "our" plan was and how easy it was to capture all of them. Sometimes I wished they had captured him.

During the meeting that night the whole story came out about what happened. The drill Sgt. asked, "Will the two guys that got caught yesterday by Parks and the Sarge stand up?" They both reluctantly stood up. The Sgt. asked, "I thought you two dummies told me you learned something yesterday."

They both said, "Yeah...but it wasn't our fault. We all got caught."

The Sgt. said, "In real life you would have been dead! You should have remembered what you were taught yesterday about turning your back on someone. As I told you guys yesterday, this time it was all in fun, but it will not always be that way. Next time it will be your lives on the line. I just hope you have all learned to watch your back door! Charley loves to do just what the Sarge and Parks did today. V.C. love to ambush from behind. They love to hit you when you're at ease or sleeping on the job. Remember that!"

He said we all passed the course scholastically. But he added he had his doubts if all of us would get home alive. He wished all of us good luck. He said, "Stay alert...Stay alive!" Then we all got our Recondo patches.

Parks raised his hand and stood up. He said, "I don't know about the rest, but I have learned a lot while I was here. The lessons I learned here really showed me what I could do if I use my head rather than rush right in, as I've been taught in the past. I've learned a lot of tricks and moves that I really think will save my life someday. I just want to say thanks!" Then he sat back down. Then just about everyone started to say about the same thing.

I had to agree with everyone else. It was a good course and it showed me a lot of better ways of doing certain things myself. But to me the best teacher of all was the real thing. For some strange unexplained reason, I wanted to get back to the real thing. For some reason I just couldn't wait to see Charley's smiling face once again. Now I know I must be getting soft in the head, I thought.

The next morning there was a lot of hand shaking and good-byes like always. We all got ready to board our choppers back to where ever we all came from. One of the two guys Parks and I captured both days on our missions came up to me. He said with his hand out, "I know I really didn't take this stuff very seriously. But I really have learned a lot. I know we all should have had our stuff together better yesterday, but that's water under the bridge now. I just want to say it was a pleasure meeting and knowing you Sergeant! And I know for sure I wouldn't want you hunting me as an enemy!"

Just then Parks came over to us. He put out his hand and we shook. He said, "Sergeant! It's been a real pleasure working with you. I just hope that we meet again someday. I wouldn't ever want you as an enemy either!"

I said, "The only enemy you two have now is Charley. He is all the enemy any one of us can handle. Just don't ever underestimate that little sucker! He will always show you another surprise you never thought of! Good luck guys. I hope we'll meet again some day."

Parks just smiled and said, "Me too! Jim, I know I'll never see you again. I really don't know what to say except thanks for showing me how to use my head rather than my body to stop the bullets. I've learned more from you than I would have learned in any school. Now I know what you were saying those times you said it don't matter what they show you in these schools. It's how you use your brain and common sense in a tight situation. That's what really counts! Thanks for everything, Jim. I know I'll make it through this place because I've been taught by one of Charley's worst enemies. Thanks Jim. I really mean it!"

I said, "Well...thanks...but I'm no better than you are at this stuff. So far I've just been lucky."

He shook his head and said, "You're the boss! Whatever you say Sarge." Then he walked away.

Jar heads! I never knew I could get to like one of those guys, I thought. That was the last time I ever saw all but one of those men.

HEADQUARTERS
5TH SPECIAL FORCES GROUP (ABN)
1ST. SPECIAL FORCES

THIS ... THAT

SGT. E-5 ... S GIB... 128-40-9610

RECONDO NR 3006 HAS THIS ...th. DAY OF MAY 19 70

SUCCESSF... COMPLETED

MACV RECONDO SCHOOL

ASST. COMMANDANT
MACV RECONDO SCHOOL

COMMANDING OFFICER
5 th. SPECIAL FORCES GROUP (ABN)
1 st. SPECIAL FORCES
COMMANDANT

137

Recondo Team Going Out

CHAPTER 22

More Ghost Time

Soon I jumped on a chopper that was going north to make one of its stops near Quy Nhon A.F.B. All the way back all I could think about was that the P.T. was over! And it was time to party out in Quy Nhon that night. Drinkin', smokin', and eatin'! Yeaaaaah! hoo! Here I come, Ted! I just hoped he was ready for it.

By the time we got to Quy Nhon, my feet and rear were numb from all the vibration of the helicopter's motor and overhead rotor blades. They made such a racket because they were spinning faster than the speed of sound. That would create a vibration that really got on my nerves after awhile.

Soon we landed at the army post next to the A.F.B. in Quy Nhon. That was where I was going to Pathfinder school. But I had a lot of time before I had to report to school. I jumped out and headed for my old Air Force buddy, Ted Springer. After I got onto the A.F.B. I quickly headed to his hooch. I knew right where to go. I walked up the stairs and into his room.

He was sitting on his bunk smoking a joint and digging on some tunes. He saw me come in and jumped down off his bunk. Handing me the joint he held, he said, "What the heck you doing back here already? What did they do, throw you out, or what?"

I said, "No! The school was only two weeks, not three! The army just screwed up again! Now I have a week to kill here before my Pathfinder course starts."

"No way!" Ted yelled, "It must be nice!"

I asked, "How come you aren't at work?" He said that morning he had hurt his back on the job so he went to sick call and got two days ghost time. I said, "Great! You aren't too hurt to party are you?"

He said, "Hurt? Who's hurt?"

I just laughed and said, "A party is just the thing to fix your back just like new!"

He said, "Ya know....I think you're right."

We both laughed and after I put my stuff into the extra locker we took off. He asked, "Well, what first?" I said that I hadn't had a good meal since I left there. The first thing I wanted to do was eat.

He said, "No kiddin'! I should have known. What else would you want to do first, except eat." He said that he was kind of hungry too so we headed for the mess hall.

We walked in and signed in as usual. I could smell that good cooking already. Ted said, "Do you want me to check out the menu?"

I said, "Don't trouble yourself for my benefit. I'll eat anything these guys cook." We got our silverware and trays and got into line. I could see they had roast beef or a fish type dinner. I hate fish so I got the roast beef. Ted got the fish. He said rare meat made him sick.

I said, "Fish bones make me choke." We sat down and pigged out.

After I finished my seconds, we got up and left. Outside I said, "Boy...that was what I needed. Now I need a good buzz to go along with that food and I'll be all set."

Ted said that he was just about out of the carton that I bought for him down at the Vill two weeks ago and said he refused to buy them from those rip off Air Police. I said, "No sweat, I'll get us more tomorrow."

He said, "Sounds good!" With that he lit up a joint and passed it to me. We walked around until it was gone. After that we headed for the club to party out. All afternoon and night we drank and smoked ourselves silly. By the time we got back to the barracks we had to help each other up the stairs we were both so screwed up.

I woke up on the floor the next morning where I last remember myself sitting. I tried to sit up. My head was about to pop! I had such a hangover. I just moaned and groaned, trying to shake the cobwebs out of my brain.

I heard the same noises coming out of Ted who somehow managed to get into his bunk above me. "Man, I'm dying," he said.

"Tell me about it," I groaned.

He asked, "Can you hand me that unopened Pepsi over there by you?" I opened one eye and saw it about two feet away from me.

I replied, "I doubt it!"

He said, "If you do, I'll make both of us feel a lot better!"

I said, "This I have to see."

I crawled over to the can of Pepsi and grabbed it and sat up and tossed the Pepsi to Ted. It nearly hit him in the head. He sat up quickly and said, "Man, if that can hit me in the head, it would have killed me!"

I said, "Yeah! But it got your dead butt up, didn't it?"

He then reached into a cabinet drawer that was built into his bunk bed's headboard, and pulled out a glass bottle of speed like Joe Son had that time down at his bar.

He said, "This stuff will put us back on our feet in no time." He opened the Pepsi and drank down a mouth full or so. Then snapped off the top of the little glass bowling pin shaped bottle and dumped the clear liquid into the Pepsi. He shook it a little and took a mouth full. "Not bad!" He said, "It's not bitter at all. Here Jim," he said as he handed me the can.

I took a big gulp. Then took another. He said, "Save some for me, you joker." So I got up and handed the can to him.

All of a sudden I could feel my whole insides start to come alive. My eyes sprang open and I felt like I was going to bust out laughing for no reason. I felt so good I could have danced up a storm. Ted gulped down another big mouthful and I grabbed the can and finished it. "No kiddin'. What is that stuff, jet fuel?!" I asked.

We sat there and rapped for an hour or so before we realized that we were going no place fast. Then we left the room and headed out. I had so much energy I could not sit down for more than two seconds. We just about ran out the door and down the stairs. Where we were going neither one of us had a clue.

For awhile I felt as though I would run right out of my skin. I never had that much energy in my life. Ted said, "I told you this was good stuff and I would get us on our feet. Lately I do it so much I just feel real good not so much rushy or speedy anymore, I just feel good. Have you ever done speed before?"

"Speed?" I replied, "That stuff is jet fuel in a bottle! Not only that, but I've never done any speed before."

"How do you like the way it gets your head buzzin'?" He asked.

I said, "My head's all right, it's my mouth and feet I can't stop from buzzin."

He laughed and said, "No sweat, it will wear off in....ooooooh about ten hours or so. Then you'll slow down a little."

I replied, "Man I hope you mean a lot!"

He just smiled and said, "Have fun dude!...go with the flow!"

Flow wasn't the word. I felt like a roaring waterfall. We went bowling and drank beer for most of the morning. Then during the afternoon we went swimming in the pool. That night we headed down to the club. We smoked joint after joint until morning, just rappin' and buzzing around playing cards all night in different barracks. Then we went back to Ted's room and played cards with some guy there.

When morning rolled around we were starting to unwind and we got a bit edgy. So Ted suggested we do some more crank. I said, "Let's go!" He opened another bottle of crank and can of Pepsi. He mixed our jet fuel cocktail and down the hatch it went.

Shortly after that we were in orbit once again. He asked, "How about going to the Vill today for more joints?"

I replied, "Yeah man...we ain't there yet?" He laughed. Then I asked him, "Do you want to go too?"

He said, "Yeah....but first I have to report to sick call." He told me that he was going to try for more ghost time.

We planned that we would meet back there at the hooch when he got back. I told him that if I wasn't here, I would be at the pool. I said, "Man, a dip would feel good right about now." Then he asked me if he could get the extra set of camos in my locker.

He said, "If I had them I could just change right away when I come back from sick call...if I get more ghost time."

I replied, "Good idea." I took out my extra set and gave them to him. His name tag was still on the shirt. I said, "Now just get ready when you get back if you can go and meet me at the pool."

He said, "Okay...see ya later." He walked out.

I got the shorts that I bought down at the P.X. the day before and headed out for the pool. When I got there I saw I had the pool all to myself. I went into one of the little booths they had set up around the pool to change and then dove right in. "Ooooooh!" I said, "This water sure feels nice." It was about ninety five degrees out that day. Sunny and pure blue sky. It looked like the monsoons had let up for awhile. They would last up to three months but would usually give way to a beautiful sunny day now and then. This was one of those real beautiful days. Sun and fun...That's the life for me, I thought.

Just then I started to get the feeling of missing L.Z. Uplift and the guys there. I couldn't believe it, like I was homesick or something. I just couldn't understand why I got that feeling. The friends, I could see missing them, the close ones anyway. A lot of them would be gone by the time I got back. So maybe that was what the empty, lonely feeling was all about, I thought. Oh well, I'll be back there soon enough, I thought. But for quite some time that day I just couldn't shake that feeling.

The worst part was how bad I missed Schriff. It was weird. It was the same kind of feeling I get when I'm in a group of people at a party, and I know a particular person is there with me, but I don't see them right in front of me, yet I know that they are there somewhere. I tried hard to shake the feeling but I just couldn't. I remember just floating on my back in the shallow end of the pool thinking about all the guys and Uplift and all kinds of things.

I even began, for the first time, to start feeling guilty about all the drugs and drinking that I'd been doing. I knew I was abusing myself bad! But for some reason when you're hooked you just don't see it, or you don't want to face it. Partying was one thing, but I was getting bad! That's about all I wanted to do anymore.

I never realized it then but I found out years later that I was self-medicating myself trying to forget and deal with the horrors of combat. I was reaching out, trying to find a place where all that torment would fade for whatever amount of time I could get. Some place to hide for awhile, if you will. Also the army itself was no help. The first thing they did to reward us for a "job well done" was give us a pass to where they told us not to go in the first place, the Vill. They gave us talks and warnings to stay a long way from such places but there was no place else to go. They told us to stay clear of whores and dope but where did they let us go? To the Vill. What did they think we were going to do there? Toast marshmallows and sing campfire songs with Momma-son and the ladies or what? They knew that is where you buy booze, ladies, and dope. Don't get me wrong, I'm not dumping the whole load on the army but they were all part of the problem like everything else.

Back before I joined the army I drank a few beers and like that. I was no angel or whatever. But never pot or drugs of any kind. In fact I looked at people that did do dope as totally dumb and real weird, a hippie freak! That is until the day I started doing drugs. I did them just to fit in is all, like everyone else. The whole place was like being in a very infectious area, a leper colony. Everyone around you had the sickness and you had no vaccine against it. It was passed from one guy to the next….how could you help but catch it? Then it was too late…

A very important thing to remember about substance abuse is this…At first it's like all sin; it fascinates and hooks you into believing you're having fun until you go out of control…then it assassinates!

I kind of drifted away as I floated in dreamland. Many times during my life I could sense different things for good and for bad.

Suddenly I heard Ted's voice. "So what the f*%#! Are you dead out there or what!?"

I jumped for a second and I stood up. I saw Ted standing right over me, just looking down at me with a frown. "What's with the face? You look ticked off." I asked. Ted said that he had been standing there and spoke to me twice and I never said a word.

He said, "I thought you were dead or something."

I replied, "I was just day dreaming." He was all dressed in my extra uniform and ready to go.

He said, "Well, do you want to swim some more or head out?" I said that I was waterlogged enough and I jumped out and went into a booth and changed.

We walked back toward his hooch and I put my swimsuit away. Then we headed out. "How did you make out with your ghost time?" I asked. He said that they told him he could take the rest of the day but to try and report for work tomorrow.

He said, "Screw those doctors. I was gonna' work tomorrow anyway! But then I planned to head right back to sick call right after work tomorrow and tell them I screwed my back up again even worse. That way I'll get more ghost time for sure!"

I replied, "Sounds like a plan to me. I think while you're at work tomorrow I'll go and find out where I have to report to Pathfinder school on the army post next door. Just to get oriented with the place."

Ted told me that the army fort was very small. He said that most of the men were stationed out around the A.F.B. perimeter. He said just the few officers and N.C.O.s were there…mostly just men for pulling guard duty and stuff like that. He said, "You'll have no sweat finding out what to do and where to go. By the way, what is a Pathfinder anyway?"

I said, "I really know very little about what their function is except I've heard they are sent to try to analyze and set up a landing zone situation out in the boonies. A scout, I guess. If Headquarters wanted to send out a Line Co. to work in a particular place, maybe to build a new L.Z. or fort, the Pathfinder would go in to guide in all the aircraft needed to bring in all the men and supplies. In other words, just to make sure someone was there, to guide that whole mess in without having any crack-ups or accidents, like that. That is about all I know about the Pathfinder right now."

Ted said, "That doesn't sound very dangerous anyway."

I said, "It's not…unless Charley is out there to meet you. On a mission you may have one or two more people with you is all. Most pathfinder missions are run by one or two men."

Ted said. "No kiddin'? No way would I go into the boonies by myself! No way!"

I said, "Every job I do is about as dangerous as it can get. But that's what I asked for when I was well, 'forced' to join the Army for three years. I would have joined anyway though."

He asked as he shook his head, "Forced?"

I replied, "I had a choice….the army or jail."

He replied, "Oh man! Well it's better you than me! I would be dead meat the first mission out!"

I said, "That's how it ends up for many guys. But I still wouldn't want your job. Jockeyin' bombs around post! You got to be nuts! With me, I have me to depend on. And I trust myself 100% at all times. With a bomb, all you have to put your trust in is a good or bad fuse!"

Ted looked at me and said, "You jerk! I never thought of it like that!"

As we talked we walked right out the A.F.B. gate no sweat at all. As we walked through the A.F.B. guard shack there was no sign of Ted's Air Force Police buddy. We ran across Highway #1 and right into the big cat house on the other side.

As we went in I smelled something very rotten when I passed an old Momma-son sitting near the door. She had some banana leaves lying on the mat she was sitting on. On the leaves was some fish that looked weird or rotten. I nearly barfed it smelled so bad. Ted said, "What the….is that?"

I said, "I've never seen any but I've heard of it. I think it's called Nukmau. They take fish and bury it in leaves. Then they dig it up in time and use that oily stuff on greens, sort of salad dressing. Then they eat that nasty looking fish."

Ted said, "Man, you have to be messin' with me!"

I said, "You can see can't you?"

He just gulped and said, "I still can't believe that! How could they get it past their nose?"

I replied, "Yeeeeah!"

As I looked further into the hooch I could see a young girl I'd never saw before. She was very pretty and had one bright blue eye, the other was brown. I waved her over and told her to get us a couple of lime drinks. "Nice!" Ted said.

"Not too shabby," I replied. Then we both got far enough away from Momma-son's rank smelling fish so as not to get sick smelling it and we sat down.

Ted and I sat around getting stoned as we rapped with dudes coming and going. None of them stayed very long. Then the girl I sent out for drinks came back with them. Ted immediately tried to grab her attention by asking her for a carton of joints. She told a younger girl to go get them. She came right over to me and sat down on my lap and kept staring at me. Then she started to mess and play with my hair. She understood very little English, except, "You new guy Joe?" Stuff like that. All I kept thinking about was the night I spent with the three girls back at Joe's place. I thought, here I go again!

I replied, "Just new to Quy Nhon."

She said, "Okay G.I." That could have meant about anything. She stood up holding my hand and pulling me up saying, "Come!"

Ted said, "I wish she would tell me that!" She just kept pulling me up. Ted said, "Go on, you dummy! She wants you."

I replied, "No kiddin'! dummy. I know it."

I got up and walked into a room with her. As soon as we got into the room she took off her clothes. Then she started to undress me. I could feel my face turning bright red. I was going to blow it again. I just knew it. All I kept thinking about were the ten million G.I.s that were with her all day long and my girl back home. Guilt City here I come again, I thought. We lay down on her bed and she tried every way she knew to get me going. That's bad when a "lady of the night, or day" can't get me going, I thought. That just made things worse! No way! I felt dead from the belt line down.

After about half an hour of that I owed her five dollars and I never got anything for it. All I did was get screwed out of five bucks. She said, "Hey Joe, you no likie Linda?"

I said, "Ooooh yeeeah! I like Linda all right, don't get me wrong! Aaaaaa but me....have headache!" What else could I say?

I got up and got dressed as she did and we walked out. I was hotter than a sex starved Billy goat! But I had a mental block about catching something and my chick at home and all that just wouldn't quit!

When we got back out where I left Ted he wasn't in the room. He was still with a girl. Linda and I just sat around and rapped. She said, "No sweat Joe."

I replied, "Yeeeeah!"

Soon Ted came back in the room and he sat down. He asked, "Did everything come out all right." Then he laughed.

I said, "Ooooh yeeeah! No sweat."

He asked, "Did you get my joints yet?"

I said, "No." Then I asked Linda to get a carton. As soon as she got back with them she handed them to me. Ted paid her and I lit up a joint. I put the carton into my lower pant leg pocket. For the most part of the day all we did was stay high. After we got tired of sitting around we duffed out. I really couldn't sit any longer with the speed buzz I had going.

We walked outside and ran across the street and headed back toward the A.F.B. We only walked about fifty yards and an army truck pulled over. The driver asked, "How about a lift?"

We said, "Sure..."

"Well jump in back and let's go." He replied. There were four army guys sitting in the back of the truck. The truck was just like the one I had come there from Uplift on. It had a bench seat on both sides of the rear box. The seats would hold about six men next to each other on either side. The truck was about the size of a stake body truck, one ton or so. Ted and I sat on the end in back across from each other. I was up next to the tail gate.

We were almost to the A.F.B. gate when the guy driving the truck yelled back to us, "I hope none of you are carrying dope! They have dope sniffing K- 9's at the gate. I think they're checking for weed! Looks like the Air police don't want anyone cutting into their dope business I guess!" See what I said about an infectious disease? Even the cops were into it big time!

Oh man! I thought. I had the carton of joints in my lower pants leg pocket. Ted looked at me with his eyes wide open and said, "We're dead!...I never thought about that! They do that sometimes!" He told me that from time to time they bring in pot sniffing mutts to try and catch guys bringing dope into the A.F.B. Ted said, "Get rid of that carton over board. Quick! before we get there!"

But it was too late. We were just about to stop at the gate. There was no place to heave it. If I had whipped the carton out they would see me toss it for sure, I thought. I looked over my shoulder and saw an A.P. walking a six foot long German police dog around the truck very slowly. As the dog got closer I pushed the carton of joints from the outside of my leg to the inside and between my legs and I squeezed it tightly. When the dog got around to the back of the truck he sort of stood up on his hind legs and looked at me and sniffed. His nose was only about one foot away from the carton of joints. As he stood there with his hind feet on the ground and his front paws up on the back of the tailgate, I said, "Nice boy! Hey buddy, how ya doin?" and I patted his head. That dog was a monster! Without a

145

doubt the biggest dog I had ever seen! I never thought they could grow them that huge! I said, "Nice boy!" as I petted his huge head.

He just squeaked and moaned once or twice and the A. P. jerked him back saying, "Watch yourself! These dogs are mean! You never know when they might bite!"

I said, "Oh Wow! I better be careful. This one looks real mean...and smart too!" Ted looked like he was going faint! He was as white as a sheet.

The A.P. slapped the side of the truck and we rode through the gate into the A.F.B. On the other side Ted and I jumped out of the truck. When we got far away from the guard shack Ted took a deep breath and said, "I don't believe that! We were all out busted! But still we somehow got through. I don't believe my eyes. If I didn't see it myself I would never believe it!"

I replied, "Tell me about it! Shut up and keep walking."

We finally got to Ted's hooch and stashed the joints. He quickly changed uniforms and sat down. He said, "Do you realize how close that was?"

I said, "Tell me about it! Just be thankful that dog had a plugged up sniffer or we would be slammers right now!"

Ted said, "Man that scared the snot out of me. My heart still feels like it's going to pop!"

I replied, "I think that was sort of cool! Getting away with it, I mean!"

We both sat back and relaxed for a few minutes. Then I said, "Let's eat, I'm starving!"

Ted replied, "Let's catch a buzz first! I need it to calm down."

After chow we walked around and rapped awhile about everything. And soon we ran into Captain Nelson the pilot that flew me to Nha Trang. He said, "Hey guys, what's going on?"

I said, "Not too much, Sir. How about you?"

He said, "I see you got through Recondo school all right. That's a nice looking patch. How was it?"

"Just the same old butt kickin' bull, Sir, like always." I replied.

He said, "If you guys aren't doing anything stop over to my hooch later for a drink."

I said, "Sounds good, maybe later."

Nelson said, "Cool. See you men later."

We walked away. "Nice guy! Not your usual hard nose officer," Ted said.

"He seems okay to me," I replied.

Ted said. "Yeah...He don't get on anyone except when something looks wrong or screwed up on his plane. For an officer he has his stuff together."

I replied, "I still don't believe he took the chance of giving me a ride in his jet. Not many guys would do something like that for you would they?"

"One or two....not many would! He's a good guy," Ted replied.

I asked Ted, "What day is this? Wednesday, right?"

He said, "Yeah!"

"That means, I still have until Sunday 1800 to report to Pathfinder school. Four more whole days of ghostin', my favorite," I said.

Ted asked, "What are you going to do when you have to work for a living again?"

I said, "Yeah, no kiddin'! This place is making me soft. I will probably have a hard time going back to all of that. But shortly after I report back into Uplift, I'll be going to Sniper school for three weeks or so...more ghost time."

Ted said, "Sniper school! Really?! You're going to be a Sniper too? You must have been through just about every combat school there is...no?"

I replied, "Yeah! Just about. Everything but O.C.S. I'm no leader and I never wanted to be."

Ted asked me what schools I went through.

I said, "Well, I went from basic to A. I. T. Then I went to Airborne or jump school. I was assigned to a Ranger/Recon Co. when I got to the Nam. Then I went to Recondo/Ranger school. Next I go to Pathfinder school....then Sniper school."

Ted said. "No wonder you guys are totally nuts! All that stuff about killin' dudes and all has got to make a guy crazy."

I replied, "That may or may not drive a dude crazy....But I don't think it helps much! I do know now one thing for sure though, all that training was set up for a reason. A guy with a job like mine needs all the help and schooling of that kind he can get to help him make it through. Sometimes on missions, I know I would never have made it on my knowledge alone. The physical work and classroom and field instruction helped me a lot since I've been here. All my teachers really knew just what they were talking about. The stuff they teach you really does work if you use your head and the info. right."

We were just about back at the barracks and we decided to get a good night's sleep that night. Ted had to work the next day and I was going to nose around the army post to check out where I had to report for Pathfinder school. It was only about 2000 and the barracks was buzzing with men talking and radios playing.

Vietnam had only one radio station worth a hoot. It was the American Forces Radio Network. Each morning the guy would come on at 0600 and say, "Goooooooooooood morning Vietnam!" I guess from where he was sitting it would be a good morning, being stationed in Saigon and all. Saigon was a beautiful place. At one time I heard they used to call it the Paris of the Orient. The whole country really was a beautiful place, if weren't for that evil war! And the evil men that kept it going. The place was beautiful if one stopped and really looked at it, over the smoke and barbed wire, that is.

Ted said he was homesick and felt like making a tape to send home to his chick. So I said I was going down to take a shower. He said he was next after he made his tape. I asked Ted if I could use one of his towels. He said, "Here," as he handed me one from his locker.

I said, "You have to show me where the laundry shack is so I can get my clothes cleaned tomorrow."

He replied, "No sweat, it's just behind the mess hall, and I know you know where that is!"

I said, "Don't start with that." And I left the room.

When I came back from my shower Ted was out cold. I don't think he ever

147

got his tape made, because the back of the tape player was off and the batteries were all over his bed. He probably just said screw the dead batteries and fell asleep.

I turned out the light and jumped into bed. As I lay there, I started to think about how nice it would be to be home with my girl who I missed so badly. And my family who always worried about me even if I just stayed overnight at a friend's house. They were the ones that really worried and missed me. I thought they are the ones that really didn't know how I was, or even if I was still alive. I knew right where they were. My Mom must be worried sick, I thought, that's how she was. She never said much when she was worried, but you could just tell. Dad...he was a tough old bird, nothing was really too big or tough for him to handle. And my chick....God, I missed her sweet smell and voice. I thought, please God, bring me home safe. Not just for me, but for them. He knows I mean it, I thought as I drifted off to sleep.

"Goooooooooooood morning Vietnam! This is the American Forces Radio Network. Rise and shine! It's another beautiful sunny day. Looks like the monsoons have granted us another beauuuuutiful day! Get up! Troops! Wash the sleep out of your eyes and just get up! This is your Deeee-da-deeeee-jaaaay sayin' rise and shine dudes and dudettes! What a beeeeeeautifull day for a war!"

I could hear the D.J. on a radio yelling out his message as he did every morning. I could hear Ted found some new batteries no doubt! It's morning already, I thought. I could hear that dope down in Saigon still believed he was in Daytona Beach, Florida or something. Men were buzzing up and down the hallway outside the door. And radios blasting Mr. Sunshine's message and music out all over the barracks. That's how it was no matter where I went. I sat up and stretched.

It was another day alright but I didn't quite feel the enthusiasm the guy on the radio did. I thought, I guess I'll get my stuff together and check out my next school as long as Ted has to work today. At least I'll know where to go and what's going on Sunday afternoon when I go to report in.

Speaking of Ted, I thought. I got up and saw he was not in bed. Just his radio\tape player blasting away. So I got dressed and sat down to get my stuff together. About five minutes or so went by and Ted walked in.

"Man, did that shower feel good!" he said.

I replied, "I was wondering where you went. I thought maybe work."

"No I don't have to be at the motor pool until 0800. How are you feeling?" he asked.

I said, "I feel good and rested and ready for a good breakfast."

"Me too!" He got dressed and we left for the mess hall.

After breakfast Ted and I parted ways and we headed out for our day's activities. Ted said, "I will try to be back at the hooch about 1600."

I said, "See ya."

I walked down the road toward the army post. The day was really beautiful, with a pure blue sky and lots of sunshine. Maybe that jerk on the radio isn't so bad after all, I thought. Soon I could see the small gate and sign up ahead. "Welcome to U.S. Army Light Infantry Division at Quy Nhon." I went through the gate and down the road. I could see the headquarters building so I walked up the stairs in front and went inside.

At the desk sat a P.F.C. looking about as bored as one could get. I asked him if he knew anything about the Pathfinder course that was supposed to be held on post. He said, "Yeah man!...But you're only about two days early."

I said, "I never like to be late for anything."

He replied, "I guess not." Then he went on to say, "Now I suppose you want a barracks and bunk, right?"

"Wrong!" I said.

"How come?" he asked.

I said, "If you want to set me up for Sunday night, that is all right with me. But for now, I have a place to stay on the Air Force Base with a friend."

He said, "How did you swing that?"

I said, "I have connections!"

"Must be nice!" He replied.

"That's what I thought too! Look...seeing how you're so busy, don't bother yourself. I'll just wait until Sunday night."

He said, "No sweat man. I don't have nothin' else to do anyway. Come on, I'll show you where you'll be set up. We have everything ready for you guys. 1st Lt. Schaffer will be your instructor for the class. He is Pathfinder qualified and he knows his stuff. He is a good dude! Schaffer isn't around now or I would introduce you to him. He is helping out with pay call detail."

I said, "My name is Jim...What's yours?"

He said, "Sam Tillotson."

"Sam!...glad to meet you." I said as I held out my hand.

Sam asked, "How did you luck out and grab this cream puff course?"

I replied, "Just lucky, I guess."

He said, "I've never been through the course but from what I've learned from Schaffer about it, it sounds very interesting."

"No P.T., I hope." I replied.

He said, "What's that?" That was all I wanted to hear. I had had enough of that.

"Around here all we have to do is our jobs. Not much else." Sam told me.

I said, "The last school I just came from had lots of that extra physical bologna."

"Well, you won't see any of that here. Most of this unit is stationed near Saigon. This is a very small portion of that unit and around here we try not to be too gung-ho! Or very strict about most things."

I said, "Sounds good to me."

He said, "I never could see what all that bull was for. Just as long as you know your job and do it right that's really all that counts to me!"

I said, "El correcto dude."

As we walked down the road, Sam pointed up ahead about twenty yards. "Here we go. This is the barracks we set up for you guys. There will be fifteen men in your class, if everyone shows up. Right there," he pointed across the street, "is your class room. Each day, you'll all come and report there for class." Pointing up the street again Sam told me, "Just beyond the outhouses around the corner is our mess hall, I think the outhouse is probably where they get our food from. Anyway, all the classes will start at 0800 each morning. Unless you have to wait for Schaffer to show up. He never does anything on time...it's just his nature. But for the most part, I think you'll like it while you're here. I won't assign you a bunk or locker yet, because Sunday afternoon we'll have plenty of time. If you want to just walk around the place and check it out, go ahead." Sam said, "As for me, I had better get back to my paperwork back in the office that I started earlier."

I said, "Thanks man! I really appreciate the grand tour and I'll see you Sunday about noon or so."

"Good enough." He said, as he turned and headed back to H.Q. office.

I walked around the post for about an hour. As Sam told me the place was small and had very few points of interest. As I walked past the mess hall, I could see a few men lined up for pay call. I looked inside and saw a 1st Lt. counting out some money. He sat at a small table in front of a line of men. The first guy in line counted his money and saluted the Lt. The next guy came up and said, "Sp-4 Joe Swarts...Reporting for pay call, Sir!" The Lt. counted out some more money and he handed it to him and so on. So that's Lt. Schaffer, I thought. Well, at least now I know what he looks like. That sucker must go 6' 6" at least. Man! What a bean pole, I thought. He looked to be in his mid-twenties, thin and tall. Well, enough of this I thought.

I walked down the street back towards the Air Force Base. I walked out the gate of the army post and slowly back to Ted's hooch. I went upstairs and into his room. On Ted's bed I saw some writing paper and free mailer envelopes. I felt then was the time to write a letter home to my girl, seeing how it was so quiet in there. So I sat down and nearly wrote a book. I just kept writing and writing about everything. All the fun things anyway. I told her how bad I missed her and how I wanted to come home. But I still had over six months to go before I reached thirteen months and all. I told her all I could do is wait my time out.

Before I knew it, it was 1630 and I could hear Ted laughing out in the hall with someone. I was done with my letter so I put the pages into an envelope and sealed it. Then I put it into my pocket to keep it safe until I could mail it.

I walked out into the hall and I saw Ted talking to an Air Force Sgt. He came up and introduced me to his friend. "Jim...This is Sgt. Thomas, my boss down at work."

Thomas said, "I've heard a lot about you."

I said, "Good or bad."

He said, "More good than bad."

"Well!" I said "I can't ask for more than that."

He asked, "How long are you going to be around?"

I said, "Until late Sunday morning."

He said, "Well maybe I'll see you guys down to the club. I'll buy you guys a cold one."

"Sounds good!" I said. And off we went.

Ted said he was off until Monday. He said he played up his hurt back at work and Thomas told him to report to sick call about two o'clock. He said the Doc gave him ghost time until Monday morning. Then he had to go back to see him again. So I said, "What do you want to get into now?"

He said, "Let's get buzzed out!"

I said, "I thought you would never ask." He laughed and lit a joint. We smoked the joint and listened to a new tape Ted picked up at the main P.X. on post that day. It was a tape by the group called "Traffic." The name of the tape was "Last Exit." The name sounded appropriate for Nam anyway, I thought. It was a pretty good tape and we listened to it all, smoking another joint before it was over. Stoned to the bone we both had a bad case of the munchies and we decided to go to the club for a steak and brew.

Out the door and down the steps we went, headed to the club. When we got to the club we went inside and we saw the place was packed already because everyone was off work by then. So we found a table and sat down. A waitress came over and we ordered. Ted got a Tom Collins and a well done Delmonico. I said, "Same for me except rare on the meat." We got our drinks and sat back to relax.

As we sat there, I kept seeing a guy giving me all kinds of stares. I was about to go over and tell him he wasn't the right sex. But I thought about it and decided I would just leave the bonehead alone. But sure as shootin' I could hear his big mouth yelling out stuff about what big pussies Rangers were and all kinds of things like that. Ted said, "Shhhhii!…There is that big mouth Smitty. He is a pro boxer, or he said he is anyway. He loves to screw with everyone, especially when he is half in the bag. Don't pay any attention to him. They will throw him out as soon as he gets loud enough…they always do!"

I said, "Big sucker!, that's for sure!"

"He's big alright," Ted replied.

Smitty was sitting with four other guys that looked like wimps to me. So I didn't sweat them jumping in anyway. I just kept a grin on my face and ignored him. Just about the time our steaks came, I saw the big dope get up.

He walked over to our table and said, "Hey Pussy!" I started eating my steak and I kept on paying no attention to him. "Hey creampuff! You got icing blockin' up your ears? You deaf or what?"

I slowly pushed back my chair, and still seated I sat right in front of him looking up at him. The place started to get quiet and I could see everyone looking at us.

He said, "I hear to become a Recondo, you first have to be a faggot to be qualified!"

I replied, "With all the faggot's in this world, I hope you don't think that the Air Force had them all."

I heard Ted say, "Oh f#**#! here we go!"

Big mouth said, "Well, let me just show you how an Air Force faggot eats up Recondos." He reached out his arms in front of him to grab my shirt. As fast, and as hard as I could, I came up under him like a rocket and I heaved a mega-punch, and nailed him right on the chin.

It was the hardest punch I ever threw! Big mouth fell right across our table landing belly down on top of my steak…out cold! I grabbed his side by his belt and dumped his cold cocked body on the floor. The place was dead quiet except for the music that was playing on the stereo system. I said, "Mess with my steak, will ya!" I reached down and grabbed the steak with my hand and I took a huge bite out of it. Everyone in the place went nuts! They yelled and screamed, "Yeeeeeah!" I walked toward the door and I handed our waitress a twenty as we passed her with Ted right on my heels. I could hear guys saying stuff like, "Man! What a punch!," all that kind of stuff.

I stopped by the exit and turned around to see if old dead-to-the-world had come-to yet. He was still out on "Queer Street." I saw everyone laughing and talking about the sucker punch of the year that I just taught them. I smiled and walked to the door with my steak still in my hand.

We got about five feet from the exit door when Ted's buddy Sgt. Thomas came running over. He said, "Holy cow! Man, what a punch! That big mouth never knew what hit him….He's still out of it right now. Man, I think you killed him he went down so hard! You could hear that punch all over the room. That was great! Everyone in the place wanted to see someone K.O. that boy. I'll bet he'll keep his trap shut for a while now."

I replied, "I doubt it! Dopes like that never learn!"

Just then the door flew open. It was two A.P.'s. They had big sticks with them and were ready to bust heads. So all three of us kept walking right out the door and duffed toward Ted's hooch. We ran back to the hooch and we went upstairs into Ted's room. We were out of breath from running and laughing so hard and we sat down to catch our breath.

Ted said, "I'll never forget that one, man. I thought we would get our butts kicked before we got out of there one way or another!"

I said, "I just couldn't pass up a sucker punch like that one."

Thomas said, "I would give a hundred bucks to see that one all over again….no kiddin'! It was just beautiful! Especially to that jerk!"

After we all stopped laughing and caught our breath, we could hear some guys coming up the hallway talking about the army dude that flattened Smitty. They came in our room and one of them said, "There's the guy."

"'Hey Ranger, nice move. Smitty's jaw looks broke and his two front teeth are smashed out!"

Another guy said, "The A.P.'s wanted to know who did it. But no one knew nothin! Know what I mean? I think Smitty's pals were scared to tell the A.P's anything either. They're probably scared they may run into you again someday. So they just took Smitty to the hospital. Man! his mouth looked like a pound of raw liver! What a punch!"

We all sat down and got buzzed out. We rapped for awhile about the one punch fight until they all left, except Ted and Thomas. We played poker and smoked joints for quite a while. For the rest of the night and all of Saturday I laid low. I didn't want to get arrested for smashing that dope's face up…although for him, any alteration was a help to his looks! So I just hung out near the barracks. Sunday morning I packed my duffel bag about 1000 and told Ted I would see him later. I was going to report into Pathfinder school.

CHAPTER 23

Flighty Looker Control

I walked out of the barracks and down the stairs. The road was fairly quiet. Soon I could see the army post just ahead. As I got closer to the Company clerk's office I could see some guys sitting outside on the steps out front. There were five men with duffel bags sitting around talking. I walked up to them and asked if they were there to report for Pathfinder school. One guy said, "This is it." So I sat down with the guys for a few minutes. They told me the P.F.C. inside told them to just relax and he would be out shortly to show us where to go. I could see the guys were from all over Vietnam by the unit patches they wore. We all started to talk about where we were from and what unit and place we each came from.

Soon the P.F.C. I had met the other day in the office came out and said, "Let's go, I'll set you guys up with a place to put your stuff." We all walked over to our barracks and went inside. We were all given a bunk and locker. The P.F.C. told everyone that he and I met the other day and asked if I would be so kind as to explain to the other guys that didn't know yet where the class room, mess hall, and things like that were. So I said, "No sweat...I'll show them."

The P.F.C. said, "I have to go back to the company office to catch anyone else as they come in. So I'll just leave you all in the hands of the Sergeant over here!"

We all got settled in. Then we went outside and I showed the men each building. Then we saw the P.F.C. coming back with four more men. While we were outside, he stopped to show them the buildings we all had to know about. He said, "In about half an hour, Lt. Schaffer will be over in the class room to meet each of you and to give you a short talk about your next week here." Week! I thought. Don't tell me I have another extra week of ghost time! My orders said this class was two weeks long. Good deal! I thought.

After everyone got settled in I went into our class room to relax and check it out. Inside I saw four maps on the walls and five radios sitting on a table up front. There were six long benches in the middle of the room. I sat down and started to rap with the men as they came in. Soon all the men were there...fifteen in all. We all sat around for a short time until 1st Lt. Schaffer showed up.

He came in and stood up in front of the table of radios and he asked, "Could I have your attention please?" He had a very deep low voice, "My name is Lt. Schaffer. For the next week I will be your instructor for the course of Pathfinder, or Senior Scout school." On his shirt was a patch I never saw before, especially where it was displayed. It was on his blouse or shirt pocket. Not many patches I'd ever seen were placed there, except for my Recondo patch.

He said, "I am Pathfinder qualified and I have pulled many Pathfinder missions. Not very often is a Pathfinder called on. But when we are needed the army wants to have some on hand. That is why the army has started this school over here in Nam. We will be working a lot with radios, radio code book translations, compass and map reading. When a Pathfinder goes out there are many tools of the trade that he uses. There are many colors of smoke grenades and they mean a lot of different things to chopper pilots. When you men start on the field exercises we do here, you will be working with choppers that have the call name of Casper. Casper choppers usually have a picture of Casper the friendly ghost painted on the nose of the aircraft. This picture will keep things straight between one unit of choppers and other units, which will have different names and pictures. The names were started by each squadron of choppers. But now we will use them as a means of identification. Sometimes we will have a very large number of choppers in the air at one time. Things can get turned into a real mess very quickly!"

Schaffer continued, "The main job of a Pathfinder is to responsibility land and discharge equipment and men. You will be responsible for many lives. When you get a whole cluster of choppers landing at random you can have a very big mess on your hands if you don't have it together! You have to control them while they're still airborne from smashing into each other. That is what we do as Pathfinders. Our call sign on the radio is 'Flighty Looker Control.' On a real mission we have eye to eye and radio contact with each pilot as they land to dump their cargo. Whether it be men or equipment, they are all very important and you will be trained to protect the men on board and safely land each piece of equipment."

He walked to the back of the room. "That will end the class for today. On Monday we will get right into it. But for now, I just wanted to explain briefly what the Pathfinder's function is. If you have any questions I'll answer them on Monday. So think about what I said and I'll see all of you then. You guys are off duty and can go wherever you like until Monday morning at 0800. I'll see you all here then. Class dismissed." He walked out the door.

After we all got outside we saw Schaffer standing around smoking a cigar and started to rap with him about the week ahead. He told us by the end of the week he would have us landing choppers in spots so tight we would never believe it possible. He said that we would have a lot of responsibility while on the job. He said that the chopper pilots respected Pathfinders for their ability to bring them in and out of very tight spots - even in a hot L.Z. situation where things can go very wrong very quickly. He said, "Well I just hope you guys learn and use what I am about to teach you because we have a very important job to do!"

The first thing I did after talking to Schaffer was head over to the club. I was dry just from listening to Schaffer talk. As I walked away, I heard the company clerk call to me. "Hey, Sarge, where you headed?"

I said, "The club."

"Come on, I'll buy you one," he said as he ran up to me.

We walked up the road toward the club and I saw nearly the whole class following right behind us. In a short time we were all half in the bag and had a blast drinking, talking and shooting pool.

For the next five days we spent our time in the classroom learning all about proper radio operation and using codes to give out landing instructions and all kinds of things. We learned how to land choppers safely by preplanned flight and controlled landing formations. We also learned what green, red, orange, yellow, and purple colored smoke meant to the pilots. We learned many hand signals. They were used to talk to and direct pilots as they were coming in to land. They told them where to go and what to do. Pilots were taught to learn and obey our instructions completely, because their lives depended on us.

Soon Friday came and we went out into a large field with all kinds of obstacles and small marked out areas to see what setups or types of landing areas we would have to prepare in the boonies for landing choppers. We were about to see and use what we had been taught. On that Saturday we guided in choppers by radio, smoke and hand signals. No matter what we said by radio or by hand signal the pilots would do it. If we gave them the wrong signal, they would do the wrong thing. This was to show us if we screwed up so would the chopper. It was weird because it was just like we were flying the choppers by remote control. Whatever we said or did the chopper pilot would react to it. Everyone did very well. We all kept our interest up and learned what we had to.

Saturday night we had a meeting back at the class room to talk about our on-the-job testing and how each of us did. Near the end of the class that night Schaffer said, "You guys all did very well. The chopper pilots that we worked with today all complimented you on your ability as good landing instructors. I think all of you did an excellent job. If any one of you were called on to run a Pathfinder mission none of you would have a problem doing it well!" Schaffer said that we probably wouldn't be called on to work very many Pathfinder missions.

He said, "As you all know it's only once in a while that a mass assault or landing will be used. Most of the time it's just one or two choppers coming in at a time. But if they needed this type of mass assault and landing you Pathfinders would be there to make sure every man and chopper would land and get airborne safely. Good job men." Then he handed out our certificates and patches. "Congratulations men! You are all Pathfinder qualified. Good luck and thank you for being so cooperative during this past week." He told us that he was going to buy each of us a cold one and it was already set it up with the bartender at the club. We all said, "Thanks!" as we ran out of the classroom and up the street.

As I walked towards the club I thought about how my schools were over, for a while anyway. Soon my ghost time would also be over and back to the boonies I would go again. Nuts!, I thought. As always all good things come to an end.

The next morning I packed my things and headed out towards the Air Force Base and back to Ted's hooch. It was Sunday and there was not much going on. I walked up the stairs and into Ted's room. Ted was sitting on his bunk listening to a tape from home. He said, "Hey, Sarge!…what's up? How was Pathfinder school?" I sat down and rapped with him for a while.

Ted told me he was about to head out on R&R for two weeks in Hawaii. There he was going to meet his chick and party hardy. He said he had been in the Nam for almost a year and it was R&R time. He said he was leaving the following Friday at noon. I said, "Super!…Man, it must be nice going to Hawaii and all." He told me no doubt and that it meant he only had to pull five months and days after he got back then and he was as free as a bird. "Man that's great! No kiddin'!" I replied.

He told me, "Man, I can hardly wait!"

We screwed around the barracks playing poker and we talked about the rest and relaxation in Hawaii and about my week at Pathfinder school and we crashed out about midnight. All week Ted worked his job and I just lay around and went swimming or did whatever I wanted to. The week went fast as all ghost time did.

Soon it was Thursday night and Ted packed all his things for the trip to Hawaii. He asked, "When are you going back to Uplift?"

I said, "I will probably start back tomorrow when you leave."

He said, "Do you want me to get a chopper set up to give you a ride back?"

"No, I don't have to be back until Sunday 1800 so I am going to take my time getting back and party in a couple of Vills on the way."

He said, "Sounds good then!" We both crashed out early to get some rest.

It wasn't long and I could hear Mr. Happy on the radio telling us how good the morning was again. So I got up and ready to go. After we got outside Ted put out his hand and said, "Jim…take care! Be careful out there so we can party out when you get back this way again. I'll be back in two weeks. Make sure you stop by the next time you're around."

I replied, "I don't know when I will be back again…but when I do I'll see you then for sure!" We shook hands and walked our separate ways.

After I got to the main road leading off post, I passed the guard shack and walked down the street to Highway #1. I ran across the road and went into the big house. Inside I saw Linda, the girl I met a few days ago with Ted. She was sitting on the floor with a guy I had met at Pathfinder school. I also saw a black dude that I had never seen before sitting in the corner of the room. He was very high on something and he was almost out cold as he sat there, just barely keeping his eyes open. He looked so non-military, except for his mixed army uniform, that I really took special notice of him right away. His hair was all knotted, dirty, and all the way down the back of his neck. He had a beard that looked like he hadn't shaved in a couple of months or more. In general he was a dirty mess. His clothes were all full of rips, from his pants to his totally unmatched army shirt.

He looked at me long and hard and he said, "What?…"

I replied, "How's it goin', brother?"

He looked at me like he was about to put a bullet in me and he said as he raised the muzzle of his M-16, "Don't you be callin' me no moooo-F#$%^ bro! Mo-f$#%@ white boy! Ya'll don't look like no mooo-f#$%@ bro a mine!"

I replied, "I hear you! You got it!"

I could see right then and there that this man was a deserter and he would have killed me just as soon as he would have killed any enemy. To him we were all the enemy, as well as Charley. Those guys had everyone out to get them. They could be spotted now and again from time to time around Nam. But they usually only came out at night and kept well hidden from everyone. I could see that this guy just didn't really care anymore what happened to him. He was like a loost mad dog that just kept to himself and trusted no one. I kept right on going and I walked up to Jim, the guy that I had met at Pathfinder school, who was sitting with Linda.

He said, "Sarge." I sat down with them and we smoked joints. Before too long we were both out there. His name was Jim Baxter from somewhere in New Jersey. He was a nice dude. But no one to mess with. He stood about six foot two and went about two hundred plus pounds. He had a very goofy way about him. That is, he was a riot to be around. He acted dumb, but he really was quite witty. His old man owned a fairly large appliance store in New Jersey and he told me he was going to take over the business one day. The guy spent money like it was water. If you were around him you never had to buy anything. He would just say, "Put your money away, it's no good here!"

I was thinking about starting back toward Uplift that day and I planned to stay at another Vill down the road further, closer to Uplift. But I was so screwed up when it was time to go I knew that was the only place I would get to that day. It was about 1700 and most G.Is were gone or had made arrangements to stay there for the night. Baxter asked, "Are you staying over here tonight?"

I replied, with blood shot eyes, "I am now! Seeing how you got me all screwed up!"

He laughed and said, "Good deal! We'll party out all night!"

He said he didn't have to be back at his unit up north farther until late the next day and he said he had plenty of time to get there. He said he could make it in a day's travel, no sweat. I asked, "Where is your Fire base located?"

He said, "Camp Radkey in An Khe....I'm with the 4th Infantry Div."

I asked him if he knew anything about the Sniper school that was starting up out there. He said he didn't but he didn't really pay any attention to what was going on around the post. He said he spent most of his time in the jungle and hung out in the village of An Khe whenever he got a chance. He looked far-off, like he was thinking of home and he said, "Sin City....Now there is a party town! Things go on there you just wouldn't believe."

Sin City was the understatement of the year for that place! He said if you had money, down at the Vill you could do or get anything! He said, "I mean anything!" Baxter told me that one could buy anything from gold to girls. "I don't mean just hookers, I mean slave girls. Chinese, Korean, Cambodian and Laotian woman. Broads that will do anything! S&M, you name it. Money talks in that place. You'll have to look me up sometime if you're ever out that way. I've got connections in that town!"

I replied, "It may be soon. As soon as Sniper school starts, I'm going to be sent to camp Radkey. That is where my C.O. said the school was."

Baxter said, "Now that you mention that stuff, just before I left post I wondered what the army engineers were building on the outskirts of the post. It looked like a rifle range and some new hooches were going up near by."

I said, "I was told it was a new school, just like Pathfinder school and Recondo school."

He replied, "I bet that's it. And if you do get there make sure you look me up. I'll show you around Sin City."

We talked about An Khe for awhile, then about most anything we could think of. He told me about the Mang Yang Pass where a large amount of French soldiers got creamed trying to get up the Mountain and up the steep pass that leads to the camp.

It got late and I fell asleep on the mat I was sitting on. Then I felt something soft and warm under my arm. When I opened my eyes I saw that it was one of Momma-son's ducks trying to get comfortable. I tossed the little dude across the floor and got up to stretch. My head felt like a blimp so I sat back down and lit a joint. No one was up and moving. It was still dark outside. I just sat back and dozed off again. That time I crashed hard and slept until about 0800 or so.

CHAPTER 24

Extra Bad News!

I felt someone kick my boot. Slowly I opened my eyes and saw Babbles smiling and looking down at me. He said, "So! This is what the army sent you to school for, right? So you can sharpen your skills in a whore house!?"

I said, "You sucker! How! What? How come you're here?" I was half asleep yet and sort of thought I was dreaming.

He said, "What nothin'…I'm catching a bird home, sucker!"

I jumped up and said, "No way! You're really going home? Really?"

He replied, "Yep! I'm leaving today on a big old bird for the world, dude!"

I said, "Sit down sucker and tell me what's going on back at Uplift and about you going home."

He told me that his time was up and he got his orders to swoop! He had his flight scheduled for noon that day out of Quy Nhon Air Force Base to the Bay. From there he would jump a bird for the world. He was so happy he could hardly talk fast enough. I was just about as happy as he was to know someone that was really going to finally make it home outside a body bag.

After we talked about his going home, I asked about Uplift. His smile quickly vanished from his face. I asked, "What's wrong?"

He said, "Uplift ain't the same anymore since you left."

"How has it changed?" I asked.

He said, "About a week after you left Uplift they started moving all the Rangers further south to a place called L.Z. Tangerine. All of the 173rd Rangers are now stationed at Tangerine. Only Recon is left on the hill, that and the fire support and radio shack."

Babbles told me that it took about three weeks to move everyone to Tangerine with all their equipment and men. He told me none of us were assigned to a Ranger Company any longer but were now assigned to Recon….We were strictly Recondo from now on. Hunter 1 was dead. He told me that Kabbatt was at Sniper school in An Khe and all Snipers were now assigned to Recon as well. He said, "The new company commander is a total bummer! A real A##hole gung-hoooo, and strict about everything. You won't like the place at all anymore. It's just not the same. The new C.O. thinks he's Audie Murph! He's changed the place big time."

I replied, "They really screwed the place up that bad?"

He rolled his eyes and said, "You'll see! I'm just glad I'm the hell out of that nightmare. A guy could get killed in that place now! No doubt!" Babbles told me that he had heard that Updike, my homey, was coming back to Uplift. He was the guy that got hit on my first mission out, during the ambush we got into down in the creek bed.

I said, "No way! After he got wounded and all? I figured he would have been sent home."

Babbles said, "Yeeeah! I saw his leg that day too. And it looked messed up to me. But it must not have been that bad or he extended and just wanted to come back. Anyway, that's what I heard."

I said, "With this new C.O. I just hope my orders for Sniper school don't get all screwed up."

Babbles said, "I think you're all right because our other C.O., Captain Willis had you all set up for it before he shipped out for Tangerine. They only have so many openings and you got one. So I don't think you'll get screwed."

"I hope not!" I replied.

"How about old Schriff? Did he book back to the world yet?" Babbles said nothing, just looked down.

I looked at him and said, "Yeah! Boy! That lucky stiff! He's probably sitting at home just kickin' back by now!...Know what I mean? I know that dude, right Babbles?" Babbles wiped his eyes, then he dropped to one knee with his head down.

Suddenly I felt a shock come over me from my hair to my heels. Babbles choked out, "The mother f#**# greased 'um last week just before he was supposed to go home!"

I screamed, "No! way! No! way!" He just kept nodding his head yes and wiping his eyes. I said, "This dirty rotten place sucks so bad I don't believe it! What a rat hole! Babbles, you can't be right! He can't be dead! He just can't be. He's too short. And too good."

He replied, "I saw him...I had to put what was left of him in a body bag. There wasn't enough of him left to carry any other way!" I felt a hate and grief like I never felt before cover me from head to toe. I sat down on my rear and I felt sick. I just knew. I felt it a few days earlier in the pool back on the A.F.B.

We both sat there for who knows how long. Finally Babbles said, "We only had one more day left before we were to come in. It was early morning. Schriff wanted to pull point because most of the team was cherry except Kabbatt, Schriff and I. I had the radio, Kabbatt was on rear guard. We just left B Co. about fifteen minutes out. It was no big deal, just routine. We were only supposed to check out a small area and set up some booby traps with Claymores then get back to the Line Co. That afternoon we were going back in. Schriff and I had to start processing out and Kabbatt was going to Sniper school. We walked right into a f@#*in' ambush! Schriff caught the biggest part of a blast...musta' been a Claymore, he was tore up real bad. Anyway, he looked like a pile of cranberry sauce. We kept the enemy off us until B Co. came in to back us up. When we moved up, I fell over Schriff's mangled body. I tried to pick him up to get him out, but his body was too mashed up. We had to come back after the fire fight with a body bag to get him. I don't think he ever knew what hit him."

In shock I replied, "This stinking hole! I'll never get used to this place if stay here forever. I just can't believe he's dead! I can't believe it!" I think the initial shock of hearing about the death of a friend is real bad, but I think the way it stays with you for so many days and years hurts even more.

Babbles looked at me, "You know that I have read the Bible Jim. Sometime it's helped me cope with this stuff a little better. But anymore, I just can't reall understand why stuff like this happens. I don't know, I want to keep my faith but it's so hard sometimes. It just doesn't make sense to pray so hard and try to be good and all. It seems we only end up dead just like Schriff. I don't know if you know this but Schriff comes from a very religious family. He wasn't a pounder though. The only time he would say anything about the Bible was if you asked him something about it. Before I met Schriff, I didn't really even believe in God. I hate to even say it, or explain it, but for some reason, in a way I feel sort of good somehow about Schriff...not about him being killed, naturally, but I just feel, or know or believe, I don't know, that he's in a better place...It's crazy, maybe just wishful thinking, who knows? But I believe that's all because of a dead man that told me about the God he and his family believed in. Jokingly he told me one time that maybe he was put here to get me saved...I don't know...I don't know for sure about much anymore except that...he didn't deserve to die in this God forsaken sweat box. I know I'll never forget that Soldier....Never! Doc volunteered to escort Schriff's body home. As bad as I wanted to go home, I just couldn't do it. I couldn't see how I could have faced his family without falling apart. Doc must have some kind-a-big rocks!"

I said, "I'm going to see that you board that bird alive, if I have to hold off every s.o.b. in this country!"

He smiled and said, "I always knew you would make a good soldier. But please don't ever think that being a good soldier alone will get you through. Watch your back real good. Like Schriff told me many times, forget about home. This is your home now, like it or not. Good or bad, life or death, you have to accept it all. But I can't accept it, I can't!"

I replied, "I know what he meant by that. But I believe when God says it's time, it's time! I don't care where you are or who you are! You're out-a-here, dude! And as far as accepting this crap, forget that! You're alive and Schriff ain't, know what I mean?"

We got to our feet and he said that he had to get going so he could catch his flight and all. So we took off. As we walked across the road and toward the A.F.B., I told old Babbles about the schools and the fun I had at the A.F.B. and all. He said, "These dudes live rough here, don't they?"

I replied, "Yeeeah!...But I guess you have to understand, that a pilot risking his neck getting shot down with a ton of bombs as cargo ain't no picnic either." We both agreed that our feet on the ground felt a lot more stable than being up in the air helpless and being shot at.

We walked through the gate and headed towards the air field terminal. We sat around until Babbles' flight loaded, then we said goodbye. I looked at him and wished him luck and happiness back home. He said that no matter how long he ever lived, he would never forget Hunter 1 and all of us on that team. He said we are all a lot more than just friends, we were brothers, borne into a very strange land. But we were brothers forever, and nothing would ever change that, no matter where we were or how long we lived. I said the only thing I could choke out. "Goodbye, Babbles! I don't know how, but someday I just know we will see each other again."

He said, "You guys will be with me always, as long as I still breathe air!" We shook hands and he was gone.

To this day I've never seen him again.

CHAPTER 25

The Nightmare

I turned around and walked away. After hearing about Schriff that day, I felt a very strong change come over me. I could almost taste the hate for all Vietnamese people explode within me. I don't believe I ever looked at them with any kind of love or sympathy again. I just didn't feel like a nice guy anymore or remember if I ever was.

I had to report back to Uplift so I figured I would head back closer to the L.Z. I got back on Highway #1 and started to hitch a ride. Soon a jeep stopped to give me a lift. They were South Vietnamese soldiers. Two in back and one was driving. The guy driving asked, "Where you go, G.I.?"

I said, "Uplift."

He said, "A-okay! we go. Me go way pass Uplift!" He couldn't speak English very well but we still managed to communicate.

I felt these guys were alright, but the two in back gave me the creeps, just knowing that two Vietnamese were at my back. Reclutantly I got in and I can't really explain just why I did. The only thing that I can say about that is I remember feeling that I wanted to kill them. Maybe I was just wishing that they would start something so I could. The whole ride was really very weird. Every time I looked back at the two guys behind me they had a smile that made me wonder if they wanted to see me dead as bad as I wanted to see them dead, if you know what I mean. We drove for about an hour and I just couldn't shake the feeling of being watched. Like when two snakes watch a mouse and neither of them can figure who should strike first. So I poked the driver and I said, "Stop here."

We were just at the outskirts of a small village called Fu Bi. It was really just a ghost town as far as good party Vills go. I figured I would hang around this quiet Vill until the next day then go on into Uplift. The driver said, "No Uplift here...more far, more far!" As he pointed up ahead.

I said, "No sweat fuzz face! This is good enough. I want out, you bikh?" I quickly jumped out of the jeep and the three dudes looked at me a little strange, but they kept on going. They were just too much for me to deal with. They gave me the creeps.

I walked into a hooch and sat down. There were no American soldiers anywhere around except the ones on the road in trucks moving past. A girl that was inside the hooch asked me, "What you want Joe?"

I said, "Drink! Beer, whatever." She nodded her head and left. The place was dead. It was a very small Vill with only six or eight hooches in the whole area. Not many G.I.s ever stopped there. There was no real attraction to the place. But that was all right with me. I needed some quiet just to think.

The girl came back with my drink and she sat down with me. She looked at me with a smile and started rubbing my back. She knew exactly what I wanted. My whole body was stiff from getting so soft back in Quy Nhon and I had a headache caused by those two V.C. in the back seat of the jeep I just jumped out of.

163

That back rub was just what I needed. I talked her into letting me use a hammock that was stretched out near me. I just felt beat and I wanted to take a nap. My nerves were right on edge and I was just all tensed up. I thought a nap would be just what I needed. I got up and put my M-16 and bag just a few feet away in the corner. Then I laid down in the hammock to rest. I slept all day long until about nine or ten o'clock that night.

As I slept I dreamed I was in a coffin being loaded into an airplane. In my dream I could see blood spattered all over the inside of the coffin I was in. Outside I could hear V.C. voices but I couldn't understand a word that was being said. I felt as though my air was running out as I dreamed I was locked and closed inside.

In my dream I could hear Schriff saying, "I told you to be careful! I told you to watch your back! Now look at you!" I started to thrash back and forth in my coffin trying to get up and get out. But it seemed impossible. I could hear voices again which made me thrash even harder.

Just then I opened my eyes and saw three older Vietnamese men looking down at me with frowns on their faces. I sat up and grabbed one by the neck. He started to yell like I was killing him and I knew then I had only been dreaming. All three of them flipped out and took off screaming as they went running out of the hooch.

I looked next to me on the floor and I saw the young girl I talked to earlier. She looked at me like she was scared stupid. I got out of the hammock. She looked at me and said, "You boo-koo! dinky-dow! Joe."

I said, "I'm dinky-dow all right, just for being in this blasted country to begin with. Man, I must be crazy is right!"

I lay back down and lit a joint. The girl started to swing me slowly back and forth. I just lay back wiping the sweat off my face. Man, I thought to myself. That nightmare was so real! I couldn't believe it. I threw what was left of my joint on the dirt floor and took a deep breath. I lay there for about fifteen minutes.

Then I heard a Vietnamese man's voice in the next room. The guy sounded very demanding and persistent about something. Just a few seconds went by and then I saw some beaded ropes like drapes that hung down as a sort of partition or door between the rooms move.

Suddenly a young man about twenty years old, my age or a year or two older, looked inside the room I was in. Then I saw the barrel of a gun pointing through the beaded ropes. I knew no one was allowed to carry a weapon except U.S. and A.R.V.N. soldiers. But we carried M-16's. This was no M-16! It was an AK-47! Jesus, I thought. It was Charley himself standing just about fifteen feet away from me just outside in the hallway. I froze and felt a lack of air I got so freaked out.

Then I quickly started to think how the heck I was going to get out of that one. What do I do now? I thought. Over in the corner of the room I saw my M-16. I may as well have been a mile away. It was too far away to go for it. I knew I was a dead man if I even tried. Charley looked over at my M-16, then at me. Then he began to smile with a grin from ear to ear. He knew he had me dead if he wanted. Maybe my nightmare was about to come true! I thought.

Charley stood there smiling at me with his big dome-shaped hat and ragged clothes, Ho Chi Minh sandals and all. This was a true V.C. enemy soldier on his night out in the Vill looking right at me. The V.C. many times were from the area. They were Communist guerilla fighters. Even if they were from out of town, from the north or whatever they still needed to party or look for a woman from time to time, as most guys did. He may even have owned the hooch I was lying around in. Maybe the young girl next to me was his wife, girlfriend, sister, you never knew. That is why he didn't shoot me dead! I think it was because he didn't want to bring any trouble down on his village or party town, or possibly his own home. Even though this was an out of the way place for Americans, killing me would have changed that big time. It would have wrecked a good place for him and his comrades to party and grab a woman now and then. Maybe my life is what he and the others were yelling about a short while ago. It made me wonder. I think the only thing that stopped him from zappin' me was that if I ever got shot there and the army ever found out, (because we also had paid local spies working for us too) the army would have destroyed the entire village just to make a statement. Charley, still smiling at me, nodded his head like he was saying hello. Then he instantly disappeared without making a sound.

In a flash I jumped up and grabbed my M-16. I flipped my safety on to semi-auto and I sat behind part of a rock fireplace. I told the girl to get out and if I saw anyone come into that room before daylight they were dead meat! I know she knew what I said because she scrambled to her feet and left as fast as she could. I never again let my guard down. I felt as though I needed to thank Schriff for warning me through the dream, or rather the nightmare I had. But when I think about it, I can see now the one he was telling me to thank was the one he believed in....not he himself.

I pulled guard duty all night long. Every hour on, no hours off.

As soon as I heard the first vehicle coming up the road in the morning I headed out of the hooch and put out my thumb. The truck stopped and I got in. Soon I was approaching L.Z. Uplift. I could see black smoke rising up from over the mountain just ahead. The place may have changed as old Babbles told me, but it still looked like home to me. The truck pulled up to the main entrance of the post and I jumped out. After walking through the gate I went up Recon Hill. When I got up to my company's office I went in to report back in. On the outside of the orderly room door it now read "173rd Recon & Sniper."

Drive by picture of the Nightmare House

CHAPTER 26

Captain A-Hole

I walked in and saw the new Captain drinking coffee, looking out his window. He asked, "What can I do for you?"

I saluted and I said, "Sgt. Gibbore reporting back to duty, Sir!"

He replied, "So you're our missing Sergeant!"

I replied, "Sir? I'm not A.W.O.L, I was at Recondo and Pathfinder school, Sir!"

He said, "According to the info. I have on those schools, they were over long ago." I told him about my other commanding officer and what he told me about and what I was ordered to do. I told him the Captain told me to go to one school then to go right to the other one after.

We both went around and around about the time that was allotted for each course, though I knew I ghosted a little bit too long between each one. But I tried to explain to him rather than going and coming two times I just found lodging where I was. I knew I was wrong but I wouldn't give in. I learned to never give in because they would hang you if you did. I knew I started off rubbing this dude the wrong way, but I was screwed one way or the other and I knew it. He shouted, "This is my Company now....it's a company of Recon and Snipers...What your last C.O. told you means nothing to me. From now on you will do things my way! You got that Sergeant?"

I said, "Yes Sir!"

He said, "You better hope so. Now, get your stuff put away and get ready for a mission you just volunteered for."

I replied, "Yes, Sir!" From that day on, he and I never got along at all!

I could see he had no Ranger or Recondo patch on the outside of his sleeve, or anything "inside" his sleeve for that matter. He was a spindly little geek. The only power he had was the power Uncle Sam gave him. I turned and started out the door.

The Captain said, "Sergeant!"

I said, "Yes Sir!"

"Did you learn anything at all while you were gone?"

I said, "Yes Sir!"

He said, "I hope so, because your whole team will be depending on what you have or have not learned."

"How's that sir?" I asked.

He replied, "You're running your own team now, Mr. Expert Soldier! I just hope you really know what you're doing, or you will have a team of dead men, Sergeant."

"Me sir?...you're giving me a team to run?"

He stood there looking at me with a jerky grin. "Well, you're some sort of expert aren't you? Now move out and get yourself and your team ready. Report to the briefing room at 1200 hours. And here!" He handed me a list of guys names that were assigned to me. Three of them I knew from the Recon and three that came with the new Captain I didn't know.

He said, "You have three cherries, so kick their butts in line before you go, or you may have a real mess on your hands when you get out there."

I asked, "Do I have a choice about taking this job?"

He said, "Oh yeeeah!...you got one choice. Now get ready!"

"Yes Sir!" I replied as I did an about face and I walked out.

Holy Moly! I said to myself. Babbles was right. The guy is Captain A@@hole.

I walked down to the hooch and I saw my cot and foot locker was gone. I asked one of the guys that was inside the hooch where my stuff was. His name was Tom Brink. Brink told me that the C.O. had a hooch set up for N.C.O.s who were team leaders. He told me the Captain had my stuff moved into that hooch. I said, "Your name is on my list as a team member."

Brink said, "I heard we are going out today."

I replied, "You heard right. Will you show me the new hooch?"

"Right away, Sarge! Come on!"

I followed him down to the very end of the long bunker or barracks building. At the end was a door with a sign nailed to it. It read, "Recon Team Leader 1,2,3."

I said, "Fancy!" Brink smiled as we walked in. It was really fairly nice. All cleaned up, with three partitioned rooms with a door and everything! "Not bad!" I said as I looked the place over.

Brink said, "It's better than you guys had it before, no?"

I said, "I wish everything was like before...I hate change."

He said, "No sweat Sarge, together we'll make a good team."

I handed him the list of names. I said, "Do you know this good team Brink?"

He said, "Oh yeah, they're around."

I said, "For right now, you're second in command on this good team. Find them and report back here to my room...And get them all! We're going to have a little chat right here."

He said, "I'll be right back." He quickly walked out.

Good team, I said to myself. I doubt it! I sat down on my cot and I lit a square (cigarette). I was once told you had to be a "square" to smoke them. At that time I didn't understand that, but now that I don't smoke I can understand that completely!

Soon I heard a knock at my door. I said, "Come in."

Brink came in and said, "Hey Sarge...I rounded up the team."

They all came in and gathered around me. Some sat on the floor and the rest stood. Still sitting on my cot I said, "Well, I guess some of you have seen me around before. But for you guys that don't know me my name is Jim." I told them that I had just come back from Pathfinder and Recondo school. I told them that I had six months in country and I had pulled many Recon and Ranger type missions. I told them that although I had pulled many missions in the past, this was the first mission for me as a team leader. And if they didn't like that idea to go talk to Captain A@@hole about it. I told them that against my will I had been put in charge of the team and I said I would do everything I could to keep them alive as long as I was the team leader. I told them that because I had never commanded any mission I was going to need their help as much as they needed mine. We were a team, not just separate people, and we all needed each other to make it out alive. I told them that for now anyway, I would accept any and all suggestions. But for the most part I was in command in the bush. But I was always open to suggestions. That way if we were all killed, it wouldn't be my fault alone. They got a kick out of that one. I wanted people working with me, not against me.

I told them I learned a lot in the schools I went to and that I was no dummy. I said we all have to start at the bottom one time or another. I told them not to be afraid of speaking their mind to me about anything. If we all learn to trust each other and learn how each of us react to whatever situation, we should make out well. I told them the team will get very good in time. But, we will all have to work hard at working together. I said we will all make mistakes. We just have to help each other out of the mistakes and pray no one gets killed.

Then I asked them, "Does anyone want to say anything?" Some guys had some questions about different things and I answered them the best I could.

I said, "I ask that you more experienced men will help the guys that have never been on a mission pack with the right stuff. I would really find it helpful to me and it may save lives. Any help would be appreciated. So if there are no more questions…Before you guys go, I want to meet you all. Some of you I already know."

I pointed to Brink and said, "Brink is the second in command. If you have questions ask him first."

A guy that sat next to Brink said, "My name is LaCoy." The next man said, "I'm Preston." The next man said, "Finch." Those three were the new men I had never seen before. The next man said, "Thompson."

I said, "I remember you, Renolds and Brink from before. Which one of you will carry my radio?"

Brink replied, "Thompson carried it before…he's a good radio man."

I replied, "Good! How about it, Thompson? You up for it?"

He said, "Sure! I'll hump the radio."

"Good then…Brink how about point? I need a man that's got his head in one bag!"

He said, "That's my favorite spot."

I said, "Renolds, you'll take rear guard, unless you've got an excuse why not."

He said. "Thanks Sarge! No problem here!"

I replied, "Cool. Everyone just stay chilly and I'll take Brink up to supply and get our food and ammo. The rest of you men get packed. We'll be right back!"

Brink and I walked up to supply and got the cases of the supplies we needed. After Brink and I got the supplies down to the rest of the team, I got my rut sack and packed it along with the rest of my team. I wanted to help the new men get packed the right way.

It was about 1100 hours and we were all set. I said, "Let's go down to the mess hall so we can eat if anyone wants to and we'll be right near the briefing room for our school work."

After we all hiked down to the main post for chow we set our stuff down outside the mess hall and went in. The first thing I thought of was that big Delmonico steak I ate the day I punched out the Air Force dude Smitty and how good it was, and how the slop inside was going to sicken me. In the chow line, I stood there looking down at the cheeseburgers boiling in their own grease. They about made me barf just to look at them. But I knew I had to choke down at least one before heading out into the jungle.

After we all got through with our gourmet meal we left the "chow" hall, which is a good name for the place, except they left out the word DOG. It was about 1150 so we picked up our rut sacks and weapons and headed next door to the briefing bunker. We sat down inside to wait.

Soon our C.O. Captain A@@hole came in followed by one intelligence man. The Captain took a seat and the Intel. man stood up front. He said, "Let me have your attention please. The V.C. activity near Ban Blech is starting to become a real problem. This place is east of Uplift near the Cambodian border, just shy of it by about twenty miles. You will be out there for about a week or so to record enemy activity. This mission will be run as a Recon mission only. Stay away from contact with them as much as possible. This area is infested with the enemy. We already know this but we don't know exactly where they are hidden. You will be sent in to find out this information. We need to find the camp so we can destroy it. Only South Vietnamese troops will be in the immediate area for your support. There are no Americans except for a few Special Forces advisers. So go easy. Try to keep contact with them at a minimal level. Use the A.R.V.N. troops only in case of an emergency. I don't want anything to break out between you and them. And you never know if one or more of them are working with the V.C. If V.C. were to get wind of you working in that area without much support....well, I think you can fill in the blanks."

I looked at the Captain sitting there with a grin on his face. I felt if I could have ever gotten him in the bush, I would have killed him for sure...accidents die happen! After all he was trying to kill me but didn't have the guts to try it, or even say so.

The Intel man went on, "The army will build a base in the area once it has been secured. But first you men have to go in, locate the enemy so we can destroy them and make it safe for others to go in and do the work of building the base. The Captain may have something he wants to say. Sir, you can dismiss your team unless you have anything to add."

He got up and said, "You men are trained to do a job. Now let's do it."

What a jerk! I thought. I wondered what he meant by " let's." I knew that dope wasn't going to be included in that statement or mission. He said, "Sergeant stand fast for more instruction."

The team walked out and I came over to the Captain. "Sergeant, here is you code book for the radio transmissions. Send all messages by code. We don't want the enemy to figure out what we're doing out there. Here is your map of the area The valley between the two mountain ranges is where we're going to eventually bring in the Line Companies to build the Fire Base. Check out this area as

Pathfinder would to find a suitable landing zone. Spend as much time there as you need. Then advance into the mountains to your east." He gave me some map coordinates and said, "This is where the Fire base will be built. I want a detailed description of the place when you get back. Good luck and I'll contact you soon. Be extra careful with the cherries you have. They have a lot of time to pull and we need all the healthy bodies we can hang on to."

Looking at him I said, "Cherries…Sir, may I ask you, how many combat missions do you have?"

He just gave me a real nasty look and said, "Get out of here! Now!"

I replied, "Yes sir!" As I turned to go I could see the Intel. man standing there with a huge smile. The Captain saw the smile too.

When I got outside I came over to the team and told all the new men to move over to one side for just a minute. They all looked as though they were about to wet their pants, just the way I looked my first time out. I said, "I just want to tell you guys that not very long ago, I stood here about to pee my pants with excitement and nervousness. I was as nervous as a demon in church my first mission out. At that time I was working as a Ranger and all the missions ever consisted of was an all out hunt to kill V.C. This mission is going to be a bit less hazardous than my hunter killer missions as a Ranger. All we're going to do is watch them, not try to kill them. If we all keep cool and use our heads, we'll be okay. Just remember! If we all move quietly, slowly, and very tactfully we will live right alongside Charley. But without him ever knowing we are there! We will become ghosts. Charley can't kill a ghost! Remember that."

I knew myself this was nothing but a mouthful of bologna that I had just handed them. But I hoped that would ease their minds. I remember my first mission was a real gut twister. I hoped it wouldn't be as bad for these guys, even though I knew it would be. I said, "If we do get into contact, just don't get freaked out. Stay cool! If nothing else just lay down, watch, and do as much as you can for the rest of the team…and yourself. But most of all, just do as I say!"

They all said, "Yeah Sarge, sure Sarge"….stuff like that. I got everyone set and we headed for the chopper pad.

After we all got in the chopper I looked at the crew chief and I nodded my head okay. The crew chief tapped the pilot on the shoulder. The chopper shook for a second or two from vibration then up we flew. We went up over Recon Mountain and off to the northwest.

As we flew I started to feel the old "gut flies" start to move into action again. I almost forgot about those little suckers with all the ghost time I'd been having. If you'd been there for your whole life, I don't believe you would ever get used to this stuff completely. I know I was just as nervous as every guy was, I don't believe you can ever lose that. But I couldn't let it show anymore. There was no more cherry left in me. For me the second I jumped into the chopper that day it hit me that this was my team. Right then and there the cherry left me. I was now totally responsible for all the lives under me. It was like a pain killer was applied to a painful area of my body, it just didn't seem to hurt anymore. I almost felt like I couldn't be killed anymore because all those lives depended on me now to get them back alive. I just couldn't let them down. I thought that's what all team leaders must feel. I wondered if Schriff had that same feeling just before he was killed.

The Good Team

CHAPTER 27

Mr. Expert Soldier

Soon we started to descend. Down below us a very large valley stretched out as far as I could see. The valley was about one mile wide and set between two very high, large mountains. They were all green and very thick. Each mountain stretched out and humped up like the backs of two sea serpents, stretching out almost endlessly. The valley below was mostly brownish green grass lands and was spotted with many banana, coconut and palm trees.

Soon we were on the ground. The second the chopper landed, we jumped out and ran for cover. The chopper lifted off and our only connection with safety was gone. We were now in Charley's front yard. I just hoped he kept his welcome wagon home that day. It was quiet except for the flocks of birds screeching as they moved in and out of the jungle area. I signed to the whole team to move in close so I could talk without making much noise. I told them that from now on only whispering was to be done if they had anything to say and to use hand signals as much as possible. I told the team to relax but keep a sharp eye out, while Brink and I checked out the valley area for tracks or signs of the enemy. I put the team into a twenty-five foot defensive circle and told them not to move and to stay quiet and motionless until I got back. I told them if they saw anything, just hide. Then Brink and I left to explore the immediate area.

Brink and I walked the edge of the lowland area for about twenty minutes. During this time we saw numerous tracks made by Charley for sure. The tracks were everywhere. The footprints were unmistakable, they were prints of what we called Ho-Chi-Minh sandals. These were sandals made of old tires cut to the size of the man's foot. Then they would cut out thin rubber strips made of old inner tubes to use as straps to keep them on. They never wore out, you would get a AAA rating for traction in mud and all terrain and you couldn't beat the price, either. I could tell that they were not made by any S.V.N. soldiers that were in the area because they wore jungle boots just like ours. So whenever I spotted a footprint that looked like a small tire tread I could never miss the identity of the owner.

When I stopped to check out some tracks to see which way they went into the jungle, I heard Brink click his fingers once. I looked up and saw Brink pointing across the flat lands. Out about six or seven hundred yards I could see six V.C. coming right toward us. I could tell they were being too careful moving along this far out to be just practicing being quiet. I told Brink to stay low and move back to the team. I told him to get on the radio and tell Uplift that we spotted V.C. and I suspected they knew we had landed. I told Brink I would be back soon and not to come back for me, just to stay put. He nodded his head and moved away.

I hid myself well and sat to watch. I could hear V.C. voices about one hundred yards out in front of me and I could see them very clearly. I could see a couple of them looking for bananas or whatever on the ground. They filled up their ragged cloth backpacks and moved about fifty yards closer to me. Two of them climbed a coconut tree as good as any monkey could, then they sat on the top as lookouts.

The other ones squatted down and ate bananas and coconuts. They stayed there for about an hour. The sun was on top of the next mountain slowly going down. There was still plenty of light but not for much longer. Just before dark the V.C. on the ground stood up and the ones in trees came down and they all headed away from me and then moved out of sight.

I slowly got up and headed back to the team. As I moved I could hear V.C. voices coming right towards me. I sure hope the team wasn't spotted, I thought as I jumped into the cover of the jungle. Soon I counted ten V.C. passing right in front of me at about fifteen to twenty yards away. I let them pass, then I moved on very slowly until I came into the area where I left my team. They were nowhere to be seen. I laid low figuring they just hid from the V.C. that had just moved through the area. I hid for about ten minutes or so and sure enough I saw Brink and the rest of the team coming back my way.

When we got together Brink whispered, "Man! Did you see that!?"

"Oh yeah, I saw ten V.C., how about you?" I asked.

He gasped, "Ten! More like forty eight!"

"Forty eight! You got to be kiddin' me!" I replied.

He said, "We sat right over there and saw forty eight move right down through here then they split up in three groups. They came right out from behind us. I thought they spotted us…at least one of us anyway! But I guess not! Man there was so many I couldn't believe it. I saw the bunch headed toward you and I figured you were in for it, but I had no way of letting you know they were on their way to you!"

I replied, "It's no sweat, I saw them first. Forty eight! No way! The word 'infested' the Intel. man used was an understatement. We best find a good place to hide before dark! This moving around is going to get us caught."

After looking at my map I located a spot about three hundred yards away up the side of the mountain next to us. There was a rocky area above that would provide good cover and keep us hidden for the night. We quickly headed up the mountain and into that area. I could see clearly down to the area we just left and we would be able to see anything that came up our way from down below us.

Once we all got there and settled, I set out guards to keep an eye out. I called Uplift and reported our sightings to them. I told Uplift that we were going to spend the night at the map coordinates that I gave them in code. I told them we would report any movement seen by our starlight scope during the night. They said they understood our transmission and that they would be standing by if anything came up during the night.

The two guys that I sent out to stand guard were new, but they needed to get some experience in staying quiet and motionless for a period of time. It took practice to build up the nerve to leave the security of the team and sit out there all alone. That is why I sent them. I told them to quickly move back with the rest of us, should anything happen. I asked the men not to heat water to cook L.R.R.P.s, because hot water makes steam and steam can carry smell a long ways. So we all ate gorilla bars and what we called "drive on." That was the grunts' word for peanut butter and jelly on crackers. It was called that because it would give us a lot of energy to "drive on."

We all took our turn on guard duty that night, two hours on, four hours off, as usual. Each shift used the P.V.S.-2 Alpha starlight scope to watch the lowlands below. All night each of us saw V.C. moving across the lowlands. First watch reported only a very small group of enemy. Then as it got later into the night more and more were sighted. All night we each kept score of how many we saw while on guard duty. I counted them up in the morning. My team had a total count of two hundred three. I reported our count to Uplift in the morning. That place was Viet Cong City!

The starlight scope was a very big help with spotting enemy troop movement at night. The P.V.S.-2 Starlight hand-held night scopes cost the army three thousand dollars each. But they were worth every penny. They were flat black in color, about sixteen inches long and were fairly light in weight for their size. The scope went from three inches in diameter in the front to about one inch at the rubber booted eyepiece. The rubber boot eyepiece was made to cup over your eye so as not to let the green light from inside the scope reflect against your face and give you away in the dark. The scope worked by taking the available light from any source at night, such as starlight or moonlight. Then it would magnify the light ten thousand times to let you see out as far as two thousand meters or more. Mounted on a rifle, we could get accuracy out to eight hundred meters in the pitch dark.

The scope omitted no ultra violet light as old ultra violet night scopes do. So we had no worry about being spotted using it as Charley had to with his old ultra violet type scopes. A starlight scope can see the ultra violet light, but there is no light coming out of a P.V.S. When you turned it on it would make a very faint, very high pitched sound that you could only hear when close enough to use it. This scope used the liquid found inside a living eye called visual purple. This is the stuff that helps us see at night, and would burn out if you turned the scope on in the day or looked right at the moon without properly darkened lenses. This was a very good piece of equipment.

There were two types of starlight scopes. The P.V.S.-2 and the P.V.S.-2A. The P.V.S.-2A was a smaller one. That model was not made for mounting on a weapon, just to spot with. This is what we had with us, the P.V.S.-2 Alpha starlight scope.

After it was well into the early morning, I called Uplift back to make an update of our night sightings. They said good work and to hold our position until they got back with us. Uplift told us to just keep out of sight and watch the area for now. So I told the team to relax and to keep all their senses working overtime. We sat there for most of that day. Finally Uplift called us back. They said they were going to send a message in code. Thompson, my radio man, got the message down in code and I deciphered it.

CHAPTER 28

Friendly? Fire

After I decoded the message we saw that Uplift wanted the team to stay in the area that day and until further notice. They said not to move around unless we had to. The next afternoon they wanted us to return to the lowlands and set up some booby traps where we saw V.C. traffic was the heaviest. Then we were to pull back to our night logger out of the way.

They said that there was a South Vietnamese Fire support base about two thousand yards up the valley from us. Uplift told us if we needed heavy gun support they would help with eight inch gunfire and four duce mortar fire. Uplift told us that they were going to start their invasion of that area within a day or so. They didn't tell us exactly when but I felt it would be soon.

All night we saw the same thing that we saw the night before. We tallied our count. Two hundred and sixty that night. The next morning I told Uplift we saw V.C. all night. They came and went throughout the whole night but we really couldn't tell for sure exactly how many. I said we saw two hundred and sixty but this number was only an estimate, as we really couldn't tell if some were counted twice because of the distance and number of men counting. The only thing for sure was that there were a lot of them.

They told us to start our ambush plans that day. The next day at 1200 we were to move below to the open area. The choppers with the army demolition crews were coming in to clear out trees or anything else that would be in the way. They were also sending in two gun ships for air support to help us in case of attack. Then they said they were going to contact us later that afternoon to give us any updated info and to find out how we were after we finished setting up our booby traps.

We got our stuff together and I told everyone to drop their packs but to keep the Claymores, det. cord, M-16 and ammo. I told Thompson to stay up in the logger with the radio to cover us in case we got hit and to guard our packs. I told him if he heard any contact below at all and we weren't back in twenty minutes to call the A.R.V.N. Fire Base for gun support fast.

We moved down the mountain to the valley below. Soon we hit the bottom. There was a path worn flat going in three different directions on the lower area of the mountainside where Charley had been moving at night. On these three main trails we set up our booby traps. Brink worked with two men and I worked with two. After we got our traps set up we were to meet back together and then move back up to our night logger. We set our mines up to go off two different ways: by trip wire or by stepping on a detonator.

Within an hour we were done and headed back. After we came back together we moved back up the mountain towards our camp. When we reached the top we sat down to wait until dark for the fireworks show we had planned for Charley.

Just as it got dark Uplift called and wanted to confirm our position and plan. We told them what we had done and that we were back at our last known position. Uplift said that they instructed the A.R.V.N. Fire base to stand by and send out eight-inch gunfire into the valley below on our command. That way when we saw the enemy from where we were, we might be able to direct the gun fire and catch a few more V.C. with high explosive gunfire, or H.E. as we called it, sent from the A.R.V.N. base camp. That is if and when the enemy was spotted by us. I told them we understood what was going on and we broke radio communications.

It was still light enough to see because of a fairly bright moon. About an hour went by and we heard our first surprise package go off. Far below we could see a puff of white gray smoke come up out of the lowland area from the booby trap that just went off below us. We could see some movement down there around the area as well. Soon there were flashes and explosions going off below every few minutes.

Then the radio sounded off. "Big Momma to Looker 1! Come in Looker 1…over !"

I grabbed the mic. "Big Momma!…This is Looker 1…We read you…over!"

"Looker 1…This is Big Momma…We have just received message from…A.R.V.N. fire base Yellow…They have advised us gun strike will begin in 05….05, do you copy?…Over?"

I replied back to Uplift, "Big Momma….This is Looker 1 we copy H.E. strike to begin 05…05…and we are standing by…Keep us advised…and warn A.R.V.N. to be careful of friendly fire…over."

I figured the Vietnamese firebase heard the Claymores going off below and wanted to begin the strike, thinking that they may catch some V.C. in the open valley. So much for me being in control of the gun strike, I thought.

One of the new men on my team asked me what "friendly fire" was. I kind of snapped at him because I was a bit edgy with all that was going on and all. And I was mad that the A.R.V.N. base was not following our plans. I told him to just stay quiet, watch, and keep his ears open. I said I was too busy and I didn't have the time to answer goofy questions like that right then. I think I hurt his feelings because he just turned and moved away.

Soon we could hear far off in the valley a very faint "boom" sound. Then about five seconds later a whistling sound came our way. Then a big!…Baaa boom!!! Just below us. I said, "Everybody! Get down! That's too close to our position! I've got to redirect that fire but quick!" I took the mic. and put in a call to Uplift. Then two more H.E. rounds were sent out and on their way. Boom!..Boom! Then two more rounds went out. Boom!..Boom! They hit even closer to us! I yelled into the mic., "Man! those dumb A.R.V.N's! There going to kill us!"

A.R.V.N. is what we called the South Vietnamese army. It stood for Army Republic of Vietnam. I knew we were in deep doo-doo because none of them could speak English so I had no way to stop them directly or I wouldn't have gone through Uplift. I called Uplift again to tell those idiots to direct their fire further down the mountain. Rounds were hitting all over the side of the mountain where we were, rather than into the valley below.

Boom! Boom! Boom! Boom! Four more high explosive rounds were on their way. I told the team, "Oh man!..We're gonna' get hit!…Stay down!" I had to yell the blasts were so loud. Boom! One hit the trees just past us about two hundred yards up ahead. Boom! Boom! Two more a little closer to us. Boom! The fourth one went off just over our heads in the trees. Huge limbs and branches fell all over us. At that time I didn't know it but a very large limb landed on the head of one of my men and killed him dead right there. It also hit one other guy as well. I kept trying to reach Uplift by radio but the blasts were so loud I couldn't hear them, or the other way around. Soon H.E. was coming in all around us. I screamed back to Uplift to stop the shelling.

By the time I reached Uplift to stop the shelling, LaCoy was dead and Finch was hit with some rocks, limbs and debris. The side of his face was cut pretty bad. Using the moonlight as best I could, I cleaned and bandaged his face and stopped the bleeding and let him rest. We all lay flat a long time to keep from being killed and we tried to get our stuff together.

When the shelling finally started to hit down in the valley where it was supposed to, I got the team up and we pulled back a ways further up the mountain, away from the fire. Then I put the team on alert and into a circle perimeter back to back to watch. Soon we could hear V.C. moving or being pushed right up the hill toward us as they were trying to get away from the H.E. fire from below.

Again I pulled the men back a little, closer to some large rocks and spread them out a little. I told everyone to get ready with some fraggs. The movement and voices got louder. I whispered, "Pull your pins and toss your grenades right where I do!" I tossed out a fragg right at where I heard movement. The rest of the team did the same.

Suddenly numerous blasts went off in front of us. Then the screaming started. Charley was hurt bad! I ordered five more fraggs. Five more blasts went off. "Now get ready," I whispered.

Suddenly some of those kamikaze-like V.C. broke through the bush yelling and screaming right at us, firing like mad. I yelled out, "Shoot at the muzzle flashes." Everyone opened up. Then I told Thompson to get Uplift on the horn quick! He radioed out to tell them we were in contact near our night logger. Uplift said to do the best that we could and at first light the gun ships would be there. We kept our positions and fought the V.C. trying to advance up to us. We fought them off and on for the rest of the night.

By day break our ammo was getting low. The V.C. kept trying to sneak around us, but we managed to keep them off, because the rocks we used for cover were so big that the enemy just couldn't get close enough to us to pick us off. We stayed ducked down behind the rocks and the enemy was in the wide open so we kept nailing them instead.

Just as soon as daylight broke we got a call from Uplift telling us that the gun ships were on their way. Soon we could hear two choppers coming. I heard a V.C. yell out, "De-de-mou!...de-de-mou!" That meant run like heck! I took out a can of yellow smoke and I popped it at our position. Then I popped a red smoke and heaved it down at where the V.C. were. Yellow meant caution to the pilots for us and red was for a hot area where the V.C. were. That's where I wanted the choppers to dump their rounds.

Soon the gun ships had everything under control and we slowly started down the mountain to the valley below. I carried LaCoy's body down the mountain over my right shoulder, his head hanging down my back. I was soaked with his blood.

As I carried him, I got all choked up so bad, knowing or feeling the guilt of letting him down and not getting him back alive. I wanted to cry so bad I thought I was going to explode inside trying to hold it back. But I couldn't cry and let the team see me. I couldn't let them see what little weakness there was still left in me. I already let one man down and that was one too many. I remember wishing I still had the chance right then to look LaCoy in the face and answer his "goofy" question....I remember whispering to him more then once as I carried him, "That was friendly fire buddy." The whole thing was killing me. But I knew I had to get over it and stay strong. I know Schriff felt the same way at times. I thought, I can't let him down too, I have to stay strong and be the team leader Schriff wanted and trained me to be.

See I believe that there is a "thing" that is given from God and it gives people special abilities or simply a "knack" for doing something. Most people think we get this "thing" from our parents, like "genealogy." I saw Schriff as my "combat parent" or the one I got my "thing," my "knack," my "war genealogy" from. Who he got his "thing" from I know not. One day someone else will get a "thing" from me, I thought. As time goes on I will rub off on someone else and he will pick up some of what I have, some of my "war genes", if you will. I just hoped that man's commander would let that man's genealogy grow and become more mature than my commander let mine mature before he had to hold so many lives in his hands. No one should have to deal with the guilt that I felt right then.

Brink helped walk Finch back down to the bottom. When we got down there I looked him over and he looked like he was doing pretty good and he said so. That made me feel a bunch better anyway. We found V.C. bodies laid out all over the place as we moved down toward the landing zone below.

After we got all the way down, two more choppers with Line Co. soldiers landed to back us up. After we got our perimeter set up we dragged twelve dead V.C. down off the mountain. I gave the team the body counts except for one that I needed. With that kill I joined the 21 Club.

I radioed Uplift to find out what was going on next. They said twenty choppers were going to be sent out with boo-koo supplies to get the new firebase started. Ten regular choppers with goods and ammo and ten two prop. Cargo and troop carriers or "Sh## Hooks" as we called them. Uplift ordered the rest of my team back in and for me to stay out there working a Pathfinder mission, bringing in the choppers, men and equipment. They said I was going to get a radio operator from a signal company to assist me in the radio contact with the choppers and Uplift during the operation.

Soon two choppers with four combat engineers and their equipment came in to help blow up obstacles like trees and other hazardous objects to clear out an L.Z. As soon as the first chopper was emptied I helped my team on board. Brink said, "I wish you were coming too, Sarge."

I said, "Just get the heck out while you can and take care of the men. I'll see you guys when I get back!" Then they lifted off waving to me until they were out of sight.

CHAPTER 29

A New L.Z.

The second chopper came in and two demolition men jumped out. We all got together and planned out the landing zone as the Line Co. squads kept guard for us. The base was going to be on the top of the mountain, about 1000 yards straight up, close to where I spent the night. The combat engineers and their demolition men started to go to work blowing up the obstacles that I indicated would be in the way. The combat engineers had a bulldozer sent out by a large cargo chopper to help with the heavy work. They worked most of the day blowing open the L.Z. area. There was a lot of work to do to get the mess cleaned up that the demo. men had made blowing trees, large rocks and opening up the thick jungle area at the bottom of the mountain. I sat and talked with the radio man Uplift sent me.

Soon it was late afternoon. All day I could feel someone had been watching our every move. Just before dark the two Line Co. squads were starting to kick back and relax. They were about to get chow started when shots came ringing out from all around us. One engineer and one demo. man were hit. Quickly, we all spread out, got to cover and formed a defensive circle. We encountered heavy sniper fire from the jungle area high above us.

The Line Co. squad leader, a 1st Lt., said he would take his two squads and go into the jungle to see if they could knock out the snipers. I told the radio man to contact Uplift and tell them what was going on. He did. I advised the Lt. to stay with us because it was getting dark and they would be in trouble out in that jungle at night. I pointed out to him that soon it was going to be too dark for Charley to hit us anyway. The 1st Lt. told me to take care of my own business. He said he knew what he was doing. I tried to convince him to stay with the rest of us, but it was no use. Talking to most officers was like talking to a stump. Without the Line squads all we had left to fight with were eleven men. I started looking around us to see if I could spot a safe place to hole up for the night. Because I knew then the line boys and Lt. Knotthead were gone, one way or the other.

Across the valley behind us, about six hundred yards away I saw a large rocky area. Rocks always were good cover to me and they saved my life more than once. The radio man told me that Uplift said that it was too late to send out any air support because it was getting dark. They wanted us to retreat to a secure area for the night and that more help would be sent out tomorrow. I called Uplift and told them what Lt. Knucklehead was up to. They told me that it was up to the squad leader to get his neck out of this one. Uplift said they would stay in radio contact with the Lt. and for us not to worry about him. They told me to take charge of who was with me, because of my combat exposure, and to find a secure place for the night and call in the night logger when we got there. I said I would contact the Lt. by radio and tell him what we were going to do and where we were going. Uplift said they copied our message and I closed radio contact with them.

I got on the radio to the Lt. and told him what Uplift wanted me to do. Once again I tried to talk him back to our position before it got too dark to see but he said he had visual contact with Charley twice and he was going to pursue him. I told him that if he got into trouble, there was nothing I could do after dark, so he was on his own. Then I told him to call Uplift and I broke contact.

I told the men that were with me what was going on and what Uplift told me to do. None of them were combat experienced. All were demo. men and engineers. They told me that they were with me all the way. We all got up from our position and headed out across the valley floor to the rocky area on the other side. We moved very quickly but carefully. Soon it was just about dark. We only had about three hundred yards to go to get to the rocky area a couple hundred feet up the other mountainside.

All of a sudden we could hear M-16 and AK fire from the other side. I stopped everyone to listen and see if they would try to contact us by radio for help. The firefight got real bad for about ten minutes. I told the men that were with me that there was nothing we could do for those men now. We only had a few minutes of light left to get to our night logger. I quickly moved up the mountain to the rocky area above.

We had just reached the safety of the rocks when I got a call from the Lt. I sat down with the men to answer him. The Lt. said he was with the second squad and they had zapped two V.C. He also told me that it was too dark in the jungle to see any longer and he told me his night logger area on the map in code. He said he had been in contact with his first squad and they were staying where they were for the night. He said they were going back to the lowlands in the morning and they would see us there. I told him by code where we were on the map and I told him I was going to make a report to Uplift shortly and I would see him in the morning. I then broke radio contact with him.

At our night logger I contacted Uplift to tell them of our plans and our night position. Uplift wasn't at all happy with the Lt. but it was too late to change anything. They said to stay put and keep our backsides covered until morning. Then I was instructed to head down to the lowlands in the morning. Then we broke contact.

After we were in our spot for about one hour we got a call from Squad #1. The team leader, a Sergeant Briggs said his squad was on red alert. He said they had movement all around them. He said he could not get in touch with the Lt. after numerous tries. He feared the radio was being "jammed." I advised him to keep low and use only fraggs if need be so as not to give away their position, to move out at first light, and to watch for being surrounded. I told them 2nd Squad was just below them near the flats. I told Briggs that was the Lt.'s last known logger. I advised him to hug the dirt and to keep in contact with me and I would report to Uplift what was going on. I told him I would try to call the Lt., but I had no better luck than he for most of the night. All night long Briggs reported to me about the movement and all they heard.

I just knew the worst was happening. I knew how Charley worked at night. If he knew where you were, he would booby trap every way out…all the way around you, carefully and quietly. Then he would move in slowly from the front, or in from the un-booby trapped area, to flush you out right into a sealed ambush area as they hid just beyond the booby traps. Whoever escaped the mines the gun fire would kill. Charley was very good at setting up ambushes in the jungle at night.

Just as it got light Briggs called and said he was moving down the mountain. The sun was not all the way up yet and it soon started to rain cats and dogs. Because of the clouds it was still fairly dark yet light enough to see. I told Briggs I would tell Squad #2 to be on the look out for them. During the night I finally got in touch with the Lt. He told me for some reason he could hear us but he couldn't get in contact with us. After Briggs and I broke radio contact I called the Lt. He told me he could still hear both of us but he could not contact 1st Squad for some unknown reason.

I called Uplift to tell them we were all moving back to the lowlands below and all about the radio trouble and everything that happened during the night. They told me that as soon as the rain let up, which was supposed to happen soon, they were going to send the invasion force in. They wanted me back at the landing area and ready A.S.A.P. to accept and guide them in. I replied, "I copy that message and we're on our way. Flighty Looker Control…out!"

We got up and moved out. We hit the lowlands and at about the same time all hell broke loose across the valley about five hundred yards from us. I took the mic. and I called Uplift to tell them about the war that was going on a few hundred yards away from me. There were loud explosions going off left and right across the valley. There was a real mess going on over there and I reported it all. I felt helpless and I really didn't know what the heck to do so I asked Uplift what they wanted us to do. I figured that way my backside wouldn't be in a ringer if I screwed up. They told me to move in but to stay back out of the way and stand by for further orders. So I moved the men I had with me slowly across the open area ahead. I just knew the worst was happening.

When we got about four hundred yards from the fighting I stopped everyone and we took cover. I put my radio man next to me and we got ready for action. Soon I got a call from Briggs and he was almost in a state of panic. He shouted, "I have a lot of guys down…I don't know for sure how many I have left!….F#**#in' V.C. are everywhere…I don't know how much…I don't think we can hold out much longer….I can't find a way out!…There is no way out….I'm going to try to hold this 10-10. We're completely surrounded!"

The Lt. came over the radio and he said he heard what was going on and they were working their way to them. Just about then it stopped raining and I could hear the sound of helicopters coming our way. I got a call from a Cobra gun ship. He wanted to know where the hot spot was. Suddenly I could see yellow smoke coming up out of the jungle ahead about five hundred yards up the mountain. I told the pilot that there were men all over up there and he should put his fire all around the smoke to within sixty yards of it.

He replied, "Roger smoke….Will direct fire to within sixty yards of smoke…over!"

I yelled back, "Roger that, but be careful! Over!"

I called Briggs. The next man in command told me Briggs was dead. I told that man to pop yellow smoke every few seconds to keep their 10-10 lit up so the gun ship would know exactly where they were…And keep down! The Cobra and the two other gun ships flew towards the yellow smoke. All three gun ships moved slowly in a circle around the yellow smoke like Indians circling a wagon train.

Then suddenly all hell broke loose. They began dumping so much firepower on the area around the smoke that I couldn't believe it. Nothing below them could ever live through that attack, I thought. I got a call from the man that was leading what was left of 1st squad and he told me that the gun ships were putting the hurt on Charley big time but they were fine and out of the way. He told me to tell the gun ships to keep laying it on 'um. So I did.

CHAPTER 30

Flighty Looker Control in Action

The lead chopper called me. He wanted to know where I wanted the rest of the force to land. I told him to send down four choppers. First two with the first two loads of men, along with two others with their supplies.

He replied, "Flighty Looker Control...This is eye in the sky...We roger that...Pop green...in first Cool L.Z...Do you copy?...Over."

I replied, "This is Flighty Looker Control....we copy...Roger green smoke at...Cool L.Z.#1, ...Over."

I got up with my radio man and I told the other men to stay put. Just then two "Chinook" troop carrying two prop. helicopters came into sight and started to descend towards me. I held my arms straight up over my head. I tossed a canister of green smoke out into the area in front of me where I wanted them to land. They swiftly swooped down and landed. The two very large troop filled choppers came down right together...one in front, one right behind. As soon as they hit the ground men started pouring out of the back of each one. They ran out then quickly moved to the edge of the jungle area and began setting up small defensive squads. I directed the two empty choppers to lift off using hand signals. Then I guided two others in that carried the squads, ammo and supplies. I stayed on that job for over two hours until all supplies that came from Uplift were safely down and unloaded.

I looked up at the mountain where the gun ships first dumped their stuff and it looked more like a blast furnace than a jungle. So I figured the two Line Squads were down off the mountain by then. I walked around to check out the two hundred plus men and supplies I just guided in. Soon I found what was left of Squad #1. Out of the twenty men they had there were only five that got out of it unharmed. Eleven men were badly hurt and four were dead. I looked for the E-4 that took over for Briggs as Squad Leader when Briggs got zapped. I found him on the ground with the men he had left, sitting with the dead ones next to him. I saw his arm and head was all bandaged up.

Pooped, I sat down with him and I said, "Bad ambush!"

He said looking at me with tears in his eyes. "You ain't said nothin' dude...Hey....you're the Sarge, the dude on the radio right?"

I said, "Yeah."

He went on. "I almost died of fright when I saw all those little son's-a-bugs comin' at us. They was comin' as fast as we could shoot 'um. It was a miracle I tell ya, or God, I don't know, that kept us alive."

I replied, "I know what you mean...If it wasn't for God and miracles I would have been dead a long time ago!"

He said, "Sarge! I just want to thank you for all you did for us! I'll never be able to thank you enough...never! You helped save our butts up there!"

I replied, "Hey dude, I know exactly what you were going through up there...Been there...done that. I just wish I could have met Briggs, he sounded like a good dude!" I jumped up on my feet.

The E-4 said, as he pulled back a blood soaked poncho liner covering a dead body next to him. "Sarge! I want you to meet Sergeant Briggs! A real good dude! We're all going to have ta' party sometime!"

Briggs looked like a bomb went off in his face. There was no way I could tell what he really looked like. I felt like I was going to choke to death on the wad of grief that came up my throat. So I quickly turned and walked away. I could see the E-4 was about to lose it. E-4….I never did find out his name.

I walked around to see if I could find Lt. Blockhead to see how he was and to see if he "knew what he was doing" that day. As I looked around the area I kept asking around where the Lt. was. A man that was in his squad told me he got hit in the hip and he went out on a chopper. He told me he wished the bullet would have been about a foot or so higher. I agreed with him totally.

Medi-evac choppers were coming and going one at a time with the dead and wounded. I just walked around for a while from one Company to another and briefed officers and N.C.O.s on what had been happening out there. There were two complete companies of men so far that had landed. Both C.O.s of the companies said that they radioed back to Uplift to ask them about what their orders were next. They both told me I did a good job as a Pathfinder and that made me feel good.

I explained, "My job as a Pathfinder was my first real mission of this type and I was pretty unsure about how it would go." One of the Captains said he thought I had my stuff together with all the men, equipment, and disorder that I had to cope with. He told me he was going to recommend a promotion for me as soon as possible. I thanked him and walked back to where my radio man was to rest and eat.

As I sat there, I saw various groups of men split into squads to check out the smoldering mountain. The gun ships were gone so men could go up the mountain to secure more area as they worked their way to the top to clear out a fire base. The top of the mountain was supposed to be the new L.Z. or Fire base. It was to be called L.Z. Green. They were going to try to secure the whole mountain to get it ready for the combat engineers to move in and build the new L.Z. With the way things were being laid out I could see it was going to look a lot like L.Z. Uplift when it was done. The Line Co. commanders said it would be no sweat to build it that week. I just knew they were full of bologna when they made that statement. I thought we'll see! A week, right!

As the squads of men went up the mountain all day long they ran into and fought Charley every step of the way. And all day long they carried dead and wounded men from both sides of the war down the mountain to the choppers and medics below. The place was no cream puff situation at all! These men really had their work cut out for them. Not only did they have old raggedy Charley to put up with, but well-trained N.V.A. soldiers to cope with as well.

There was a big difference between the V.C. and the North Vietnamese soldier. The V.C were born and raised in the area and N.V.A. soldiers were sent down from North Vietnam to fight and train Charley or the Viet-Cong a.k.a. V.C. Charley Cong was a Vietamese guerilla fighter fighting for the communist cause and under their military control. He was the guy that dressed in rags or civilian clothes like most civilian people. The North Vietnamese army wore a uniform, with a khaki color to it and a safari shaped tan hat or pith helmet. Both were very deadly...very good soldiers. Although the V.C. were under-manned and ill-equipped they could still live off the land and also raise boo-koo heck with what little he had. The V.C. were fighting two unstoppable forces, one in front of them and one behind them and were still holding their own.

I always gave Charley a lot of credit, but I still hated his guts for what I saw him doing to his own people. Killing your own people always made little sense to me. But I do know one thing for sure where I totally agreed with Charley. If it were my own country, if someone tried to invade my homeland, that is what my nickname would be too, Charley the guerilla fighter....until the day I died! I would never give up.

One time an old Pappa-son told me he, his father, his father's father and so on never knew a time that they were without war. He said a thousand years or maybe more. He told me that for countless generations people from all parts of the world were always trying to run and take over his country. He intently looked into my eyes very boldly and he said very seriously, "No one will ever take over this country except our own people!" I almost jumped back he said it so boldly and so convincingly. Even though he was so old and frail he freaked me out with just his look.

Even though the South Vietnamese had requested our help and were fighting beside us, some Vietnamese resented any outside intervention. Many of their people didn't understand what was happening any more than the Americans did.

No matter how hard we fought in the South, the V.C. could return to re-supply in the safety of North Vietnam, then come back to kill us. And every time we took an area at great cost of American lives, we would soon abandon it. I thought how could we win if we did this? But at that time I was just as confused as others and I just followed orders.

It was getting close to dark by the time Uplift got in touch with me. When they called they told me I was going to get my team sent back out to me, with one added member, a "T-2" Sniper. Kabbatt! The dude must be back from Sniper school, I thought. I was very happy with that good news. Finally, someone that was a member of Hunter 1 was on his way back to be working with me. I could use someone with some experience and a lot of "Cool." Uplift told me that Brink, my second in command, would explain our mission to me when he got there in the morning. They told me to just relax that night and rest and they would contact me the next morning after the team got out here.

That night I walked around talking to the Line Co. people and relaxed with them. I had no guard duty or radio watch. So about 0800 I strung out my hammock to sleep. I was bushed! Then it started raining again. Trying to sleep with rain pouring down on you all night was almost impossible. But I managed to sleep anyway I was so tired.

In the early morning I got up and wrung out my clothes. Then I put them back on and I headed for chow with the Line dudes. One of the Line Captains told me that he got a message from Uplift about more men that were coming in that morning.

He said my team would be among them. I told him thanks for the info. and I went back to where my radio man had set up a small tent to hang out and stay out of the rain.

The rain started to let up two hours after daylight and we could hear the choppers coming up the long valley. I got up and walked out to the L.Z. to welcome my team. Two choppers landed and the men all jumped out. I could see Brink then Thompson, then Kabbatt and Preston and Renolds. The only new guy left was Renolds. Good deal, I thought, five men I felt I could count on again. I started waving and calling them over to me. They spotted me and ran over towards me. As they got to me I saw Kabbatt was carrying a different looking weapon; one not often seen anymore. It looked like an M-14, the standard weapon the army used before we got the M-16.

He ran right over with his hand out saying "Jim, you're really gettin' to be just like an old timer! How the heck you been!?"

I replied, "Oh…pretty good I guess. How about yourself?"

He replied, "I see you got yourself a team-a-yer own now...Real big shot huh?"

I said, "Stop! You want it..? You got yourself a big shot job too, I see!"

He said, "Wait until you get yours dude! You won't believe this weapon!…What a beauty!!"

I replied, "Big deal, looks like a big heavy M-14 to me is all."

He said, "It looks like an M-14…It sounds like an M-14, without the silencer. But it's something real special. No M-14 can ever keep up with this XM-21, dude!"

I replied, "You'll have to tell me all about it later. But first let's get somewhere dry and out of the mud so we can talk."

We walked over to the Line Captain's big tent and I asked him if we could come inside for my briefing on our next mission. He said, "Sure, come right in." So we all piled into the tent and sat down on the floor over in one corner, out of the way. We just talked for awhile about the time the team spent in the rear and a little about Kabbatt's new toy. He told us it was an XM-21 U.S. army match rifle. He said it was very accurate up to 1250 meters in the day with a 10 power Redfield scope and 875 meters at night with the P.V.S.-2 Starlight scope. He said it had a glass-laid stock and a micro-grooved stainless steel-lined barrel for outstanding accuracy. He told me that they had given him specially hand-loaded match ammo to shoot. The bullet was only 30 cal. but it would mushroom out to 50 cal. It was against the Geneva Convention to use ammo of this type because the Convention only allowed bullets of 30 cal. or less to be used on humans. But he also said Snipers were against the Geneva Convention too. He said. "I guess no one gives a squat!"

After Kabbatt gave us a brief on his new weapon he told me of our mission. He said we were going in by chopper to the top of the mountain to try to establish some sort of perimeter on top for the new firebase. He said after an air strike on the mountain, which was going to happen the next day, we would be put up there to help guard the people that were going with us. The engineers and demo. men were going to build some bunkers and all the hooches and buildings. Intel. thought he could zap V.C. from long ranges in the day as well as at night. He said our mission was a "Hunter-killer" type mission. He said it was going to be just like an old Hunter 1 mission. We were instructed to kill any V.C. on sight unless we thought we could capture them, of course. He said those were our orders until further notice.

Our code name was "Hunter Killer." Kabbatt told us that intel. knew that the V.C. monitor our radio talk at times as well as "jam" our radio transmissions. He said that they wanted to let Charley know he was going to be watched day and night and he would be killed on sight. He said they wanted this new firebase built without delay big time. Then he told us Intel. wanted us to just lay low until after the air strike the next day and they would contact us about what they wanted us to do next.

So that is just what we did. We laid around and took it easy trying to stay dry. It poured for the next two days as we waited for the air strike to begin. Finally it stopped raining the second night. About 0700 the third morning many gun ships came swooping up the valley out of nowhere and rocketed the mountaintop. Also one after the other "cargo choppers" dropped skids of fifty five-gallon drums of gasoline down on top of the mountain to clear off the foliage. The mountaintop burned two days and nights.

Uplift called me and gave me our orders in code. Three choppers were to come in to take my team and two Line Co. squads and equipment up first. The demo. men, engineers and the rest were going to be sent up when we had the top secured. Uplift told me to take the signal man that I had been using to be our radio man.

We all moved outside of the mess hall tent to where the two Line Co. squads were standing to wait for our choppers. Soon we could hear them coming. They landed and we jumped right in. We lifted off and banked towards the mountain top above. The chopper we rode up in moved in first while the two other choppers idled high above us, keeping watch with their guns ready. My team was sent in first to see if we could draw any enemy fire from below while the two other choppers hovered high above with guns ready. We descended until we touched down. Then we all jumped out and I set up a circle perimeter. Our chopper quickly lifted off and I popped a yellow smoke to bring in the other two ships. They descended on to the burned out L.Z. and unloaded their men and supplies. As soon as the men landed we all got in a large circle perimeter and kept watch. I radioed down below for the engineers to start up. We started to spread open the circle, making it larger until we reached the outer limits of the mountaintop. I called two choppers of engineers in and they landed. They were followed by a large cargo chopper with building material, ammo and pre-filled sand bags to use as make-shift defensive bunkers. They also brought food, water and more men.

After the mountaintop was secured my team picked out good spots around the mountain top to pull guard while the engineers and Line Co. men went to work building bunkers and filling hundreds of sand bags. All day the men worked, digging out some rocket craters that were blown open by the gun ships. They piled sand bags around the holes to use as bunkers or bullet stops. The whole area was a black burnt mess! Sitting out in the open we knew we would be screwed if Charley started lobbing rockets and mortars at us. So we had to get our stuff put together fast!

Just before nightfall we had all worked hard and we had a fairly nice little landing zone set up and secure, we thought. There were bunkers all around the L.Z. perimeter and enough ammo and supplies to start our own small army. But no one slept that night at all. Small weapons fire and mortars came in all night. During the next day the mortars let up for a while but we caught small arms sniper fire from all around the mountain area. Kabbatt wasn't much help because the jungle was so thick around us his weapon was about useless. The mountain we were on was the tallest one around, but the other mountains around us were just about as high. Charley could snipe at us from all around. We were wide open and he was totally hidden in the thick jungle around us. I thought to myself, there goes the Intelligence corps thinking again! Charley could see us but we could not see him.

This sort of nightmare went on for two days and nights. We just never knew when it was our time to get blown up by an incoming rocket or mortar...or hit by sniper fire. The Line Co. squads went out hunting and tried to help, but it was no use. They were losing men fast!

CHAPTER 31
A Losing Battle

It was the fourth night out and still no let up from Charley. The Line Companies just had too much area to cover to try to keep secure. All night we got hit with mortars and rockets. That fourth and last day we spent on that hill was terrible! Just about dawn the fourth day the V.C. made their move. As I looked over the mountain's edge all I could see were V.C. charging with their AK-47's and rockets. They were attacking with every man they had available to them. There must have been two hundred!

As they advanced toward us we shot as many as we could as fast as we could. In the small bunker I was in, there was an M-60 belt-fed machine gun that would almost fire non-stop all day if you let it. I got it so hot from firing so continuously the gun barrel glowed red hot and I had to break the belt of ammo to get it to stop firing all by itself. This is known as "Hot rounds." The barrel can get so hot inside that the almost white hot inside will set a bullet primer off instantly as it enters the chamber, and the gun will keep firing by itself until you take its food away.

There were just too many V.C. kamikazes coming at us at once and we had to start making preparations to evacuate the hill because we were beginning to be overrun. I called Uplift to tell them what we and the line squads were up against. They told us to booby trap our bunkers or blow them up with our supplies in place and get ready to move out. We were told to leave Charley nothing. They wanted nothing left on the hill that V.C. could use against us. So as many men as could be spared worked setting charges to blow up our goods and ammo.

Late that afternoon the V.C. were nearly on our backs. We shot, clubbed and killed them as fast as we could to keep them off us. All day helicopter gun ships came in and zapped as many V.C. as they could see and held them off while we retreated, setting booby traps and blowing up supplies. My team was the last to be air lifted out.

Just before our chopper landed it was hit by a rocket. The chopper exploded into a ball of flame, killing everyone on board. The V.C. were swarming over our barbed wire and sand bag perimeter like ants. I knew there was no time to hold them off any longer. I ordered my team to blow our supply bunker, then we headed over the hill. We were the only Americans on that mountain and I wanted out of there immediately! I wasn't sticking around for another chopper to be sent up. I headed down the mountain with my team right behind me as I pulled point. Every step of the way we ran into V.C., but I just kept moving on instinct. As we ran, jumped, fell, and dove we dodged gunfire all the way. I just kept saying Our Lord's Prayer non-stop in my mind as I ran. I saw my team was still together, but almost in a state of panic.

When we hit a small rocky area I stopped and we took cover. Then I grabbed the radio mic. and I called the line company below for some help of any kind. I got no answer from them. So I got us up and we headed down again. We ran, fell, and flew just about all the way down those near sheer rock cliffs. I saw Kabbatt was cut all over from falling down on the rocks and I tried to help. He said, "Just keep on moving!" The rest of my team was beat to a bloody pulp as well. We were all cut and scraped up very badly.

I heard the radio come on, so I grabbed it. I could hear someone saying, "Keep coming the way you are….straight down. We can see you now. Keep on course straight down…come on! You're almost home free!"

I could see the lowlands far below us. I could also see the Line Co. men through the trees. There were men on their way up to help us. Now they could see us from below and help was coming. I kept saying, "Thank you, God!" as I kept on running with my team. kept saying that over and over until I collapsed on the lowlands below. Somehow we all made it. I know now, many years later, that it wasn't our skills alone that got the whole team off that mountain alive and in one piece that day.

We all lay on the ground flat out trying to catch our breath, thankful that we were all still very much alive. I think we all lay down in the mud for over an hour before we even tried to get up we were so exhausted. When Uplift called they told me they wanted us to come back in on the next chopper out of there.

As we all walked towards our chopper I heard someone yell out my name. I turned around and saw someone I thought I would never see again…It was Becham! I dropped my pack and all my stuff on the ground and ran towards him. We ran head on into each other and hugged each other as hard as we could. I was muddy and all bloody. But he didn't care. We just hugged each other anyway.

Bec yelled out, "You bad! azz mother f#**#…..Don't tell me that was you and your team up there! I didn't know that was you, I just heard it was a bunch a crazy Recondos up there! You sorry….!" We both almost got misty right there.

"Man, I never thought I would see you again!" I replied all choked up.

He said, "If I only knew it was you in so much danger up there, I would have come up for you guys myself! Everyone here knows about you guys and what's been goin' on and all. We've all been worried about you guys!"

After we got calmed down, I told my team to get on board the chopper, while they were waiting for me. I told Bec, "When you guys come in come right up to Recon Hill. I'll get you into Recon with me, if ya want to."

He smiled, "Do you think you can?"

I said, "Get your butt up there as soon as you get back in."

He replied, "You know it buddy! I'll be there as soon as I get back!"

I squeezed his hand and said, "See you back in the rear sucker!"

He said, "For sure!"

I grabbed my rut sack and weapon and jumped on board my chopper with the rest of my team and up we went. I waved to Bec and he faded out of sight. We flew for about half an hour and there she was, L.Z. Uplift, Home. As soon as we landed I dismissed the team and I told them they did a super good job and I would see them after my briefing up on the hill.

I asked the Signal Corps radio man to stick with me for a few seconds to talk. I said, "You did a good job with that radio the whole time out. If this wasn't the nasty job it is I would like to have you with me always!"

He replied, "Thanks Sarge! But no thanks! I was about to crap my pants at any second out there! That was something I will never forget as long as I live. I don't know how you could take a steady diet of that!"

I said, "I know what you mean! Even with all my experience in combat, I'm going to have to check my pants as soon as I get a chance myself." He laughed.

I said, "For a while there I really had my doubts about getting out of that mess. I have been in combat for going on seven months now but I think this mission was one of the worst."

He said, "I thought you ran the team very well, I'm just glad that it wasn't my responsibility to get all of us off that damn mountain. I was frozen with fright...I had no clue what to do. Let alone try to figure out what to do next!"

I said, "Well, I only acted on instinct to tell you the truth, not skill. Things were just going too fast to really do any positive thinking or planning."

He said, "I only know I wouldn't want this type of work for all the money in the world, let alone what we get paid!" We walked and rapped until I got to the briefing bunker.

Then I said, "Thanks again. You've been a lot of help."

He said, "No sweat! It's been nice knowing you, but real dangerous working with you! I just hope you live to see your next birthday."

"Me too!" I replied as I walked down into our briefing bunker.

Inside I saw an Intelligence man. He came right over and started to fire questions at me as fast as I could answer them. He wanted to know if I thought we could ever take and hold the hill, if I knew how many V.C. were there and things that were so dumb I had to laugh. I said, "First, that mountain is a V.C. infested hive! Second, you'll need a large sized army to hold and keep it. And third, forget about it dude! Look, I'm beat to death. I'm a bloody, muddy mess. I've been out, I don't know how long now in the rain. I haven't had any sleep or what you could call food in I don't know long! And you want me to stand here answering dumb questions like your askin? Get real dude."

He said, "You guys did an excellent job out there, please don't get me wrong...with none of you getting killed and all. That was really some leadership under the conditions and all...But..."

I interrupted, "Yeah, I wish Captain A*#hole could hear that."

He said, "Better yet, the Battalion Commander was pleased with your work, but he was not happy that we couldn't keep the hill. He said maybe next time. We're going to keep trying."

I said, "Maybe next time the Colonel should come out there with us to show us how to do that little thing."

He looked at me with a big frown. He said, "Don't ever say that around him."

I said, "Hey, with him being a big shot bird Colonel and all, he must have some brilliant idea on how we should take that hill. Why don't you ask him your silly-azz questions?"

He said, "With an attitude like that, all you're in for is trouble around here, soldier!"

I said, "Whether I'm here or out in the bush, I'm always in trouble, so what's the diff?"

He said, "You don't know this but you have been put in for a promotion to E-6 Staff Sergeant."

I said, "Ooooh! You mean the promotion the Line Co. Captain said he was going to put me in for. No, I didn't hear about that!"

He said, "How you ever got the rank you have now, I'll never know."

I said, "The only thing rank means around here is more work!"

He said, "If it was up to me, I would bust you down two ranks for being such a wise guy."

I said, "Look, I do my job and do it well. I didn't ask anyone to promote me this far, and I never will. Besides, you wouldn't want to lose a team leader now would ya? All I want to know is when I am going to Sniper school."

He said, "If it was up to me, never. But you've been set up for the third class starting in two weeks. But don't worry about that! You still have two weeks before that happens and a lot could happen in two weeks."

I replied, "Oh you're right, a lot can happen in two weeks. Like a rocket could come buzzin' right in here at anytime and hit you square upside the head. One never knows when one's time is up, does one!?"

I felt so good inside knowing he knew just how I felt about him. The feeling was now officially mutual. I knew he would try to screw me over every time he had a chance just like my Captain; I saw both of them as butt buddies anyway.

It was about 2100 at that time, and time way overdue to get a big buzz on. I would never get high in the field. That was no place to be having fun or for relaxing one second. That's all the time it took for a bullet to blow your brains out. I walked up to the men's hooch to see if anyone was around. I saw Thompson just coming out of the N.C.O. hooch so I yelled, "What's up guy?"

He said, "Oh, there you are Sarge! I've been looking for you."

I said, "What can I do for ya?"

He said, "Come on into our hooch, I want to show you something."

I walked into their hooch and saw my whole team standing around with big smiles. In the middle of all of them was Kabbatt. He had a chair in front of where he stood and with a smile he held out his hand. I looked into it. I asked, "A pin!? What's this? What's this mean? I'm a big prick or what?" They all laughed.

Kabbatt said, "I speak for everyone here. With all the honor and prestige that goes with this, I want to welcome you to the old timers "21" Club. Have a seat on your throne, Sir!"

I said, "Oh man, get out-a-here! I'm not ready for this!"

Kabbatt said, "You don't want to be the first one to reject this award do you?" So I shook my head and gave up, then I sat down. He said, "With this sacred pin, I do welcome you to the "21" Club." He then grabbed my left ear lobe and stuck the pin through it. Then he took a gold earring from Brink's hand and put it in my lobe.

They all said, "Congratulations on your 21st kill."

I said, "Thanks, now who has the joints?! I need a mouthful!"

Everyone started to dig into their pockets, footlockers and everywhere else you could stash joints. In just seconds I had a lap full. Even though we were a tired and hadn't had much sleep we stayed up and partied talking about how scared we all were on our last mission out and about almost everything that you can think of. We laughed at how Kabbatt, while running from the V.C. on the mountain smashed his new gun, scopes and all, going on his butt so many times. He said he was going to get a week's pass to go back to Sniper school to get the equipment fixed or replaced. We all had a good time that night then we all crashed out.

In the morning I was on my way back from breakfast and just about to cross the road to go up Recon Hill, when I saw the Captain and 1st Sgt. standing on the other side of the road ready to cross. Peppy was gone by then and this guy was all right but he was no Sgt. Peppy. As we passed each other I saluted and said, "Good morning Sir."

He just passed me and said nothing. Then he stopped dead in the road. He turned around and said, "Soldier!" I stopped and asked what he wanted.

He said, "Get your butt back here! Now!" I walked up to him and stopped about two feet away. He said, "What the f*#*!? is that in your ear?!"

I replied, "I think it's an earring, Sir."

He said, "I must be seeing things."

I said, "Like what, sir!"

He said, "Like an earring in your ear!"

The First Sgt. said, "Excuse me, Sir, but it's an old custom of some Rangers to award a gold earring to anyone with 21 kills."

My Captain said, "Well, that's just what it is all right, an old custom. From now on the new custom is looking like a soldier! No more of that stuff!"

I replied, "I don't know what you're so upset about, the army done it to me, it made me this way." He got bright red in the face and his eyes bugged out. He was fit to be tied! With a crazed look on his mug he reached over on his side and un-clipped a Swiss Army knife.

He said, "If you can't do it yourself, I'll help you get that ring out of your ear!" As he came at me with the knife, I stepped back and pushed the button and loaded my M-16, one in the chamber, and nineteen behind it.

I said, "If you take one more step, Sir! In self-defense, I will blow your s*#! away, Sir!"

He looked like I just kicked him in the slats. Then he yelled, "Sergent! You heard that! He threatened my life! I want that, that, whatever he is in my office at noon today!"

My First Sergent replied, "Well sir, I also saw you threaten his life first!"

Then he looked at me with half a smile and said, "I think you screwed up this time guy!"

I said, "What's he gonna' do?...Send me into the boonies?" Then they both walked quickly away.

I went back to my hooch and wrote a letter to my chick. Then the Company clerk came down to get me. He said, "The C.O....or I mean Captain A-hole wants to see you...Now."

I said, "Yeah I know, what time is it?"

He replied, "1230."

I walked up Recon Hill, went in and saluted the Captain. As he sat behind his desk he said, "You have pushed me long enough. You are a disgrace to that uniform you wear and to the U.S. Army! You..."

I interrupted and said, "That's only your opinion, Sir!"

He went on, "Around here, my opinion is the only one that counts! From now on, I am going to make life as horrible as possible for you. First, I'm going to tear up your E-6 promotion and bust you to E-4 for insubordination. Second, I'm imposing a two hundred-dollar fine as well. And third, I...I...Do you have anything to say for yourself?"

I said, "Sir, I could probably think of something. But I'm sure you wouldn't dig it! As for the demotion, I never wanted the rank or the responsibility anyway! And the fine, I only make one hundred ten bucks a month anyway. To me, nothin' from nothin' leaves nothin' anyway, Sir."

He looked so ticked off I thought he would flip out! He screamed out, "Get the... Get out of my sight! Right now!...out of my sight or I'll have your butt locked up right now!"

I replied, "Yes Sir. You're the boss!" I saluted him and yelled "Airborne Rangers...All the way!" I did an about face.

As I walked out I heard him slam his fist on his desk. Quickly I turned just long enough to see him grimace in pain as he held his hand. "Get out!" he screamed. Quietly I busted out laughing as I left the room.

The next morning I was moved back into the main hooch with what use to be "my" team. Brink got my job as team leader, even I couldn't have made a better choice and I told him so. That day I had lost all my respect for the military completely, especially for all its puppet officers. From that day on it was F.T.A. all the way. All I kept in mind from then on was watch out for #1 and screw the other guy. Brink felt real bad about the whole thing, as did my whole team. Before we left on our mission that day, they all walked up to the C.O.'s office to protest his decision. He just told them to get out or they would get what I got. Little did they know then, but they already "got it!" just being with or standing up for me.

Brink asked me if I would be team leader out in the bush or at least help him do the job. I told him I was going to look out for #1. I told him that if I thought he was about to get me killed, I would tell him so. Other than that the team was his baby now.

A hate came over me that I could almost taste. I took the point position every mission just to make sure I got the first kill. For weeks we sat out in the rain and pulled one Recon mission after another. The only thing A-hole wanted to do was make life as unbearable as possible for me and everyone around me. I found out from my 1st Sergeant that the Captain quit Ranger school because he couldn't hack the punishment. That was why he hated Rangers so bad. It figured.

After two weeks of being marinated in the rain and mud, we got a call that we were to come in for stand down. So we were picked up and loaded on a chopper headed back to Uplift. As soon as we got back in A-hole sent word for me to report to his office. So I did.

After I got cleaned up I came in and saluted him. He said, "How did you like your sunny vacation in the boonies?"

196

I replied, "I love it! At least out there your enemy has the guts to hit you face to face."

He said, "I'm glad you like it, but I'm going to have to spoil your fun. I've been instructed by higher ups to release you for awhile to go to Sniper school. Just think though, after Sniper school I'll be able to let you go right back to all the fun you were having. Why, maybe I'll let you live out where you like it so much. You'll be in big demand. As a sniper you'll have to go with anyone that needs you. Line Companies, Ranger and Recon teams, you just name it. I think I can just about...No! I can assure you, you will have just about as much time in the bush as Charley. Maybe even more! Won't that be nice?"

I said, "What ever you say, Sir!"

He said, "I have a lot to say, but my rank prevents me from doing so!"

I replied, "Same here, sir! Your rank prevents me from doing a lot of things too, Sir!"

He asked, "Is that a threat?"

I replied, "No Sir!"

He handed me my orders for Sniper school and said, "Get out of here before I can figure out a way to take this away from you!"

I said, "And spoil all my future fun! Only an A-hole wouldn't do that, Sir."

He screamed out, "Get out of my face!"

I saluted him saying, "Airborne Sniper! All the way! Sir!" I then did an about face and I walked out.

After walking down to the hooch I told the team I was headed for Sniper school. Kabbatt said, "You'll love it. It's neat dude. Whether A-hole knows it or not, he really did you a big favor. Every thirty days it's mandatory that you get eight days off to go back to Sniper school to re-zero your weapon."

I yelled out, "A whole week of ghost time? No way!"

He replied, "You'll love the school and all the ghost time you get out of it."

I said, "Before I forget Kabbatt...You're on good terms with A-hole, aren't you?"

Kabbatt replied, "Yeeeah!...I guess so, as good as one can be I guess."

I asked, "Would you do me a favor and ask him if an old buddy of mine named Dave Becham from B Co. could be transferred up here to Recon? This guy and I go way back! I told him I would try to get him in Recon."

Kabbatt said, "No sweat. That's no biggy. The worst he can say is no. I'll take care of it, no problem!"

I said, "Just tell A-hole Bec is your long lost buddy or whatever, know what I mean?"

"No sweat, I'll make Bec sound gung - flippin'- ho...A-hole loves that stuff!"

I said, "Thanks boo-koo buddy. I really want to get Bec into Recon before the Line kills him!"

We all rapped for a while, then I got packed for my trip. I was to leave the next morning. I planned my first stop would be Quy Nhon A.F.B. to see my old Air Force buddy Ted and to finally get a good meal for a change, instead of eating Army dog chow.

Morning came quickly as usual. But that morning I felt very good! I was getting away from puke face Captain A-hole for four whole weeks! I said goodbye to the team and I headed down Recon Hill to the road below.

When I got to the bottom of Recon Hill I saw a jeep pull up to the main gate of Uplift with two M.P.'s in it. They also had a prisoner. It was that black dude that I saw down at the big white cat house in Ophu Cat a while back. The one M.P., an E-5, got out of the jeep and he started talking to the guy on road-guard duty just across the street from me. i could hear everything they said. The black deserter was sitting in the back of the jeep all chained and cuffed up with the second M.P. sitting next to him, guarding him.

The E-5 said to the guard at the gate to the main post area, "I want to stash this F$#%^* nigger deserter in that container over there for safe keeping for a half hour. My partner and I want to grab some chow before we head further on up the road. That black boy is heading for a military prison for a lot of years at very hard labor! Will you keep an eye on him for me?"

The guard said, "Deserter? Really?" He stretched out his neck to check the guy out.

The M.P. replied, "He's a f$#%^* runaway all right."

Just the sound of the word "runaway" sent chills up my spine. Sure, he was a deserter. Sure, he gave me a hard time back at the cat house and I had no love for him. But when that M.P. said "runaway" the guy just looked so pitiful sitting there all chained up and helpless that it broke my heart. All I could think of was that this was how it must have looked, way back in the eighteen hundreds.

The road guard said, "Sure, I'll be here for a while. I don't care if you stick him in that container. It's got a bolt on the outside so he ain't goin' no where once you put him in there! But don't forget that it is about a zillion degrees in there, and there is paint and thinner and stuff in there with the sun beating on it. Wow, fume city! But I could give a s#$% if you don't!"

The container they were talking about was a large, heavy gauge, solid steel, ten-foot square storage box. The E-5 kind of nodded his head at the other M.P. sitting next to the deserter. The M.P. pulled the guy out of the jeep and all three of them walked to the large steel storage box that was just inside the gate, near the road to the main post. The E-5 opened the large steel door and they shoved the dude in and closed the heavy door.

It must have been really hot inside with no air because the deserter went totally wild! He began to scream and carry on like he was being cooked alive! He kicked the door and cursed like a mad man. The M.P.'s both yelled at him that they were going to pull him right out and beat him bad if he didn't shut up. Be he went even crazier and it got even worse.

When the M.P.'s opened the door I could see that the black dude had kicked open many gallon cans of paint and burst them open by stomping on them and there were about twenty colors of paint flowing right out the door. What a scene! The M.P.'s grabbed him and all three slid to the floor on the paint and fell into it wallowing in it. The M.P.'s went nuts and began to beat the tar out of him with their clubs. But not before the guy had them rolling in resh paint. I just about died laughing right there! What a sight!

1 Shot, 1 Kill, 27 Cents

I crossed the road and walked over to the chopper pad to see if one of the two choppers that just came in were going my way. I asked the crew chief of one chopper where they were headed. He said, "We're going South to Phan Rang, but the other guys are headed to Ophu Cat just North of Quy Nhon."

So I walked over to the other chopper and I asked their crew chief for a lift. He said, "Jump aboard dude!" So I did.

The ride by chopper was a pleasant one because I knew I wasn't going to have to put up with any of Charley's bologna when I landed...at least for a while anyway. So I sat back to enjoy my ride. Soon we were descending on the A.F.B. at Quy Nhon. We landed and I hopped out. The crew chief told me that they made that stop just for me but it wasn't out of their way at all. I told him thanks as they lifted off once again.

I walked into the terminal building and down towards the area where Ted worked. I got to the area and I looked around. Soon I saw his orange-red hair. You could see it a mile away. His back was towards me as he helped unload some rockets from his truck. I set my stuff down and crawled up behind him. I slapped the side of his head and said, "Hey, fly boy, when was the last time you had your butt kicked?"

He and all his friends and co-workers jumped back and looked kind of surprised. Ted turned around and said, "You big...You scared the snot out of me. What the heck are you doing here?"

I replied, "I'm on my way to Sniper school."

He said, "Good deal! How long do you have to ghost?"

I said, "Today's Friday, which is officially party night! Plus I don't have to report to An Khe until Sunday afternoon before 1800 hours."

Ted replied, "Good! I get off in another four hours. So book over to the hooch and rest up for tonight's party! Your gonna need all the rest you can get between now and then....Yeeeeee-yaaaaaahhh!"

I asked, "What party?"

He said, "A party just like we always have when you come to town. It's always a party whenever you're around!"

I said, "Totally cool! I'll see you back at the hooch later."

He replied, "Good, I'll see you then."

I picked up my duffel bag and M-16 and I headed over to the chow hall first. As soon as I got in line at the chow hall I could see my buddy the cook was slicing a huge roast beef. When he spotted me he used hand signals to ask if I wanted a big piece. I just gave him a big smile. After I was stuffed full of very good roast beef I headed over to Ted's hooch, went up the stairs and down the hall to Ted's room. I put my stuff into the extra locker then lay down to rest until Ted got there.

It felt as though I just shut my eyes and Ted was poking, punching and yelling at me. "Get up you candy azz Ranger."

I jumped up and got my brain together as Ted lit a joint. I asked, "How was your R&R in Hawaii?"

As he passed me the joint he said, "Totally awesome! How have you been since I seen you last?"

I said, "Since I saw you last I've spent just about every single day getting shot at. Then I was given a Recon team of my own and they took it away. I was almost promoted to E-6, but got busted for insubordination down to E-4 and things have been goin' down hill ever since! Me? Oh, I've been havin' a regular blast!"

He replied, "No way! Not a good time I see!"

"Not a good time at all! F.T.A. all the way! Let's forget that and talk about what you did on R&R."

So as we got buzzed out he told me all about meeting his chick and all the fun times they had in Hawaii. All that weekend we partied out! Smoking, drinking, going to the club and swimming. The two days I spent there were very sunny and just beautiful! On Saturday Ted arranged a chopper ride to get me to An Khe on Sunday.

Soon Sunday came and we walked to the chopper pad area. He said, "I hate to see you go. We have a lot of fun together, but I do need the rest after you leave. You are hard to keep up with!"

I replied, "Yeah! I need a rest myself when I leave here. But in three weeks or so I'll be back so get rested up fly boy."

Ted replied, "Yeah I'll try real hard!"

"You do that!" I said.

I got on the chopper he pointed out to me and we said goodbye for a little while as the chopper started its motor. He shouted, "Goodbye! See ya soon!" Up I went towards Camp Radkey An Khe Sniper school here I come! I thought.

An Khe was about thirty or forty miles north of Quy Nhon. Camp Radkey was a Fire support base of the 4th Infantry Div., an army post that sat on top of a large mountain, overlooking the city of An Khe. This post was where the Sniper school was located.

We soon landed and I asked a G.I. which way to go to the Sniper school location. He said, "It's about a quarter of a mile over that way," pointing in a direction just ahead. He told me to just keep walking straight down the road I was on until I came to the rifle ranges. Then turn right and he said I couldn't miss the Sniper school area. He told me that it was well marked with a big sign out front. I thanked him and I walked on.

Soon I saw the ranges. There was an area in front of the ranges that looked like an outdoor pavilion. It had only a roof supported by twelve 4 by 4 beams. On the concrete slab on the floor I could see yellow lines painted on the cement. These lines divided each shooter's area. Down range I could see human silhouette targets like the ones back in training at Fort Dix, New Jersey and elsewhere. I also saw some targets that were way the heck out there, so far away I could hardly see them. I couldn't see how anyone could hit a target that far away. It looked impossible to me.

I walked back onto the road and turned right like the guy told me to. Soon could see a big white with black lettered sign supported by two 4x4 poles, eigh foot high. The sign read "4ᵗʰ Infantry Division." Under that was a picture of two crossed M-14 rifles and a 4ᵗʰ Inf. Div. Patch between them. Under that were the words "Sniper School." Like the guy said, it was well marked. I walked up to the door and went in.

Inside I could see a classroom with an easel and a large black board behind it. I saw a door up front marked Arms Room. So I opened it and looked inside. It looked like a weapons parts or Fix-it Shop, like a gun shop. Inside sat a white haired plump old E-7 at his bench working on a stock. He was sanding away with a piece of sandpaper on the stock. He spoke with what sounded to me to be a German accent.

"Can I help you?" he asked.

"Sergeant, I am here to report to Sniper school." He told me that his name was Joe Swanson and he was the mechanic in charge of the repairing and fitting of the weapons. He said if I went out the door I came in and walked outside to the front I could sign in and get my bunk and locker. So I said thanks and walked out.

I walked around to the front of the building and went in. There were two E-7s inside sitting around talking. One of them asked if I was there reporting in for school. I said, "Yes."

He said, "Good! We need all the crack shots we can get!"

After signing in and giving them my order papers they introduced themselves. The first one I spoke to told me he was our Range Instructor. His name was Sgt. Kelley and the other man was our classroom instructor named Sgt. Walters.

Kelley said, "About ten students are in the hooch now, so let's get you all set up." We walked outside and on into the hooch billet. Once inside Kelley introduced me to the men. He said there were twelve men in our class and they were expecting one more man.

After I put my stuff away I walked back to the Arms Room to talk to Sgt. Swanson about the XM-21. After I looked inside I asked if I could come in and look around. He said sure. After I got done looking around a few minutes I started asking him all kinds of questions about our new weapon. He said he didn't want to say much then because we were going to start classes the next day and he wanted to tell us all in depth about the XM-21 army match rifle at that time. He did say that it was the hottest thing the Army had to date. As he was looking at an XM-21 he had just put together he said, "This is the most accurate killing machine in the world…a beautiful piece of work."

I asked him how long the course would last. He said that the course itself was officially eighteen days long, but the last two classes had only lasted sixteen or seventeen days. He explained, "If everyone catches on well to what we teach you, we will usually give you guys the extra two days to get back to your units." So far I thought everything looked very relaxed and done with no big hurry which was just fine with me.

Joe said, "Everyone that comes here is an expert marksman. You have to have an expert marksman's rating to be accepted to the school to begin with. The army made sure that the men taking this course has an expert rating from basic training all the way here. All we do here is fine-tune the skill and accuracy you men already have. The army gives you the best equipment available to a sniper in the world. You men also have the best instructors anywhere. They have competed in Olympic match competition themselves and they have won many awards. If you think you are a good shot now, wait until you finish this course. You won't believe how good you will become! One shot, one kill, 27 cents." I asked what he meant by that. All he said was he would explain it all the first day of class.

We all felt at ease there and we were put under no pressure. These instructors were just like everyone else…just regular men. We got to go anywhere we wanted on post. So I walked over to the enlisted man's club and drank a couple beers. I felt a little tired so I went back to my hooch to sleep.

When I got over to my bunk there was a guy I had never seen before. I figured he was the guy that Sgt. Kelley said they were expecting. I sat down on the lower bunk just beneath him and untied my boots. Just as I sat down I nodded my head and asked him, "How's it going, guy?"

He said, "Good, I just got here a little while ago."

I said, "Yeah, I didn't see you around here earlier."

"What a bummer getting here up that mountain road," he replied.

I said, "Yeah?! I didn't come by road, I flew by chopper."

He said, "My name is Radkey."

I said, "No way! Just like the camp's name?"

He snickered, "Yeeeah, years ago when they built this fort my uncle was a commander in this area. So when they built the place, they named it after him."

I said, "You're kidding me."

He said, "No I'm not."

I said, "What's your uncle, a General or something?"

He said, "Yeah, something like that."

I said, "Must be nice to have that kind of rank in the family."

He said, "I've never asked him for a favor in my life! I never will!"

He said he had been in the army six years. And he just re-upped for six more. He said with all the re-enlistment bonus checks he was saving along with his pay he was going to buy a fishing boat to charter fishing tours back in Florida (where he was from) when he retired someday. He said he was going on his third tour in Vietnam. He was a combat soldier in a line company with the same unit I was with….the 173rd Abn. He was an E-6 and he looked to be in his late twenties. But he was so small and thin I really couldn't tell how old he was. His hair was fire engine red and he had freckles everywhere! He was covered!

He told me that he had been shot three times already. He showed me a big scar on his calf. Then he showed me the scar on his chest from an AK-47 bullet and one in his right shoulder. I said, "You must be crazy man. Why do you stay here and take so many chances?"

He said, "I love to kill V.C! The army keeps trying to get me to stay home, but I just keep extending and re-enlisting for combat duty." He was told if he gets hit again and lives they would not allow him back ever again. He said most of his near fatal mistakes were made going down into holes and caves after V.C….Remember what I said about caves and underground passage ways? That's why I only made one trip down into one of those death traps! I was real lucky to have gotten out of that one. He said that's how he got hit and almost killed twice!

He was a short skinny little dude, but I just had the feeling he was everything he said he was.

After we got done rappin' we both crashed out. In the morning we were all up at 0530. We ate chow and we were told by our instructors to be in the classroom by seven. So Rad and I headed towards our classroom. He and I talked about the different companies he had been with during his tours in Nam. And I probed him on different tricks he'd used on Charley that might help me one day. I thought what he knew would help keep me from getting shot, seeing how he was the expert on getting shot. He had many helpful things to tell me about.

We were seated inside our classroom with everyone else and the instructors came in. Sgt. Walters, our classroom instructor, said, "May I have your attention? I am Sgt. Walters. Some of you know me from yesterday when you all reported in." He explained about the three instructors, he and Kelley and Swanson and what their jobs were. He said, "All three of us, Kelley, Swanson and myself, are here to help you men get better at what you already do so well. For most of the classroom instruction I will be your teacher. Sgt. Swanson is the man that fits, repairs and builds all the weapons you will be issued here. Now, let me give the floor to Sgt. Swanson so he can tell you all about your new toys!"

Swanson got up and Walters sat down by Sgt. Kelley. Swanson said, "I will be your gunsmith for the 'Experimental Model 21' U.S. Army match rifle. That is what XM-21 means. This weapon is the newest thing in hand held, long range, light infantry weaponry and it is never to be taken apart, cleaned, or re-zeroed unless you're here doing it. These weapons were handmade one at a time in Belgium. While you're here I will fit each weapon to each one of you separately because no two men are exactly the same. They were sold to the army for a basic cost of two thousand dollars each. The day scope is valued at twelve hundred bucks and the PVS-2 Starlight night scopes are three thousand dollars each. So you can see why we try not to screw these weapons up in any way. It also costs the Army three thousand dollars per man to go through this course. So when you figure it out the Army just invested over nine thousand dollars or so for each man here taking this course. We believe when you get through here you men will be the most accurate and most deadly small arms force in the world. So deadly in fact, the N.V.A. have posted a 50,000 dollar reward for a sniper and or his XM-21. I hear the reward goes up everyday.

"The XM-21 rifle is made to fit each man exactly. Today your stocks will be fit to each of you, one at a time. The stocks are fiberglass bedded for a perfect stock to barrel fit. Every time it is taken apart it will fit perfectly together again in the same exact position the barrel was in before. The machining on the gas-fed semi-automatic bolt and breach assembly is absolutely perfect. They measure things with light instead of by thousandths of an inch."

He went on to say the inner barrel was stainless steel with a micro-grooved twist to it. This meant there were twice as many rifling twists in the barrel than in the standard M-14, to make the bullet spin twice as fast, putting a gyro effect on the bullet to help keep it on course better. He said, "You will learn by shooting and with the instructions of Sergeants Kelley and Walters just how accurate these beauties really are." He said we would get dead accuracy up to 1250 meters in the day and with the P.V.S.-2 night scope, 875 meters at night. The bullets were hand loaded and spun balanced match ammo. The bullet was a .30 cal. full metal jacket, semi-hard point, boat-tail bullet that would expand, or more like explode, up to .50 cal. He told us it would inflict awesome damage to the enemy.

He continued, "We aren't supposed to use this ammo according to the Geneva Convention. But as for right now, what they don't know will be more help to us, if you know what I mean! You will be told more about the Geneva Convention and their laws about snipers and our equipment during your time here. Snipers, according to the Convention, are just dirty pool. We happen to believe dirty pool or not, Snipers really work! So far the classes before you are now getting kills in record numbers." Swanson talked for about forty five minutes or so and told us things about rifles I had never heard before. Then Swanson said, "I've run my jaws enough for now, so I'll give the floor to your range instructor, Sgt. Kelley."

Kelley stood up and said, "I will be instructing you men at the range. I will teach you how to shoot the eye out of a mosquito at two hundred yards." Then he laughed saying, "Well, maybe not two hundred yards…more like one hundred fifty." We all chuckled. He said, "All jokes aside for now. I just want to tell you what you've heard so far about the XM-21 is very true. This weapon will really amaze you when you get to know how to use it. But first I have to explain ballistics…range and drop, breathing control, control of the weapon, trigger pull and lock time, windage, and how to control every shot. There are many things that add up to a dead shot or zero. We have a saying around here. It goes like this…One shot, one kill, 27 cents. That's just what we intend to teach you while you're here. With one shot you will kill one enemy soldier for the cost to the army of 27 cents. Snipers keep the cost effectiveness value to the army lower than any other unit or piece of armory in the army. More bang for the buck, so to speak. All you need is one well placed shot to complete your mission. These weapons are semi-automatic, not fully auto. Unlike other sniper weapons like a bolt action rifle for example, you don't have to even move a muscle to have another round instantly rechambered into your weapon, in case you have multiple targets and need to shoot quickly to hit more than one target within just a few seconds. This makes staying locked onto a target so much easier because you don't have to relocate your targets after each shot. But just because you have the capibility of shot after shot, take your time and make each shot count! Remember, 1 shot, 1 kill, 27 cents."

Kelley went on to say that there were two more goodies that went with the weapon. But they weren't quite finished making enough of them yet. They were a silencer and noise suppressor. He said we would get them when finished, as needed. He explained, "The silencer does just what the name says. The only noise when firing the weapon will be the sound of the semi-automatic breach bolt flying back to throw another round into the chamber. The noise suppressor is only used to distort the sound of the shots to keep the enemy guessing which way the shot came from. The flash suppressor is already built onto the end of the barrel. It will kill the flash of the muzzle when firing, so you will not be spotted by the enemy, giving your position away, especially at night."

Then Kelley told us that the day scope was invented by an ex-army Lieutenant.

He told the army about his discovery and the army didn't like his idea, so he quit. He sold the idea to a telescope manufacturing company which made him very rich. Now the army buys them for a cost of twelve hundred dollars each. He said, "Sometimes we all make mistakes, even the army."

Kelley continued, "The scope will show you how to hit exactly on target as it automatically zeroes itself on target by the use of a cam and visual picture. As you look down through the scope, the picture inside is basically the standard cross hairs. But on these crosshairs are four small lines, mounted up and down and side to side, so that as you look at a target, you will put the cross hairs centered on your target. Then each of the smaller lines on the sides and up and down on the cross hairs will line up shoulder to shoulder and head to belt line. The two small horizontal lines should be exactly touching each shoulder of the human silhouette target. The other two top and bottom or vertical lines should be placed one flat on top of the target's head and one right at the belt line. When all four lines are set, one touching each shoulder, one at the top of the head and one at the belt or waist line and the regular cross hairs are dead center, the bullet will hit dead center. By turning the cam ring on the scope the small lines will adjust in or out which will change where the bullet will hit at whatever range. If your target perfectly fits inside the picture in the scope at one hundred meters, moving your view or target out to three hundred meters your picture will be way too small to fit exactly into your hair-line picture. The only thing that will look dead center to you is the regular cross hairs. All the small lines from the head to waist line and side to side will be too far apart. All you have to do to make the shot hit perfect again is to turn the cam or move the cam ring on the scope to make your side and top hair line picture fit exactly perfect on the target once again. It's that easy."

Kelley went on to say, "The distance between an average man from the top of his head to his belt line is about twenty eight to thirty inches. A man's average chest span from shoulder to shoulder is around twenty inches. So when your hand adjusts the cam ring, the lines will move in and out to adjust themselves.

"I've told you how the picture adjusts itself. Now I'll tell you how it changes the trajectory or angle of the bullet. The cam has an oblong shape to it. As you turn the ring, the cam rides up or down on the spring-loaded base, which automatically makes the picture go out of center. To make the center look on target again you will instinctively raise or lower the barrel according to the lining up of the center cross hairs, which will range the shot. You will automatically re-line the target back up perfectly dead center once again. With a few basic pointers you cannot miss, if you don't jerk the trigger. There is an adjusting screw on your triggers that will adjust to find the most comfortable pull for each of you. You must learn not to jerk the trigger. That will send the bullet off target. These rifles have a clip-on bi-pod that can be quickly mounted on the front of the weapon at the gas tube, near the end of the barrel. This bi-pod is used so that while in the prone position when lying on uneven or even flat terrain, you can still lie down and keep the barrel flat and totally steady. The bi-pod will hold that position for you to keep you from swaying all over your target."

Most of that day, except for fifteen minute breaks every couple of hours, we trained. The instructors told us how to breathe, how to hold our XM-21 and how not to flinch or jerk the trigger. We were all measured for a perfect stock fit and we were taught from a classroom for all of the first week of school. On Saturday of the first week we all got our personalized custom-made XM-21 army match rifles. This weapon was custom fit and made for each one of us. That Monday morning we were to go to the range to start live fire.

Early Monday morning we all walked out to the range to zero our new weapons. After all we'd heard and learned about the XM-21 we were all dying to use it and see if it was as good as it was cracked up to be. When we got there Swanson was unloading some tri-pod, single eyepiece, high powered spotting telescopes. They were fairly large and had long tri-pods hooked to them to hold them steady. We all set our weapons into the weapons rack and got out allotment of ammo. When we were finished we were all called up to the shooting line under the roof of the pavilion I first saw the day I got there. There were six thick rubber mats on the floor between the yellow marked lines.

Kelley said, "As you have all been told before, you will be shooting in pairs, a.k.a. 'sniper team.' One of you will shoot and the other man will be the spotter. The spotter will use the spotter scopes Sgt. Swanson just got done setting up. The spotter will be able to just about see the bullet going down range to its target. These scopes are 100 power. As you spotters look down range it will look all wavy, like you've seen on a hot black-top road on a hot sunny day. What you see are only heat waves, it doesn't really mean that you smoked too much dope last night. One man will do the shooting, the other man will use the spotter scope.

"Spotters, when you hear the sound of the rifle going off, watch in the lower part of the scope. You will see a small shock wave caused by the bullet plowing its way through the heat waves as it moves down range. You will not see the bullet itself, only the shock wave about two feet behind the bullet. Using your eyes, follow the shock wave. Watch closely and you will see exactly where your Sniper hit the target. The wave will look like a small boat or fast moving bug on the top of a still lake. You will see it buzz down range to the target. If anyone needs help catching on, just sing out. I'll help you as we go.

"Shooters, you will fire three shots at the target per firing round. Then you will clear the weapon and you will get up, leaving the weapon in place. Don't worry where your shots hit, just keep aiming every shot dead center of the target. You will adjust to center as we go. You need to get a good shot group first. Then you can tell how to adjust and which way you need to adjust for a good 'zero' to dead center. Now, pair off and I'll get your first three rounds each."

Rad and I got together. I said, "I'll spot if you want to shoot first."

He said, "Okay." So he got his XM-21. I sat down and adjusted my spotter scope to a suitable height for me. Rad opened up the bi-pod on the front of the XM-21 and set it down. Then he got into a prone position.

Kelley said, "Spotters, I'm going to hand you six rounds, three for the first set and three for the second set. Load one magazine with three rounds." So we did. He went on, "Shooters, look at the first set of targets down range. We will group the weapons at fifty meters. Once you get your weapons grouped you will then zero them dead center at fifty meters. For now all you'll have to do is hit the targets. Turn your cam ring to its lowest setting. This will automatically put you in range for a fifty-meter shot. Shooters…Spotters!…Are you ready?" We all said yes.

Kelley went on, "Shooters, lock and load one three round clip of ammo into your weapons. Spotters, watch the fifty-meter target. Shooters, take your time, and aim carefully! Remember to squeeze! Ready on the firing line left! Ready on the firing line right! Commence fire at will."

Boom! Rad's shot rang out with the rest. It was just like Kelley said. I could see a little V-shaped object cutting into the heat waves as it flew down range. Just like a water bug you might see moving across the top of a very smooth pond. Then…splat! I could see the bullet's puff of smoke as it hit about two o'clock high. I told Rad just exactly where it hit. He said, "Get ready!"

I said, "Fire when ready." Boom! Another shot went out. Splat! "Darn near hit the same spot. Go ahead, I'm still watching." Boom! The third round moved down range.

I said, "Hot! Diggity, same spot again. Good group!" He laid the butt of the stock down and he removed the empty ammo clip. Then he looked into the gun breach to make sure it was empty and got up.

After the shooters got done we were told not to make any adjustments. Kelley just told us we were only getting the feel of the weapon right now. Adjustments would be made later after we all got a shot recording card. He said we would be told about the cards later. He said, "Shooters, put your weapons back into the rack and spotters, secure yours. Then trade places." All morning we just kept doing this switching back and forth to get the feel of the weapon going off and to practice pulling the trigger.

After noon chow we went back out to the ranges to zero the weapons. Each spotter got a card with pictures of human silhouettes on them. They looked like the targets down range. Kelley said, "Now Spotters, when your man shoots put a dot right on the picture exactly where your shooter hits the target. Shooters, do the same as before. Shoot a three round shot group once again. Hold your cross hairs dead center each shot. After we see on paper where you put your three shots, we can move the shot group dead center with our left or right adjusting screws." In a short time we all got to zero our weapons and we were hitting the target dead center every shot. After that we moved out to one hundred hundred meters, then two hundred and beyond.

The XM-21 was incredible! All you had to do was just turn your scope cam ring until your target's picture was dead center in the cross hairs and not jerk. You couldn't miss. At three hundred meters we were putting two out of three bullets into a hole about the size of a dime. The weapon was so easy to shoot that it built our confidence up, thinking no target was too far away. And we were not far from being right. Most of every day of the second week was spent at the ranges. We just shot and shot day after day, until we could hit darn near any spot that our spotter picked out.

On Friday of our second week our instructor Sgt. Kelley told us that we were going to spend the next two days discussing the PVS-2 starlight scope and get into night shooting. So all day Saturday and Sunday was spent on classroom instruction on our night scope. Sgt. Walters was our classroom instructor on the PVS-2. He told us the scope was just as much a high performance piece of equipment as was our XM-21 and day scope and that they cost the army three thousand dollars each. He said inside the scope was a special piece of equipment that took the light from any light source, like the moon and stars, and magnified the light ten thousand times. He said it could be burned right out and be made worthless unless used correctly. He told us to never use it in daylight. Even with the special filters for the front, it just wasn't worth taking the chance. He told us the scope didn't need any light at all really and could still do it's job fairly well. Sgt. Walters said, "Inside the scope is a liquid like what is found in a living eye. This liquid is called visual purple. Visual purple is what enables people or animals to slowly adjust to a dark room or area. If you sit in a dark area long enough, you will eventually be able to see fairly well. But if someone turns on a light your eyes or sight will go totally black until your eyes adjust again to the darkness as your eyes re-supply their visual purple. If you burn out the visual purple type liquid in the PVS-2 or PVS-2A, it is gone for good. The scope will become useless. So to ensure the safety of that liquid in your scopes from even strong moonlight like a full moon, I advise you to use the filters we provide you.

"The P.V.S is a three thousand dollar scope but totally worthless when burnt out. The P.V.S. scope will not automatically zero itself on target as your day scopes do. You must learn how to use it. When looking inside the Starlight scope, you will first see that it looks green in color, like if you were looking through green sunglasses. Second, you will notice that there are crosshair lines inside the PVS-2, but they are larger. They go from top to bottom and from side to side, crossing dead center of the scope lenses as a day scope does. Third, on these cross hair lines you will see very small slash marks all the way across horizontally as well as vertically. From the dead center point to the first mark up, down, left, or right, each mark stands for ten meters. With this scope you will have to rely on your own judgement as far as windage and distance. But I will teach you how to even lead a moving target and hit it using the small slash marks in the P.V.S.

"Men, this is a frightful piece of equipment to the enemy. Just imagine if you will. You're walking across a rice patty dike at night in the total dark. Maybe just enough light to see your way, feeling fairly safe because your enemy can't see you in the dark. Then suddenly out of nowhere…Bam!..You just traded in your weapon for a harp and a set of wings! Think about that!"

Kelley continued, "We will zero the P.V.S. scopes at fifty meters just the way we did with your day scopes. Once you have them set for one hundred meter zero all you will have to do is guess-ta-mate the range of a target, say at two hundred meters. Count ten marks up and that will give you another one hundred meters in extra range. It will then be dead center for two hundred yards counting ten slash marks up from the center dot. Twenty marks is three hundred and so on. For less than one hundred meters, just hold the target on the two lower marks is all. Don't worry about putting your shot into a dime size circle. The bullet you use will do a job on the enemy no matter where you nail them."

To help us all get our ranges right, we used a small pocket-size range finder. You looked at your target and it would tell you fairly close what the distance was.

The rest was up to the shooter. The slash marks going left or right were for a moving or walking target. These marks would tell you the right distance to lead a moving target, left or right.

Our instructor said we would have the next day off from our shooting duties, while Sgt. Swanson fitted us for our Starlight scopes to be mounted on our weapons. But then, after dark that next night we were going back on the range for our first night of starlight practice.

During the day we went down range to check our targets for wear and tear. All Monday morning we worked out on the range repairing or changing the battered up targets. The targets were 3/8" steel targets and some were almost torn apart. I couldn't even comprehend what they would do to a soft human target. We were told to be in class by dusk for our night shoot.

For the next three nights, we practiced using the PVS-2 at night. The fourth night we were tested. We all passed the night shoot course and Saturday was our final daytime shoot test. We had to get one hundred seventy-five kill shots out of two hundred total shots at all different ranges out to one thousand meters. Shooting that perfectly, shot after shot, when they changed the range of the shot each and every shot was no easy task. But we all made the grade, no one failed.

Sunday morning we all got our Sniper Certification paper and sniper number. Our last meeting Sunday night, after we got our certificates Sgt. Kelley said, "During this course we watched you men get better and better. You men, as far as we can see, are probably some of the best-trained and equipped shooters of this type in the world. But anyone can shoot and hit a target. Not many men can watch a perfectly healthy human being from a distance and take his life for no other reason other than the fact that he is the enemy. Can you? Will you? That is the most important question that each one of you has to answer and face individually.

"You men are very special. Out of the thousands of men in Vietnam there are only twenty eight of you now in the whole world that have been certified as U.S. Army trained Snipers to this day. But as good as you are, and with all the training and equipment that you have, it is worthless and for naught unless you can answer 'yes' to the question I just asked you. Can you, will you, take that all-important shot when the time comes?" (These questions bothered me then but I did not realize just how relevant they would be to my service.)

"You men can be very proud of who you are, you're the best of the best. It's been a pleasure working with each one of you these past seventeen days. I'll be looking forward to seeing each of you every thirty days until you leave country. Every month you will be tested just as hard as you have been. If you fail, ever, we will take your XM-21 and you will no longer work the M.O.S. of Tango-2, a United States Army trained Sniper. May God be with you all. And remember, never let one of those XM-21's fall into Charley's hands. That is why you must never be without an incendiary bomb. You need to melt the rifle and scopes together completely, before you're overrun or captured, so the enemy can never copy them. You know what damage he could cause with them. I'll see you soon. Oh, keep a count of your kills for our records if you would! We want to know how you make out with these weapons. See you soon." He then walked out.

Swanson and Walters stuck around a while and they talked with us about all kinds of different things that weren't talked about in class. More detailed stuff about our weapons and extra tips on shooting and all kinds of things. Then we all said goodbye to each. We went back to the hooch and got our things packed to leave.

When I left there I had a duffel bag and two rifles and a fairly large two-scope case. The XM-21 was in a gun case and my M-16 was slung on my one shoulder, the duffel bag slung over the other shoulder, and I carried the large scope case in my hand. I must have looked like I was ready for anything. On my travel orders the instructors put the next day's date down as our last day of class. Now I could have extra time to get back to Uplift with no big rush. They allowed us extra days for travel. That made my reporting date back to Uplift Wednesday. That was really cool of them, giving us lots of party time so we would be able to take a slow relaxed trip back.

Rad and I headed out of the hooch when we were ready to leave and we walked on down "Range Road" towards the Air Field to see if I could catch a flight back. I was stationed at L.Z. Uplift with the 173rd Airborne and he was stationed about forty miles South with the 173rd Airborne at Fire base Orange, where all the Rangers went during the big move. We walked slow and rapped as we went. We knew like always that one never knows if we will ever meet again. Times like that to me were a total bummer! Neither one of us knew if we would be killed, or if we may by-pass each other during our re-zero times or whatever. To me saying goodbye always sucked.

Rad said, "I can't wait until I see how this weapon works."

I replied, "Yeah, me too." I stopped to look back towards the school just kind of thinking to myself a minute. As we stood there we talked about how much we liked our new XM-21 rifles and how cool the course was.

I was looking towards the middle of the post and I could see a mountain setting almost dead center of the army camp. I said to Rad, "That's weird that they would build an army camp around a big hill like that."

Rad said, "At one time in the early days that mountain was chock full of V.C. that had tunneled under from the outside into it without anyone even knowing about it. The men here could never figure out how V.C. were getting inside the fort and blowing up things every night, until they caught Charley sneaking in and out of that mountain one day. A lot of men got killed before they caught on to those little jokers! I know that happened for sure because my uncle told me all about it."

"No way?" I asked.

"Yeah way!" Rad replied.

We were soon at the post L.Z. and we parted ways. He kept on going down the road to the Mang Yang Pass road. He told me he wanted to travel by road so he could party with a girl he knew down the road a piece. He said, "See you next month." Then he walked away.

Author (far left) and three other Snipers
at 4th Infantry Sniper School
May, 1970

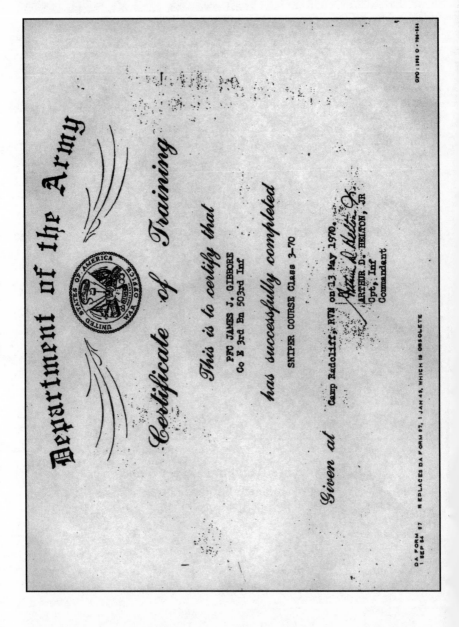

Department of the Army

Certificate of Training

This is to certify that

PFC JAMES J. GIBBORE
Co E 3rd Bn 503rd Inf

has successfully completed

SNIPER COURSE Class 3-70

Given at   Camp Radcliff, RVN on 13 May 1970.

ARTHUR D. HELTON, JR
Cpt, Inf
Commandant

DA FORM 87   REPLACES DA FORM 87, 1 JAN 45, WHICH IS OBSOLETE
1 SEP 64

GPO : 1965 O · 781-844

212

James Gibbore, Sniper

CHAPTER 33
Party Time

I walked around looking for a chopper that was headed south and I finally found one. I got in and soon we took off for towards Quy Nhon A.F.B. As I flew I got a tired and lonely feeling, I just wanted to go home. Even with my new killing machine and being one of only twenty eight snipers and all, I was just tired of the same old thing and I didn't feel very special at all. I was into my eighth month in Nam and knew I would have to make up my mind soon about whether to go home in the next four months or pull the whole last year of my active duty in Fort Bragg, N.C. Extending for six more months there in Nam would get me out of the army early. But, I thought, would my luck run out?

Then I got a picture of the ugliest, doofiest, most loathsome jerk in the world in my mind's eye. A dude I wanted to see dead more then any V.C. I ever had the misfortune to run into. I thought of ten more months with Captain A-hole! What was worse? Ten months with him, or a whole extra year in the U.S. Army! One way or the other I was screwed with no palatable option to choose from. No matter how I looked at it I was stuck in Stink Vill!

As we flew I could feel that I needed some change of scenery. Just what I didn't know. But I really felt like doing something different. I rapped with the crew chief of the chopper about how he liked his job and all. He said, "It's not bad, I get to move all over Vietnam from place to place, wherever I'm needed. I get to see boo-koo things, good and bad." I asked if there was any better place to party for a couple of days than Quy Nhon. He said, "You just left the best place to party besides Quy Nhon or Ophu Cat, around this area. Sin City, or An Khe is just about the best. You should have stayed there if you wanted to party."

I said, "Yeeeah? I'll be back there once every thirty days to re-zero my weapon, so I'll see that place soon enough."

He said, "Ophu Cat A.F.B. is a good place to party. The town is fairly good sized. There are a lot of gook bars downtown to party at. Strippers, lots of good dope and the chicks ain't too bad at all."

I said, "Yeah?…maybe I'll get there someday."

He said, "Do you want to check it out now?"

I asked, "You mean go there today?"

He said, "Yeah…That's where me and the pilots are stationed."

I said, "I'm with you all the way!"

He said, "Good, I live there and I know the Vill well, so I'll show you around own tonight. I'm Dave Jameson, what's your name?" I told him and we became nstant friends. In the Nam that's about how fast you made friends…and also made enemies just that fast too.

Soon we were on the ground at Ophu Cat Air base. Dave unloaded two large uffel bags of letters for the army post. I waited for him to help secure his aircraft nd then we headed towards the gate that led deeper into the airfield. Within the irfield I could see very large airplanes unlike any I had seen at Quy Nhon. They were mostly medi-evac aircraft for taking wounded G.I.s to Cam Rhon Bay hospital and elsewhere, so I was told by Dave. He said, "You can catch a plane to about anywhere in Vietnam from here."

We approached the air field exit gate and crossed the road onto the other side. There were stores and shops of all types. You could have your portrait sketched by a Vietnamese artist or buy T-shirts with just about any saying you wanted on it and souvenirs of all types. There were G.I.s and Vietnamese dashing everywhere. The whole place was almost like a carnival.

Dave said, "How about we head over to my hooch, so we can put your stuff away and get our stuff together."

I replied, "Excellent idea…Lugging all this stuff is killin' me."

We headed down the road towards the Army hooches through a gate. We walked right through the gates and up the street. Just past the gate to our right was a two-story building. It was made of sheet tin and wood and sort of looked like a two-story apartment building. Dave pointed up ahead, "There's my hooch. I live up on the second floor. Most of us are connected with aviation or in a medical unit. The hospital here on the base is the last step before the Cam Rhon Bay hospital for the wounded. G.I.s. that are sent home after they get hit go from the hospital here to Cam Rhon bay hospital. Then it's home to the world for those guys. You should see some of those poor suckers; I've helped load some of them into the medi-evac air planes to be shipped home. Man, you would get sick looking at them all messed up and all. Shot, burnt up, blown up. Man, you name it!"

I replied, "You should see those poor suckers before they get all bandaged up and washed off. Torn to pieces, limbs hanging by a thread, guts torn open and hanging out, limbs blown and shot off. Try carrying a buddy on your back that's been shot up and blown to pieces. Or a man like I carried once with his head smashed almost flat as his blood ran down the crack-a-my butt as I carried him about a mile down a mountain. Talk about making you sick. Friends that have their faces half blown off trying to scream, but have no face or throat left to scream with. Or the guy with his whole stomach blown open running around half crazy with fear and pain, stringing his guts all over the thick brush. Then watch him face to face, up close as he goes into shock and dies in your arms! That's sickening."

Dave shouted, "Stop! Jesus! Man, you're making my knees shake."

I said, "Sorry, I just can't help getting carried away sometimes. I have about had it with this place up to my ears! I swear, I'll go nuts before I leave here! I hate this place so bad I can hardly stand it anymore!"

Dave said, "Yeah! I know what you mean! I've been here about seven months now and I've about had it myself. And with the job you have, Man, it really must be a bummer!"

I replied, "Thank God you don't know the half of it!"

Dave said, "Yeah!"

After we got to the top of the stairs to the second floor I could see that pig must have been living there. The hallway was a mess, with all kinds of trash and junk everywhere. The place looked and sounded like a bunker back at Uplift, only more lit up. There was hard rock music coming from every room. Each room housed three to five men. About the sixth room down was Dave's. As we walked inside his room I saw black light posters on every square inch of every wall. It looked as though he wallpapered the entire room with them. The place must have been a real trip with the many black lights hung around the room turned on after dropping a hit or two of LSD, I thought. There were all kinds of beads and many dope related things and pot paraphernalia all over the room. The guy could have opened up a head shop and made himself a bunch of money just selling the extra stuff he didn't use that was scattered around the room everywhere.

I asked, "Who the heck lives here? A bunch of hippies or what?"

He said, "No! Me, this is my hooch, dude."

I replied, "Holy molly! If I didn't know better, I'd swear I was in an apartment in Hippie City."

Pot and opium smoke filled the air. All I had to do to get a buzz on was breathe deeply and get high for free. The music was so loud coming from every room you could hardly stand it. Songs by Iron Butterfly, Jimi Hendrix, the Rolling Stones, you name it! There was no doubt that this was some party hooch of a different kind. That place was the only place I ever ran into where so-called "normal" people did dope and the weirdos stayed sober. I looked around the room and tried to spot an open area of the room to set my things down. But I couldn't find a place so I just held onto my stuff for right then.

I looked at Dave and I said, "Man, this place is a nut house! The music and yelling and screaming. How the heck can you stand that all the time?"

Dave replied, "Here we have a saying. It goes….F.T.A."

I replied, "I thought I thought that one up!"

Dave said, "Well who knows maybe you did, but we try to show it every chance we get and in every way we can!"

I said, "You dudes are showin' um all right! I can relate to that and I go along with you 100%. With all the pipes and dope laying around, how about we light up a bowl of the good stuff?"

Dave smiled and asked, "How about some of this?"

He tossed me a bar of Cambodian Red hash. It was about the size of a Hershey bar…but about one inch thick. I said, "That will get us started!"

Dave replied, "And you call me a hippie pot freak."

I said, "I don't care what you are, as long as you're not queer. And if you are, just don't come after me."

He said, "Well, I ain't queer, so let's party dude!"

I said, "How about letting me check my weapons into an Arms Room or some place safe before I get too stoned out to give a squat."

He said, "Come on! I got just the ticket!"

We walked out of what he called his pad and down some stairs on the inside of the hooch. We went down into the basement area of the building. The fairly large room that we entered had a floor to roof heavy wire link fence from one side of the room to the other. Dave buzzed a buzzer mounted on the caged door. Soon a Sp-4 came out of a second caged door just behind the first one. He said, "Jameson! What's up?"

Dave said, "My Sniper buddy here wants to check his weapons in for a day or so."

The guy said, "Come on in." We followed the guy in through the two caged doors to a large locked up steel cabinet. Inside there were many M-16s stacked side by side. The guy gave me a card with my XM-21 and my M-16's serial number written on it. We both signed it. He kept one copy and I got one. Dave and I said, "Thanks!" Then we booked back up to his room for a buzz.

As we sucked on a big fat bowl of red hash Dave pulled out a quart of Jack Daniel's whiskey and we began to pound that. After I took a big gulp of Jack I blew out an enormous lung full of hash smoke and I said, "Man, what a combination of tastes. Ummmmm that's tasty!"

Dave replied, "Yes sir! I would say that's one of my favorite combos. I love that Jack! That's some real good stuff alright." Dave took the pipe and filled the bowl again with the red hash and he handed it back to me. Soon we were all messed up from the half-quart of Jack we just drank and half ounce of hash we just blew away.

Dave asked, "Do you get into toothpaste?"

I said, "What the heck you talking about, toothpaste? Yeah, every time I brush my fangs. Why? What do ya do, smoke that too? How do ya get high on that?"

He reached under his bunk and he took out a locked metal box. Then he opened it and said, "Not the toothpaste you brush your choppers with, you idiot! This…Morphine!"

He handed me a very small tube that looked like a tube of super glue, with a needle already mounted on the top. I said, "Oh that, I pumped the stuff into dudes that got hit before, yeah! I've seen this stuff before out in the bush. Medics carry this dope all the time. But you gotta' stick yourself with a needle! I don't do that."

He said, "This stuff is a number Moat!"

I said, "I don't think I'll try any of that."

Dave asked, "Do you mind if I do some up?"

I said, "No, knock yourself out! Do all you want." By that time for me, the whole room was spinning around like a chopper blade. Man, I couldn't understand how this idiot could even handle a bigger buzz than what we had.

I knew I was about to pass out so to help me stay on my feet I asked him if he had any speed. He said, "Yeah!" He opened his box again and pulled out a small bottle of crank. He snapped open the bottle and I poured the whole thing in my mouth and chased it with Jack.

As I sat there waiting for the crank to kick in, I watched Dave pull up his sleeve and stick the needle of morphine into his upper arm. Instantly he looked so messed up I had to ask him if he was all right. He didn't look it. He slowly fell over on his side with a goofy smile and he just nodded his head and winked his eye. I was starting to get off on the speed and I was coming back to life in a big way. I grabbed the bottle of Jack and drank as I started to walk around the room like an expecting father. Dave mumbled out, "Do you want to head down to the Vill and party? Catch a buzz…like that…" I was wired out big time.

I replied, "Ready to rock dude! We ain't out a here yet? Get up dude, let's swoop!"

So I got Dave up and he staggered towards the door. I opened the door and walked out into the hallway. As I took my two first steps I heard a thud on the floor behind me. I turned around and saw Dave flat on his face on the floor. So I said, "Get up. Man, why don't you just go do another hit of that RipVan Winkle in a tube? Looks like good stuff." He just groaned and got up on his knees and elbows. I helped him up and we tripped on down the hall toward the stairs.

Once we hit the road and fresh air Dave started to get his brain back together enough to walk on his own. He asked, "Do you want to check out the 21 Club down the street?"

I replied, "Sure! I've never been there before." So he led the way across the street and into the 21 Club. Inside there was an oriental band playing and they dressed in clothes that looked like the psychedelic posters in Dave's room. There were G.I.s and girls everywhere.

I looked at Dave and said, "What the heck is this? The whole country taking LSD except for me or what?"

He said, "If you think this is crazy, you should party down at An Khe! That place is really ripped out!"

I just shook my head and said, "The American hippie has finally rubbed off on the Vietnamese people! This is the last place I ever thought I would see hippies."

Dave said, "Man, loosen up. That's how things are, get used to it. You'll dig it if you just give it a chance."

I said, "Next thing I know, the army will be passing out psychedelic cammy's for me to wear and I'll be weaving flowers onto my XM-21."

Dave laughed and said, "I rather doubt that."

I said, "I really wouldn't doubt anything any more."

He said, "Shut up and watch the show. Man, you're bringin' me down dude!" So I sat back, choking down the show and making the best of it.

Soon I had enough and I suggested we go some place else. We wandered around the streets for about three hours going from one joint to another. Then we headed back to Dave's hooch, because I couldn't take anymore of that psychedelic bologna any longer, especially the hippie looking Vietnamese. They looked so funny I couldn't believe it!

Back at Dave's hooch we partied all night until morning. Dave told me that he had to go to work but if I wanted to stay in the hooch to just do so. I asked, "Are you guys going anywhere near Quy Nhon today?"

He said, "Yep, right next to it." So I asked for a lift back that way.

He said, "No sweat." So I caught a ride with him all the way back to the army post where I went to Pathfinder school. I wanted to see if I could find Ted and party with him that night.

After I got my weapons checked out we both left for the air field. We got his chopper all loaded up with out-going mail bags and the rest of the cargo, then we took off. Soon down below I could see a small compound that was all fenced in. I could see some people down below dressed up like nuns. Dave said, "That's a leper colony. Those poor suckers down there are really something to see. The nuns are from the U.S. and Vietnam. They live there with the sick and take care of them."

I said, "I would not go near that place with a hundred foot cattle prod! No way! That's got to be a real bad way to go!"

Dave said, "You ain't said nothin'. Rotting alive just has to smart!"

In just a short time we flew over the village of Quy Nhon and on to the small fire base next to the A.F.B. We touched down and I jumped out.

Dave said, "Look me up when you get to Ophu Cat again, buddy."

I said, "For sure! Thanks for everything!" I never saw Dave again.

After I got into the A.F.B. I walked across the ball field just behind Ted's hooch. I could see a big guy coming my way. As we got closer to each other I could see who it was. I said to myself, Oh great! It's that big dope Smitty, the dude I knocked out a while back, walking right at me.

Smitty said, "I just want to talk. I don't want no trouble." When we got about twenty feet apart from each other he looked at me real hard. Then he said, "Hey Ranger! I only want to talk."

I said, "Talk then." He kept coming closer to me. I said, "If you want to say something, stop and say it over there." I walked away from him.

He said, "I got no hard feelings."

I replied, "Just a hard head. So what do you want then, another dance?"

We were about ten feet apart as we walked parallel to each other. He said, "I just wanted to tell you I know I had it coming that night in the club. I was drinking pretty heavy that night and I get mouthy when I'm drunk."

I said, "We all do that when we drink, juice does that to ya." I ran up the stairs when I reached to Ted's hooch and I turned to look down at Smitty. I figured if he came up to get me I would be able to kick his head off his neck. I liked to be higher up than my enemy, easier to swoop down on him than up.

He looked up and said, "You don't have to be worried about me coming back after you or nothing. The last punch I got from you was like getting kicked by a horse."

I said, "I just don't like to be screwed with. I never did and never will!"

He said, "I should have known you were a bad mother! I've learned my lesson. But even with all that, I would still like to go three rounds in a ring with you sometime. You know, just to see how bad you really are!" I laughed, I just knew dummies like that never learn their lessons.

I replied, "Rings and gloves are for big dumb hard-headed idiots that never learn their lesson."

I turned and walked inside Ted's hooch and down the hall and into Ted's room. I looked out the window and saw Smitty walking away towards the airfield. For me that's how it always was my whole life. I guess I just had the look or a face people wanted to punch. Everyone I ever met either liked me right off the bat or wanted to punch me in the face right off the bat. Back in school that is how I made most of my friends, after I got in a fight with them. I guess it's like they say…If you can't beat 'um…know what I mean?

I put my stuff in the extra locker and I lay down to rest until Ted came back from work. I was bushed but still speeding my brains out from the night before. I didn't think I could sleep but I went out cold in just a couple of minutes. Then started to feel my hand getting numb so I turned over on my back. I opened my eyes slightly and I could see Ted putting his laundry away.

I sat up and rubbed my eyes, stretched and yawned. He looked over at me and said, "Is that all that Rangers do is sleep?"

I said, "With all the partyin' we have to do, we need to rest sometime!"

He laughed and asked, "So how you been?"

I replied, "Good, I guess."

He asked me about Sniper school as he lit up a joint. I told him all about the course as we got high. He asked, "How long do you have?"

I said, "Tomorrow I have to head back."

He asked, "You staying here tonight?" I told him that I planned on it. So he said there was a card game going on that night. He said, "There's gonna' be a good bunch of guys here tonight that don't mind me taking their money every week."

I said, "Sounds good to me. I could always use some extra spending money."

He said, "I hope you're prepared to lose what little you have."

I said, "Don't worry about me, sucker. After you lose what you have, my little pile won't look so little any more."

He said, "We'll see whose pile looks the smallest when the smoke clears."

I replied, "No sweat, fly boy. The only smoke I see around here is the smoke coming out your ears."

It was chow time and we were both starved so we went to the mess hall to eat. After we stuffed our faces we headed back to Ted's hooch and into his room. Soon a couple of guys showed up for the game that night. We all sat around for a while smoking joints and talking as we waited for the others to show up. About seven o'clock everyone was there that was going to play poker. There were seven of us that gathered together at a guy's room at the end of the hall. For some reason that room was a bit larger then the rest.

After we all got seated at a table Ted asked, "What will it be tonight, gents? Five Card no peek, Jacks or Better? What? You name it." We all decided on five card poker, Jacks or better progressive. Ted dealt the first hand cards.

In less than three hours everyone was flat broke except Ted and I. Ted was so hyped up he couldn't stop smiling and looked like he was having a real good time. The rest of the guys got all upset and left. The guy that had the room we were playing in came down to Ted's room to party with us. Ted's friend named Walter asked me all about my patches and wanted to know all about being a Sniper.

I said, "As yet I haven't been on any Sniper missions. But I do have just the toy for the job."

I walked over to the spare locker and got out the leather case and I took out my XM-21 and handed it to Ted. His eyes bugged out as he said, "Holy cow…Will you look at this mother."

I asked, "Nice hmm?"

He said, "Nice ain't the word!" He looked through the day scope after I mounted it on the weapon. I told them both all about the weapon and how accurate it was. They were amazed by how it looked but never knew about how amazing it really was. I put the 21 away and showed them my P.V.S. 2 night scope. They both wanted to look through it but there was just too much light outside with all the building lights and street lights so I said no. I just couldn't take the chance of burning it out. They both understood so I put it away.

We partied for a while then we all crashed for the night. I got up early so I could get a shower and some chow before heading back. Ted and I walked to the motor pool to get his truck. I told Ted that I was going back by road that time so I could grab some dope at a Vill before I got back to Uplift. Once we got into his truck he gave me a ride to the main gate. When he stopped I said, "Well, see you next month buddy."

He said, "You have to boogy back this way every month?"

I replied, "Yep! Once a month I have to go back to Sniper school to re-zero."

He said, "Man, that's cool! Every month you get some ghost time and a chance to get out of the boonies a while."

I said, "I hear they give us seven or eight days to go and come back. With your flight connections, I'll be able to get a flight fairly easily so I can spend more time partying out down here."

He said, "A chopper ride is no sweat for me to set up anytime, no sweat."

I said, "Well, thanks again dude, and I'll see you in about four weeks or so." We shook hands and I jumped out.

I walked out the gate and down the street. I crossed Highway #1 and ran into the big house. I sat down and ordered the carton of joints I needed and I was only there for about five minutes when I saw Becham walk in.

I jumped up and said, "You sucker! I don't believe this one!" He ran over and he shook my hand.

He said, "I don't believe it either! Meeting in these off the wall places."

I said, "Man, sit down! We've got a lot of catching up to do."

He said, "No kiddin'! Where do I begin?"

I said, "First, what the heck are you doing with that duffel bag? You goin' A.W.O.L. or what?"

He laughed and said, "No way! I don't know how you did it! But you did it!"

I asked, "I did what?"

He said, "You got me into Recon."

I said, "No way! A-hole let you in?"

He said, "Not only that, but he just got me a slot in Sniper school because of my past marksmanship record."

I said, "I think I'm dreaming!"

He said, "I still don't believe it myself!"

I said, "Tell me how it happened."

He said, "Your big muscle bound Hawaiian buddy there, Kabbatt. He came down to the L.Z. the day I came in, just after I ran into you out in the boonies."

I replied, "Yeah! Then what?"

Bec went on, "Well, two weeks after I saw you we came back into Uplift. Your buddy Kabbatt walked up to me and that monster stands there looking at my name tag. He says to me, 'Are you Jim's buddy Dave?' I thought you got zapped or something. I thought, Oh no! Know what I mean?"

I said, "Yeah yeah, go on."

Bec said, "Kabbatt told me to report to Recon orderly room at the top of the hill and to talk to the Captain if I was still nuts enough and wanted to get into Recon. He told me not to mention your name to the Captain, but you were the one to thank for getting things set up. So I told Kabbatt thanks for getting me in. Kabbatt told me, don't thank me, thank Jim when you see him! I was so happy I could have fainted! Just to think I had a way out of that no mind suicide company I was stuck with. In all the months I've been in country I only seen Uplift three times."

I said, "No way, man. Those Line Companies are suicide for sure!"

He said, "Sleeping in the mud, getting bit by everything with a mouth or stinger. Man, it's total hell being doomed to a Line Company! Living out in the bush not just for a couple of weeks at a time, I mean months at a time you're out there! I thought I would die from exposure before long, Jim! I owe you my butt for getting me out of that one. You got a friend for life!"

I said, "You owe me nothing! Bec, I'm just happy as a pig in mud that I could help!"

I told Bec now that he was going to be in Recon as a Sniper and all, we would make a good team - even better than we made before! Bec said, "We'll hit those V.C. like they never been hit before, you and me."

I replied, "Wait until you get your killing machine." I opened up my gun case and I handed the 21 to Bec. He knew just what it was and what it meant to Charley.

He said, "What a beauty! This is a killing machine for sure."

I said, "Bec, just wait until you get yours! You'll go to bed with it at night."

Bec replied, "She's a real beauty."

I said, "I don't know how the heck you ever got snagged up into that Line Company. But you're out of there now and you will be a sniper with me."

Bec said, "That's what Captain A-hole asked me, how I ever got assigned to a line company. I told him I had no idea. He put my transfer through the same day I talked to him. I hear he has pull with the Colonel. He said my record looked very good and he said he needed real soldiers he could trust. So I just kept agreeing with everything he said. That way I got on the good side of him right way."

I said, "There ain't no good side to that mother! And don't you ever forget that!"

Bec said, "He is a jerk all right, but he still pulled me into Recon."

I said, "Only because you're new to the Company and he knows you don't know him yet. He's a user. He needs all the friends he can get! Soldiers, he has a whole Company full of them but he has no clue how to treat one. He is a total jerk, Bec. Watch the mother. Just do as he says when he's around. When he isn't, screw-um'!"

Bec said, "Everyone that I talk to says the same thing."

I said, "Remember that well!"

Bec said, "What ever you say, buddy, whatever you say!"

I told Bec that I had a very good friend on the A.F.B. I told him his name was

Ted and all about him and everything. I told Bec to look him up, mention my name and Ted would set him up with a hooch to stay in and a ride to Sniper school and real food! I told Bec all about the A.F. Base, my jet ride to Recondo school, and everything else I'd been doing since we last saw each other months ago. We rapped for about two or three hours. I just kept lighting joint after joint as we got caught up to date with everything.

It was about noon when I told Bec I would have to head out if I was going to make it back to Fort A-hole that day. I drew a map of how to get to Ted's hooch and work area so he could find him. I then wrote Ted a note on the map. I told Bec, "Just ask around these two places for Ted Springer. Someone around the A.F.B. will set you onto Ted's trail. When you meet Ted just give him this note and tell him you're my good friend. Believe me Bec, he will set you up like a king!"

Bec said, "Man, I don't know how to…"

I interrupted and said, "Shut up and go find Ted. You're into my travel time now!" I smiled and hugged him saying, "Take care Bec, I'll see you in a few weeks, dude!"

He just looked at me and said, "You know it, friend!" We walked outside. He crossed the road and headed for the A. F.B. I stuck out my thumb to catch a ride to Fort A-hole!

Ophu Cat R.V.N.

CHAPTER 34

The Change

It wasn't long at all before a truck stopped and picked me up. The driver asked, "Where ya goin'?"

I replied, "Uplift."

He said, "Goin' right past it, hop on." I threw my duffel bag and stuff in back and climbed aboard. The whole way back, all I could think about was what Captain A-hole told me about sticking me out in the woods as long as he could as soon as I became a Sniper. Just knowing that jerk, that's just what he would do. I also thought about whether or not I would extend my tour to get out of the army early. At one time and one time only I thought about staying in for twenty years. But I quickly got over that.

Soon I could see Uplift just ahead. As we got closer to the gate on the lower part of Uplift I could see many new tents that just about took up all the extra room left on the main post of Uplift. It looked as though some new battalion had moved in. Well, I thought, we could use all the support we could get. I jumped out of the truck and right away I noticed a lot of men around post were not dressed in a complete uniform. Many guys were looking very sloppy and were decked out with loud colored shirts and hats. A lot more men than usual were wearing sunglasses too.

As I walked up Recon Hill, I could see that many men looked just like the people I saw at Ophu Cat, wearing all kinds of peace signs, gold chains around their necks, necklaces of all types, and psychedelic shirts like I couldn't believe! As all black guys would pass each other, instead of just saying hello or whatever, they would go through a hand shaking routine that you would have to have lessons or a map to follow. They would slap their hands together, bump shoulders, bump elbows, bump heads, and go through indescribable contortions that you wouldn't believe.

At first I thought I stepped off in the Twilight Zone, not Uplift. After stopping dead in my tracks, I turned completely around and looked again. I said aloud, "Nope, this is Uplift," shaking my head. Before I came back to Uplift from Recondo and Pathfinder school, I saw a change in everyone's behavior, but not like this! The place changed so much in the past four weeks I couldn't believe it. Nearly everyone I passed was so stoned out they never even tried to hide it. I just couldn't believe the change!

I walked up to the Arms Room near the Company office to lock up my XM-1 until I needed it. Then I came back down toward the hooch. On the way down the hill I heard someone call to me. I looked up and saw Captain A-hole calling me up to his hooch. So I turned around and walked toward him. As I got closer he said, "Come on in, I want to talk to you."

When I walked in I said, "Yes Sir! Reporting back in from Sniper school, Sir."

He said, "At ease! And sit down." So I did. He asked how I liked my Sniper course. I told him I loved it! He asked, "Do you think you're rested up enough for a mission tomorrow?"

I asked, "As a Sniper?"

He said, "Yes!"

I said, "Sir, truthfully I can't wait to kill someone with my new XM-21."

He said, "Good! I have a very important mission to get together and I need a sniper with a lot of experience in combat. That is you! I don't have many good combat men left. If you look out the window you'll see what I mean."

He stood in front of his window looking down on Recon Hill he said, "Just look at those raggedy screw ups out there. I don't have any soldiers left, just a bunch of hippies!"

I replied, "Sir, when I first left to go to the first two schools I've just gone through, I came back to find Uplift had changed big time. At first the only real change was you. Then I began to change my thinking and attitude myself. Now frankly, I just didn't give a dump about the army any more at all. I used to be proud to be called a soldier, now I hate the word! As long as I stay here I will do my job as always. I never thought I would, but I agree with you. You don't have many soldiers you can really count on. I believe that you've turned the good soldiers you once had into the scum bags you're lookin' at. They, like myself, just don't care anymore!"

The Captain screamed out in a rage, "It's men like you that have changed this place! Men like you, that can't follow orders, that don't know what their job as a soldier is! Men like you are why I get no respect or control around here anymore!"

I replied. "You have to give respect to get some. Second, no man will ever follow chicken scratch rules in a combat zone rear area. Back here it should be time to relax a little. Third, if you have anyone to blame for this mess, you better stand in front of a mirror when you blame that person!"

A-hole said, in a low tone of voice and gritting his teeth, "I will see your dead body before I leave this mad house!"

I said, "Whatever you say, Sir! Recondo sniper...all the way!" Then I turned to walk out half saluting.

He replied, "Get out! You're dismissed."

I quickly headed out the door. Then just as I came flying around the corner of his hooch I came to a quick halt! I almost plowed head on into two Special Forces green-beanies. They jumped back and I barged my way right between them. I was so mad I saw stars! I wanted to kill A-hole so bad. Not just shoot him. I wanted to make it hurt like crazy, more like beat him to death!

When I got into my hooch I saw no one inside. All I could hear was super loud music coming from the rooms beyond. I threw down my M-16 and duffel bag and yelled as loud as I could, "Turn that crap down!" I sat down on my cot and the music got lower. I just sat there thinking about going A.W.O.L. But I had too many miles to go to reach home. So I laid back just to rest.

Soon I was awakened by my company clerk. He said the Captain was on the warpath like he never saw him before. He laughed and said, "Man, I heard you two in there. You've really driven him nuts this time!"

I said, "That no good son of a b*#@*!"

He totally agreed with me and said, "He wants you in the briefing room at 0700 hours in the morning with your new weapon, rut sack, with no mission equipment except your special ammo. He said you would get the other stuff you need where you're going."

I said, "I'll be there." Then I fell to sleep.

CHAPTER 35

Secret Mission

I slept until 0600 the next morning when I heard the radios in the hooch come on. I got up and stretched and saw that I was alone because A-hole had everyone else out in the bush. Then I headed down to chow for some coffee. After chow I picked up my XM-21 from the arms shack and went down to my hooch to get ready for the mission. After I had all of my special ammo and scopes packed I headed down the hill. It was almost 0700 so I walked into the briefing bunker. I saw two Intelligence men and two green beanies seated inside. One Intel. man jumped up and headed toward me. He said, "Here is our Shooter now. Sergeants Goodrich and Commings, I want you to meet your Sniper."

The two S.F. men got up and shook my hand. One of them said, "I think we met you yesterday, just as that tornado blew by."

I laughed and said, "Sorry about that! I was just smokin' mad at something."

He said, "No sweat!" So we all sat down. Then Captain Buttface came in and sat down with us. The Intel. man opened a map and he set it on the table in front of us for all to see.

He said, " Special Forces has been working with us on this mission and I will go over everything again for everyone's benefit." Pointing at the map at a place far up toward North Vietnam the Intelligence man said, "Along this area," then pointing along the edge of South Vietnam between S.V.N., Laos and Cambodia he said, "These three areas in particular are known V.C. supply routes. One up north near Lao Bao, down towards the center of S.V.N. about fifty miles west of Pleiku, and way down south near Hong Ngu. This mission is very important. We need to show the V.C. he is not safe even in a place we aren't supposed to be. That's why you are needed on this mission, Jim. As a sniper you can demonstrate to the V.C. they have no safe refuge. First we have to be completely quiet about telling anyone about this mission. U.S. forces are not allowed to be anywhere inside the countries of Laos or Cambodia. These countries are off limits to U.S. troops. If the North found out about our plans, we would get our butts wound up in an International illegal nightmare! We want to hit the Viet Cong where he will never expect us to be. This is above top secret. It is a top priority mission, and it is to be handled in just that way. The first mission out you will be sent north from Lao Boa and head northwest into Laos until you get to North Vietnam."

North Vietnam!, I thought. These guys must be crazy!

The Intel. man said, "This mission is a Counter Insurgency Mission. In other words, you will be sent in to stop Charley before he ever enters into South Vietnam. Use extreme caution. You must not to be spotted. Most of all, don't get captured! No help will be sent to you. Remember this mission officially will never have taken place, if you know what I mean."

He went on to say, "Jim, your mission is to quietly take out as many V.C. as you can, using the special forces team as a back up. In essence, this is the mission. As soon as you leave here you'll be flown to Sniper school to pick up your silencer.

We have pre-arranged a deal so you could get yours today. Swanson has been ordered to give it to you. There will be no questions asked. Then you and these two men will be flown to the S.F. fire base near Hue. There you will join the rest of the Special Forces team and be briefed on the entire mission. A lot more info. about the mission is in a sealed envelope waiting for you in Hue. You men will read the orders and you, Sgt. Commings, will personally see to it that the orders are burned up completely after you have read and understood them. From here you men will have as little contact with anyone as possible. With anyone! Most important of all, we need 100% secrecy on this mission. For a short time now we have been dropping small pamphlets here and there telling the Vietnamese people, 'Charley,' that there is a new and very deadly 'Superman' in town looking for them, and there is no safe place to hide. Not in this country, or in the other countries around Vietnam. This 'Superman' is you, Jim. You need to show the V.C. there is no safe place to hide - even at night, even in a country where Charley's enemies are not suppose to be; a place where he is thought to be safe. I wish you luck! Do your best not to be seen. The whole mission depends on that and making a strong statement. If you are seen just get back across the border without fail!"

Superman! I thought. I was in shock. I got up and walked outside. Now I was going to have to work with teachers. What next!? I thought.

Once outside the two S.F. men and I walked to the chopper pad. The two green beanies and I jumped into a chopper that was there waiting for us. The crew chief looked at the S.F. men. One nodded his head and the crew chief tapped the pilot on the shoulder and up we flew.

Many times in my life I had heard about missions of this type, but I never thought I would ever be part of one. It was scary, thrilling…I don't know. I guess I was more shocked than anything to know for sure that these things really did happen and were not just something we read about in a book.

We were just about to An Khe before anyone said a word. Then Sgt. Commings said, "I know this was real short notice, just coming in and swooping you off into a mission like this. But we needed a sniper. Not just any sniper, but one with lots of know-how. One I don't have to watch or teach as we go along. We don't have much time to screw around. Your Captain highly recommended you for the job."

I replied, "Really!" I knew that A-hole was nothing but diggin' on the fact that I was most likely going to be killed on that mission. I just felt that there was no other reason he would have recommended me or dragged me into that nightmare!

Sgt. Commings said, "We need someone that thinks for himself on this one. It's not going to be easy, but if we all work together I know it will be a successful mission. Our mission is to shock the life, and the fight, out of Charley. We need to show him that there is an invisible enemy out there that he can't see. One he can't kill. Hopefully this will discourage him enough to slow down his supply routes. Without supplies they will lose."

I said, "Whatever you say."

I felt that I was being used again by the army and set up by A-hole to be killed because he had already tried so many times before and failed. I sat back and looked out the door as we descended on the L.Z. at Camp Radkey at An Khe.

As soon as we touched ground a jeep was waiting to pick us up. The driver drove us right to the school. We walked into the Arms Room where Sgt. Swanson was working on a weapon. As soon as he saw me he said, "Jim, I heard you were coming."

I asked, "These guys tell you all about it did they?" The two S.F. men just stood there and said nothing.

Swanson said, "I already know what you want." He opened a small door in his workbench and he pulled out a silencer.

He handed it to me and said, "Kelley tested it. Beyond that, I know nothing."

The three of us walked out and got into the jeep and off we went to the chopper pad. Soon we were airborne and headed for parts unknown to me. As we flew, Sgt. Commings said, "We are headed to a small place just north of Hue, we have a small base there. Once we get there we will go to a briefing on the rest of our mission." I said nothing. I took out the silencer and looked at it and then I mounted it on to my XM-21 rifle.

Commings said, "I don't not know the whole story myself yet. So for now, we're all in the same boat. From now on we will hide nothing from each other....we are a team. Are you with us?" I just smiled and shook my head yes. Commings said, "The place we are headed for is a little less than two hundred miles away, so just sit back and relax for now."

I said, "Relax, you must be crazy! Here I am headed into North Vietnam with a team of men I've never met yet, except you two dudes, and you want me to relax. Don't worry, I'll do my job right, just make sure you guys have your stuff together!" Then I shut my eyes to ignore him.

Commings said, "I think you'll find out we have more on the ball than you think."

I said, "Whatever you say."

We flew for a long time it seemed, but we finally got there. I heard one S.F. man talking to someone so I opened my eyes and looked. Far below was a very small base camp just like Recon Hill but smaller, about ten bunkers and four buildings in all. We descended and then landed.

All three of us jumped out and headed towards a long building just in front of the L.Z. area. Commings said, "If you want, I'll take your things and put them away." I handed everything to him except my XM-21. He took my duffel bag and rut sack. Sgt. Goodrich the other S.F. man said, "Come with me."

We walked into the large hooch and down a hallway. Goodrich opened a door to a room and we walked in. Inside there were maps and things everywhere on the walls. Four other green beanies were sitting at a long table. Goodrich took a seat. I put my XM-21 in the corner and joined the four men sitting down. Goodrich started to introduce us. Goodrich said, "Men, this is our shooter, Jim Gibbore. Jim, I want you to meet the rest of the team."

The first guy stood up. "Sgt. Holmes, this is Jim Gibbore." We shook hands. Then the next man stood up. Goodrich said, "Jim, this is SP-6 Dixon, our medic on this mission." We shook hands. Goodrich said, "This is Sgt. Sherman, our map coordinations and locations expert." I shook his hand as he stood up. He went on.

"And this is Sargent Wassel. Each one of us is an expert at what we do. For example, Sgt. Commings is an expert in guerilla warfare and hand-to-hand combat. I'm a hand-to-hand combat expert myself and I have cross trained in light arms and demolition. Dixon over there can take out your appendix while you're running. Excellent medic. Sherman is an expert in reading maps and can find his way back from, or to anywhere blindfolded if need be. Holmes is an expert in demolition and light weapons as well, and can set booby traps that I would not try to disarm. He is good! And you Jim, are the expert Shootist. We have a team of experts here and we all know our jobs to the letter. The most important thing here is trust! All we have to do now is trust in each other completely, or we could fail our mission. We have to work together very closely, so let's make an all out effort here to trust one an other."

The door opened and Sgt. Commings came in with an S.F. Lieutenant. Someone yelled "A..tennn..hut!"

The Lt. came down front and said, "At ease. Go on Sgt. Goodrich, keep talking."

Goodrich said, "I guess I'm about done for now, Sir." So the Lt. said, "You all know me, except for the sniper." He looked at me saying, "My name is Lt. Washington. I'm the Intel. officer in this area." Looking away he said, "As you all know, this mission is to be kept absolutely secret for all kinds of reasons. The most important reason is so that Charley will never expect this surprise attack on him. Also, we are trying to demoralize him and we aren't supposed to be using Laos or Cambodia as entry points for our C.I. or C & C missions North."

The Lt. went on, "It's almost impossible to keep these two countries out of it anymore. We have no other choice but to use their land to cross over as the V.C. already do now. We just have to do it stealthier than Charley does. He had a letter in his hand. He said, "I have here your sealed orders. I will now read them to you."

He opened it and read. "You men have been picked to complete this very important mission. Each one of you is an expert in his own field. You are a vital asset to the U.S. Army and your country. The war in Vietnam will be greatly extended if we don't find a way to stop the V.C. and their supplies at the Northern border. Your mission is to eliminate as many enemy soldiers as you can using every tactic known to you. Each man was picked because he can continue the mission on his own in case any members are caught or killed. This mission is also for the gathering of any information on troop and supply movements. Gentlemen, you need to inflict as much damage as possible to the enemy. We must demoralize him in a place he thinks he is safe. If this mission is a success there will be more like it. We need to bring this war to a swift end. So do all you can to stop the enemy in his homeland. God be with you all! Signed, General W.C. Willard, commanding General Special Operations Group, R.V.N."

The Lt. said, "This letter will be destroyed now." He lit the paper and it went up in flame. The Lt. said, "You men can understand the importance of this mission." Whether it came from a General or not, all this added up to for me was another suicide run.

Lt. Washington said, "Jim!"

I stood up, "Yes sir!"

He said, "Under no circumstance let that XM-21 weapon or either scope fall into enemy hands. If you have no means of escape, use the white phosphorus incendiary canisters we will provide you and melt your equipment in one pile. Even if you think you're going to be killed or captured, put all your equipment into one pile and pop the canister on top of your equipment. As you know, the canister will burn so hot it will melt the steel and everything together so the V.C. or N.V.A. can never figure out how to build any of this equipment! That is most important."

I replied, "Yes sir!"

He said, "I wish you all luck on this mission. It will last as long as your supplies last. Start out with enough supplies for ten days. If things go crazy, just get back as quickly as possible. Don't take any chances above what you know you can get away with. If you are captured we will not acknowledge any of you were assigned this mission. So don't get caught. If the N.V.A. ever get their hands on you, it will be pure hell for you. They would make an example of you men to deter other missions of this type."

It was late afternoon and the Lt. told us to get all our things ready so we could leave that night just about dark. Washington said, "I will see you men when you all get back. I mean *all* get back!"

We all replied, "Yes sir!"

We got up and wandered into the hall. In the hallway Sgt. Commings told me to go with the rest of the team and they would help me get ready. So I followed the men into a large room in the back of the building. There were weapons of every type inside...M-14s, M-16s, AK-47s, M-60s, S.K.S., and just about every type of light weapon known to me anyway. Sgt. Commings said, "Everyone listen up! Pack your own L.R.R.P.'s and water according to how much you really have to use. Keep the weight as low as you can. We've got a lot of humping to do so make it easy on yourselves."

He went on, "I want everyone to carry extra explosives and extra ammo. Doc, take all the extra medical supplies you can carry and give some to the other men to hump too."

Dixon, our medic, carried a small surgical kit in case he had to extract a bullet or an unexpected bad appendix if need be. Even our blood types were matched up. Every person on our team had at least one other person on the team with their blood type. They had difficulty finding a match for mine because mine is quite rare.

When we were all packed we were basically a small, fully equipped team of assassins. Each one of us also carried one L.A.W. rocket launcher. L.A.W. rocket stood for Light Armored Weapon. Each is a two foot long rocket that extends open, like a telescope. When fired it would take out a small tank or reinforced bunker. It is two or so inches around and carries a small rocket inside capable of blowing open solid steel. It is a one shot rocket. The other shell is made of tubular fiberglass, which actually is the rocket launcher itself. Once you open it up and fire it, you would smash the fiberglass rocket tube so the V.C. couldn't pack it full of explosive and use it as a bomb casing or a rocket launcher for their homemade rockets. They were very light but could cause enormous damage.

After we were packed I said to Commings, "Remember when you told me that I would be surprised at what you guys knew?"

He said, "Yeah!"

I said, "I just want to say you were 100% right. I am surprised. So far you guys look like you got your stuff together to me!"

He smiled and said, "I figured once you gave us a chance to show you what we know you would see we're no bunch of idiots!"

I said, "The only idiot here is me, for even thinking any other way. But trust is hard to come by, know what I mean?"

He looked at me and said, "I know exactly what you mean!"

I said, "Airborne!" It once again felt good to really mean it.

After we were ready we ate chow which was prepared by an army guy that knew how to cook. We ate steak, potatoes and vegetables. All we could hold. Soon it was time to go. It was about 2000 hours.

CHAPTER 36

Into North Vietnam

We all secured our things and headed to the chopper pad. As we walked we all talked about what we were going to do. The plan was to fly west of Lao Boa, which was one of the northern most points in South Vietnam. There we would repel onto the ground and head out for N.V.N. We were going into N.V.N. as far as we could safely go in four or five days, then we would start to ambush known supply trails and set booby traps all the way back. This way, if we were spotted and chased we would be heading back the whole way.

The day and night would be used to knock out the enemy one by one as they tried to move about. There was going to be a nearly full moon for the next few nights. This was part of the plan because that would give me good light at night. It hung so big and low in the sky it was almost like daylight every night.

We all got into our chopper and it lifted off. As we flew I asked God to watch over us very closely that mission. I knew that this was a big favor I was asking of him, but I just didn't think the odds were much in our favor. During our meeting that day the Lt. said if we were spotted our odds would be thousands to none that we would ever make it back. The V.C. would put on an all out push to catch us. That's why not being seen was so important. We wore camouflage stick paint on every part of exposed skin and took plenty with us. Camouflage was a very important part of our equipment and it really did work.

We flew very high and soon we were there. We quickly descended to the level of about sixty feet. Two men quickly repelled down and the rest of us followed. The chopper would not land for fear of leaving skid marks on the dirt below. Even though we were still in S.V.N. this would be a dead give away that a U.S. chopper put down there.

The second all of us were on the ground the chopper quickly flew away. Commings grabbed a stick and brushed away all our footprints in the dirt. As soon as we hit the jungle area about fifty yards ahead we all got into a circle perimeter in the bush. Sgt. Sherman checked his maps using a very small, very dim red penlight. He cupped his hands over the dim light as he checked his map. Then he pointed in a westerly direction and he led the way. Commings followed, Wassel was next, then Dixon, then myself and Holmes, followed by Goodrich on rear guard....seven men in all. We walked all night.

Halfway up the side of a hill we stopped so we could watch the valley below. It was about 0400. Just up ahead in the valley we could see fire lights flickering everywhere. Commings and Goodrich went on to check it out. They were gone about half an hour. When they came back they said it was a very large base camp. They said we would have to go down into the valley and sneak around it. They said it was too thick for us to pass up above them where we were.

So very carefully we went down the hillside into the valley below. When we hit the lowlands, one at a time we ran across an open area in the valley and went around the enemy camp. After we all got to the other side we stopped to rest. About fifteen minutes passed and we saw two V.C. crossing nearly in the same spot that we did. As they came over to our side Commings and Goodrich took off but told us to stay put.

About half an hour went by and they came back with one dead V.C. each over their shoulders. I thought, Man! I don't believe this! These dudes don't even need a gun! Commings and Goodrich laid the two dead V.C. down and pulled out their fold up shovels. I could also see that both V.C. had their necks slit wide open. I-kee-rumba!, I thought to myself.

Commings and Goodrich just looked at the others on the team. Everyone took out their small fold up shovels. So I did the same. About ten feet from us I saw an eight-foot around flat rock a foot or better thick that Commings motioned us over to. The team circled the rock and Commings whispered 1-2-3. On three we picked the rock up and moved it a few feet away and we set it back down. We then went over to where the rock first laid and we all began to dig slowly and quietly, or more like pull back the dirt slightly towards us. We dug out just enough dirt to lay the bodies in so they were flush with the ground. We pushed and smoothed the dirt back over them and we all picked up the boulder and set it back exactly where it was, totally smashing the bodies flat and out of sight. The rock was so heavy it felt like it weighed as much as a small car. You could never tell what we just did. Commings fluffed up the grass and brush around the rock, being very fussy about his work. He made it look perfect. I would have never believed we stashed two bodies under there and I saw us do it.

We moved out because it was quickly getting daylight. Soon we stopped to rest until late that afternoon. From where we made our day camp we watched large numbers of V.C./ N.V.A. in the valley carrying supplies of all types. It was almost too much to believe. No wonder Charley had so many weapons and goods, I thought. The area was a perfect spot to bring in equipment and supplies to the V.C. in the south. No choppers flew over to check on them and there were no G.I.s to stop them in any way! The place was a free base for them to move around in and do whatever they wanted. Nothing was there to stop them. We were no longer in S.V.N. but not yet in North Vietnam

We started to move about 1800 hours that afternoon. We walked all night long. All the way we dodged base camp after base camp. Sherman, the point man, led our way with a starlight scope as we moved. From time to time he would stop the team to rest and to check his maps. He would make small marks and notes on the map when we stopped. The marks were preset ambush and booby trap trails. We were going to set traps there when we came back through. It also marked us out a free and clear route home...something we wouldn't have to plan out in case we were in a hurry when leaving. We would only have to follow the marks on the map to get back out.

During one of our rest stops Sherman said, "Gentlemen, welcome to North Vietnam! We are now the 'Gooks,' not Charley! We are now invading his country!" I remember that I couldn't have felt emptier and farther away from home if he told us we just landed on the moon.

The fifth night Goodrich planned that we would head back. On our way back he said we could set traps and ambushes all the way, killing as many V.C. as we could get away with on our way out. We rested all day until late afternoon on the fifth night out. Then we started across a flat area below to make our way back. Once we all crossed the flat lands and up the opposite hillside that night, Sherman once again checked his map.

Just below we could see the valley starting to curve south. Down in the valley I could see a base camp much larger than I'd ever seen before. It was three times the size of Uplift and hidden very well by the trees from above. There were campfires and V.C. everywhere.

Commings whispered, "Let's go down as close to the base camp as possible. Down there we can booby trap with Claymores and fraggs wherever they will be effective." He said the whole team would go except me. They would go in and set up traps. He wanted me to stay high above the camp to watch and pick off any V.C. that seemed to be getting in the way. He told me to shoot at my own discretion. He said to get the ones that were farthest out of the base camp area or the ones that were about to come down on the team. I told him I understood.

The men all split up and I got on top of a large rock above the camp. I could see the entire camp area. Most of the enemy was asleep and at ease. It looked like I was looking down at a moving target rifle range. I couldn't believe my eyes seeing how big the camp was. I could see about fifteen V.C. on guard scattered about the edges of the camp. As I panned around through my scope, below I could see sand and dirt mound ammo bunkers and a small caged-in area at the center of the camp. As I looked into the cage area, I could only guess it was a prisoner of war detention area. Why else would they have barbed wire ten feet high around six small shacks, I wondered. There was a small clothesline strung across the area with clothes hung on it. Some were raggedy clothing, some were pieces of Air Force and army uniforms like flight suits worn by pilots. I wanted to go in and get those men out so bad I couldn't stand it. But I would only end up dead or sitting in there with them and I knew it.

In the corner of my scope just below me, I could see members of my team starting to slink along the open area just in front of the camp. One by one they ran to the cover of some trees and behind some hooches. Soon they all disappeared from sight.

About twenty minutes went by. Then I saw them one by one run back toward the mountain I was on. I waited five minutes to start my assault on the V.C below. I figured that the team was well on their way back to me by then. I watched the enemy down below walking back and forth about one hundred meters apart all around the camp. I took aim at the farthest one out at about two hundred fifty meters.

Squeezing my trigger…Thud! A round went out. I saw the V.C. I was aiming at get hit and go flying. I panned around to see if any of the others had seen what happened. No one saw a thing. I went right down their perimeter line. As they moved to their furthest position away from each other, I hit each one, one after the other like ducks in a shooting gallery. It was almost a joke it was so easy. I had my ranging down perfectly. All I kept thinking to myself was, what a killing machine! Kabbatt was right, my whole body was totally electrified with excitement and my heart pounded like a base drum in my chest.

If you have ever been deer hunting before, I know you can remember what it feels like the few seconds after you see a huge or even a small buck slowly coming your way. Your heart begins to pound and the bigger the buck, the bigger the pound. You begin to shake, your knees begin to get weak and you find it more and more difficult to breathe as the ten-point slowly comes into range. You try to hold steady but your crosshairs shake all over the place, you're so excited. In your mind you're thinking, how far is he? Where do I hold? A little higher, or a little lower? You try to remember to pick a small area to concentrate your aim on, rather than the whole deer itself, so you won't miss. You try to remember not to jerk the trigger. But on that cold frosty morning if you miss, you just miss and you will have another frosty morning and another ten point to look forward to. In the patch of woods I was hunting in, had I missed killing just one of those bucks, my mornings would have been over permanently. I knew if I only wounded one of those V.C. and not killed him instantly he would have screamed out in pain, shaking the entire camp awake and onto our backs.

Could you, would you, have squeezed that trigger? Myself, I knew then I had answered Kelley's question. Could I, would I, take a man's life, just because he was the enemy? Would I stay cool enough to do all the things I just talked about? That answer was a definite Yes! and I just proved it, I thought.

Could you do that? Think about it. Now try to think about how it would feel to carry that picture in your mind all the days of your life. That's the time I knew I had de-evolved from a man back to some sort of animal…a thing; I didn't really know for sure just what. I felt an excitement flashing through me, like some sort of power of invincibility because I was invisible and I was causing such damage to the enemy. Then and there I really felt that I was in fact an invisible, very powerful Superman. I could feel an evil smile come to my face as I went for a chest or back shot each time giving me the largest target possible. I knew all I had to do was hit dead center each shot and that "buck" was down!

I never missed one shot. Fourteen men lay dead in the time it took for my team to get back to me. I counted each one as I pulled down on them. This is only one of the pictures my mind carries around, and will carry around all the days of my life.

When the team got back to me we all picked up our stuff and quickly moved out. We were moving as fast as we could go to put as much distance between the camp and us as possible. As it got daylight we could hear explosion after explosion going off, echoing through the valley. We knew that Charley was getting his butt kicked like he didn't believe. We also knew he was as mad as a wet hornet! We definitely showed them that there was no longer a safe place to hide or a place he couldn't be touched. They must have jumped out of their black P.J.s when they came out that morning and found all their dead buddies lying around, then finding themselves hemmed in on every side by booby traps.

It being daylight, we couldn't take the chance of being spotted crossing the valley. So we just set down to rest and make plans. The P.O.W. thing kept bothering me big time and when I talked to Commings about it he told me that he saw what I saw, and he highly recommended that I just forget it! He said it would be reported to the right people, but there was nothing right then that we could do about it. He said that problem was just too big for us to do anything about. He asked me not to bring it up again....Ever! He was right but it still got to me big time. At that time I never looked at it as some great cover-up or conspiracy or whatever. I just saw it as something too impossible to do anything about.

We stayed put and kept still, taking turns sleeping and pulling guard. On guard, we saw groups of V.C. moving below. We also noticed none of them crossed to our side of the valley. We figured it was still safe for us to move along our side.

About dark we got set to go, about 1900 hours. We slowly moved down to the lowland's edge where we could move easier. We spotted two V.C. coming at us, from about three hundred meters across the valley. Commings asked me, "Can you take those two out quick?"

I replied, "With my eyes closed!"

He smiled and told me to sick 'um. I moved out quickly into an open patch just ahead. I watched them get closer and closer to within one hundred meters down range. I had so much confidence in my 21 I knew it was all over for those two except for the funeral.

Thud!...My XM-21 barked out. The second guy in line went flying backwards. The round hit him right between the eyes, and it hit him so hard I could hear it hit him. It sounded like he got hit in the bean with a ball bat. The first V.C. in line had a real surprised look on his face as he turned to see what happened to his buddy behind him. He saw the dude lying on the ground with his head blown literally off. The guy standing quickly turned back to look all around, then in my direction. He looked right at me with an oh no! look on his face as I had my cross hairs dead center right between his eyes. Thud! I let another round go. His head burst into pieces like a blown up pumpkin. Commings said, "Damn!! Let's move out!"

We all got up and ran with Sherman leading the way. Commings ran out with Goodrich to take care of hiding the bodies. They just pulled them into the brush then headed right after the team. Soon we stopped to rest and I got down to cover Goodrich and Commings. They came over to us and dove into the bushes with us.

As I looked through the scope I saw another V.C. rounding the valley's bend towards us. I asked, "Should I take this one out? He's coming our way."

Commings said, "Wait to see if he heads into the jungle area. If so, zap

him so he'll fall into the bushes and I won't have to lug his butt into the brush."
I followed him in my scope at about seventy five to one hundred meters. Then
he turned and headed into the bush. The second he hit the thick brush I fired. I
saw it hit him right at the base of his neck. He flew head-first into the brush and
became part of history.

We all got up and moved very slowly and quietly along the valley floor
headed south. The team moved all night long and as we went we set many
booby traps along every pass and trail that we came across. I thought, God help
anyone that was trying to follow us. Sherman said he thought we should sneak
back across the valley before light and booby trap all the trails we used coming
in leading into the hills on the other side. So we moved out across the valley.

We got to the other side just as it was starting to get fairly light out. One by
one, we found the heavily used trails we came in on. For miles we set all kinds
of trip wire booby traps as we went.

Goodrich found a good spot to spend the day resting. As we stopped to rest
I spotted two V.C. coming towards us from the other side of the valley. We were
all in the brush hidden while we rested and watched. I got Cummings' attention
and motioned him to come over to me. When he got to me, I pointed out what I
saw. He told me to put those two dummies to sleep. So I lay down with my
XM-21 and I quickly changed to my day scope. I had plenty of time. I wanted
to let them get at least half way across the open area to us so they would have no
place to run but in the open.

I looked through the scope. I saw I could hit one for sure and the other one
would have at least three hundred meters in any direction to run to get to cover
once I fired if he saw what happened and tried to get away. The two V.C. were
laughing quietly and pushing each other like two kids messing around.
Commings said, "Shoot, man, shoot!"

I said, "Hold your horses! What is the rush? I want to let them get closer."

So I watched them getting closer and closer. I knew after one was hit the
other one would be in shock for a second and that was all the time I needed. I
could see both of their faces up close, like they were two feet in front of me.
They were only about eighteen years old. "God, will you look at this?" I
whispered to myself. If only they weren't humping an AK-47 each. My finger
got tighter on the trigger. Just kids, I thought. But so was I....with only a year
on them at best. Thud! The guy on my right in the rear flew backwards. I saw
his head burst before the view I had through the scope went dark. Instantly I re-
zeroed onto the next guy on my left. He turned around and he bent over to see
what had happened to his friend. Just for one second he stopped and he looked
down to see what was going on. He should run, I thought as I held the cross
hairs of my scope on his rear end. Just as he stood back up to run, I brought up
the cross hairs in my scope about one foot - Thud! I closed my eyes, took a deep
breath and I got up. I didn't need to look to see if I hit him. I just knew it
because I heard it smack him. I was so at ease and confident with that rifle I
could tell I hit dead center just as easily as I knew I'd caught a baseball in my
glove without even looking into the glove to see if the ball was there.

Commings said, "Man!, you're one damn good shot with that thing!"

I said, "If you say so, Sarge." We got up and headed out and on the move again. Not too far away Goodrich found a good place for us to hole up for the day to rest. We were all very tired. Again we took turns resting and pulling guard. On guard, we watched the lowlands as the enemy carried their goods in a southerly direction in the valley below. From time to time we could hear explosions going off all over the place. Our traps were kicking the stuffin' out of Charley but he still kept going.

That night after watching enemy all day long we decided to keep Charley up that night. I saw at least fifty or more V.C. during the day watch come across onto our side of the lowlands. I could see with my scope just about exactly where they were heading into the woods. We knew that there must have been a camp down there not far away, so we planned to ambush their camp that night if we could. We stayed on the high side of the hill area until about 1900 hrs. or so. Just before it got totally dark we headed out.

It was risky getting to the area we saw them moving to that day. There was a swamp that led all the way across and up to where I saw the enemy going into the bush all day long. We could hide as we walked through the very tall reeds and brush that grew in the swamp area. All the way there we were hounded by mosquitoes, snakes, leeches and things that love to bite. By the time we got to where we were going we had been bitten by bugs, cut by razor sharp elephant grass, covered with mud, leeches and we were soaked. It was a major job just getting through it alive.

After we got across we stopped to get our stuff back together for about fifteen minutes or so. Then we moved out to the spot where I had seen the V.C. moving into the jungle area that day. We all moved onto a very beaten down dirt path that went straight up a hill. It was so used a blind man could follow it.

After we went up about one hundred fifty meters we stopped. Commings and Goodrich went on ahead to check it out. About ten minutes went by and they came back. Commings told us that about two hundred meters up was a small camp. They said they could see about twenty V.C walking around by the light of a campfire. He said there were hooches all around the fire area in the center of the camp. He told us that there could be any number of enemy inside the hooches, but if we did our job right we could get all of them in their sleep. He told me to go back to the bottom of the hill and take out any V.C. coming this way between the lowland below and the team and he said to stay out of sight. He told me that it was imperative not to let any V.C. make it to this path. I said, "Roger that!"

He planned that the team would sneak into the camp, set down a bunch of booby traps, set off the explosives that they were going to place on the hooches, then lob some hand grenades in and run like heck back the open area to me. There we could all run along the lower open area and put some distance between the camp and us. He told me to make sure the area below was clear of all V.C. when they got to me so we would have a clear path to run. We all knew the plan and we moved out to do our job.

I quickly got back to the bottom of the hill and sat down to wait. While I waited I kept watching the open area through my starlight scope for anything coming my way. At first, I saw nothing. As I sat there it felt spooky as all get out. All kinds of sounds around me were being made by small and sometimes large animals, reptiles, you name it. Then suddenly…Baaabooom!! I just about jumped right out of my skin the blast shook me so bad. When I got my nerves back together I realized it was the almost single blast of the hooches being blown up all at the same time.

I looked up and out into the open area to see if any V.C. were coming. When I did I almost messed my pants! I could see out at about four hundred yards a whole squad of V.C.…ten or fifteen running my way fast. I figured they were a squad that belonged to the camp the team just blew up and were on their way home that night when they heard the blast.

I thought, Oh no, now what?! How was I going to warn the team? If they just came running out of the bush and into the open we would all be screwed! We would have been pinned down for a while in a firefight and we had no time to screw around, we had to get out of the area fast! There were just too many V.C. to try and take out one at a time with my rifle.

Then I got an idea. I got out two Claymore mines and det. cord and I quickly belly crawled out into the open about fifty yards in a straight line with the path I was guarding. I set the mines front toward enemy, put the Det. cord in and started to crawl backwards to the mouth of the path. I looked up and I saw the enemy with my naked eyes about two hundred yards out closing fast. I was so freaked out I thought I would faint.

When I got back to my pack and rifle, I got out my detonator and plugged in the det. cord. Behind me I could hear the team coming down the path to me. When they got to me I stopped them. Commings came right up to me and said in a whisper, "Let's go! There's a million V.C. on our backs!" I was shaking like a leaf in a wind storm. I could hear V.C. screaming as they ran towards us from the open area in front of us. I pointed them out to Commings and I told him to sit tight a few seconds because I had a surprise for them.

He said to the team, "We're sandwiched big time!" Half the team turned to guard our rear and half turned to watch the front with me.

Sherman asked, "What the hell are we waiting for? Lets move!"

I turned to the them all and I whispered, "Trust in each other….Remember?" I held the detonator in my hand as most of the team failed to see, and I watched the squad of V.C. come to within sixty yards or so of us.

Commings whispered to the team, "On my command fire!"

Just as the V.C. squad moved close together to form a line to run up the path I blew the Claymores. Baaaabooom! The blast was so close I thought it deafened all of us. Goodrich said, "Holy mother-a-peril! I think ya got 'um!"

The flash of the blast blinded us for a few seconds but when I could see again I saw numerous bodies sprawled out all over the place in front of us. The team got a real kick out of the whole thing as we grabbed our stuff and moved out quickly. I could hear all kinds of blasts going off up at the camp area as

Charley was blowing the heck out of himself with the booby traps the team set for them to find. What a slaughter from only seven men, I thought. Now we were doing to Charley what he would sometimes do to us. Now we, like he at times, were unseen and untouchable. I thought to myself, There you go Charley, you S.O.B.! What you can't see you can't kill! How does it feel?

We all looked around to see if any V.C. were coming but the coast was clear. Sherman took point and we all moved out quickly. We made very good time as we ran along the edge of the jungle in the valley. We didn't run into a single enemy soldier the two miles or more we ran before we stopped to catch our breath. Then we had to slow down because we entered another very thick swampy area once again. We couldn't see clearly because of the very thick brush within the swampy area, and the going was slow and hard.

It was starting to get towards daybreak and we knew we would have to find a place to hide for the daylight hours. Sherman told us that we were at the base of a small mountain and the higher up we went the more open it would most likely get. Goodrich figured if we could stay up high and out of sight until nightfall, we just might have a chance of getting back in another night or night and a half. We had covered so much ground that night that it wasn't funny. Sherman had us placed about four and a half miles away from safety in S.V.N., according to his map.

Commings figured the last night out I could set up somewhere close to the border and zap a few more V.C. just before crossing the border again. He said he wanted me to leave a "Statement" to show the V.C. that I had been there….and that "Superman" was real! At that time I asked what he meant by all that and he just smiled and told me, "Just kill me a gook and I'll show you what I mean! We need to make a statement…Remember?"

I replied, "Sarge, I think we already did."

He laughed and said, "No doubt about it, but let's really freak them out. That's the whole idea of this mission!"

Rest time was over so we all started up the mountain to a higher area to sleep. We went up about three hundred meters or so then moved about a quarter mile south along the mountainside. It wasn't very thick and it was much easier going. Sherman found us a good spot to rest. If Charley came along from there, we could ambush him good, there was a lot of cover and we could see anything coming a long ways away.

We were there about an hour before we finally got relaxed and felt no enemy was on our trail. One man stood watch…two hours on, four off. The rest of us slept. I felt great after my six-hour nap and I was ready for anything that night.

During my watch, I saw a very large tree about one hundred feet high. The tropical forest grew very large trees. Even as a kid I loved to climb trees so I climbed that one to use as a look-out tower. Once I got to the top part of the tree I could see the lowlands and swamp far below. The area was about 2000 meters from where I was sitting. I could see teams of V.C. from time to time moving up and down the valley near the swamp area below. I watched them for three hours or so. I figured I would let old Commings sleep some more and take his shift on guard. I was all rested and I was having fun watching Charley look for signs of us…with no luck I might add.

As I sat there, I watched through my scope from time to time. Suddenly I heard some V.C. talking a short distance away. About one hundred meters away on the ground, just a short distance from the team, I saw six V.C. coming. I thought, if one of the team makes any noise or gets up, we'll be spotted for sure. It was thick below but I could still see for quite a ways around because I was so high up. As they came closer and closer to the team I watched them through my rifle scope.

Soon they were only about twenty feet from the team. One V.C. said something to the others. They were only about one hundred feet down below me. I put my scope cross hairs on one, then another. I just didn't know which one to smack first. It looked to me as though they just thought we moved non-stop through the area and they kept on going past the team as they slept on the ground twenty feet away. V.C. were very good trackers and I couldn't believe they didn't walk right into our camp. Thank God they kept going, I thought. I waited until they were long gone then I came down out of the tree. I sat quietly until Holmes and Goodrich woke up. Soon the whole team was up as I whispered to Holmes and Goodrich what just happened. I didn't tell them exactly how close it was though.

Goodrich said, "They're on to us big time. We'll have to be careful of ambush from now on. If I were them, I would setup all along the open area below. Tonight we are going to have to be on our toes more then ever and we're going to have to slow down and be extra careful!"

CHAPTER 37

Superman and the Crimson Light

We sat back and waited for dusk. Then finally 2000 hours rolled around and we got up to move. We headed down the mountain. Going through pitch-black thick jungle was a real job in itself.

We soon hit the valley area below and we moved as quickly and quietly as we could. I had my night scope mounted and I helped pull point with Sherman and Commings who used the P.V.S.-2A night scope. We slowly but surely moved the team ahead in the dark as we went.

After most of the night went by we finally reached a familiar place to me. Only about a quarter mile away was our home plate. We could see S.V.N. from where we stood. We had to be careful we were not spotted as we had to cross a long stretch of open area ahead. The stretch was about 800-1000 yards or so to the S.V.N. side of the valley we were in. We stopped so we could take a rest and check things out before we crossed over and into the open area. Goodrich said, "That's it over there. If we make it we're home free." He pointed to the spot I recognized as S.V.N., where we first got dropped off. I kept looking through my starlight scope to see if anything was moving out there. I didn't want to get caught in a surprise ambush out in the middle of that wide-open area by V.C. that might be camped out.

As I looked out across the valley through my night scope, out about two hundred meters, I saw a crimson red light come on and move back and forth, up, down and all around from up high in a tree. As it moved back and forth it shined a couple of times right into my scope, nearly blinding my scope eye. I said, "What the heck?" I pulled the scope away from my eye and I looked around. But all I saw was dark. Nothing! I looked through my starlight scope again. "Holy cow, look at this!!" I said. As I looked through my scope I could see the reddish colored light once again.

Commings asked, "What's wrong? What the heck are you seeing?"

I said, "I don't know, but just stay put, don't move around."

He motioned for the team to lay back down, as they were about ready to move out. I got up and moved to a large rock just a few feet away. I looked out into the open area again through the scope. Once again I saw the beam of reddish light coming from the top of a banana tree. Then back in my mind I could hear Sgt. Swanson, my 21 gunsmith back at sniper school, say, "The P.V.S.-2 can see any source of light, even ultra-violet light on the old fashioned ultra-violet type of sniper scopes Charley uses." Right then I knew I was looking at the light made by an ultra-violet sniper scope! It was a V.C. sniper! I got a sharp twinge in my gut.

I looked up the banana tree and sure as shootin'! A V.C. sniper! I could see him clear as day. If we would have walked out into that wide-open area our butts would have been cooked! I settled the butt of the stock of my XM-21 down into a small crack in the rock to hold the rifle steady and tight. I then put my cross hairs on the sniper's chest. As I started to squeeze the trigger, Charley started to move and the red light went out. He sat up kind of to re-position himself. I stopped the pressure on my trigger. Then I saw Charley put his feet in a firm position and he looked back into the scope. Then the light came on again. It looked like he was sitting in the tree with a bright red flashlight on. I could see him plain as day. I took my eye off my scope and saw nothing but pitch dark. Then I sort of chuckled in amazement at the difference in our equipment. I felt like a cat about to pounce on a bird, as I sort of sat back and just watched him as he thought he was the one with the big edge. Little did he know that he was on his way to hell very shortly, whenever I felt like sending him there.

A sniper's call sign on the radio was "god." We used to say we could take a life just as fast and as quietly as he could. Today the thought of that sickens me.

Commings asked, "What the heck is it?"

I said, "Look at the banana tree out about three hundred meters."

He asked, "What banana tree?"

I said, "Use your P.V.S and look out there!" He did. He quickly brought the starlight scope back down. With his eyes wide open for a second he said, "Kill that little mother f#@**!"

I got lined up and set once again. The light from Charley's scope was so bright I thought I would have to put my light filter on the scope. I took dead aim. He turned his scope and rifle slowly to look around, and as he was checking out the area in front and all around him. The red light shined into my crosshairs dead center. Thud!

Commings said, "What a shot! Ya smacked him right in the head!" He watched the whole thing with his P.V.S.-2A scope. Commings said, " If I hadn't seen it, I wouldn't a believed it! I don't know if you realize it or not, but you just saved this whole team and mission."

I replied, "No sweat, Sarge. You're talking to Superman…Remember?"

He snickered, "You jerk! If we would have moved out, that one gook out there would have blown the purpose of this whole mission! And he would have opened up, pinning our butts out there! That would have brought the whole valley full of V.C. down on us."

We both moved back over to the team and Commings told them what happened. The whole team congratulated me on the shot that supposedly saved all their lives and all. Myself, I was glad to do it, seeing how one of those lives was mine.

I watched out and covered each man as they ran across the open area to the S.V.N. side of the valley. Goodrich and I got up together and we moved out. We both ran right towards the V.C. sniper I shot out of the tree. As we ran he told me that he wanted to visit the dead sniper, and pay his last respects. He said he also wanted proof that the V.C. were using snipers too. He said that with proof Intel. could present it to the right people when the V.C. came down on our backs for having snipers. He had to have proof and he wanted to make a strong "statement." He felt we now had both. I kept thinking to myself, rules in war, you got to be kidding me! What a joke!

When we got there we saw the dead sniper lying on the ground. I hit him right in the eye and the whole back of his head was blown away…only his face was left. He looked unreal to me, like a big doll or something. Goodrich asked me to get the plastic wrapped piece of paper out of the small pocket in the center of his rut sack. He told me to open it and look at it. It was a 6x6 inch piece of paper with a sketch of an XM-21 sniper rifle. There were all kinds of Vietnamese writing, telling them all about the "super gun" and the "Superman" that was out to kill them.

The Sarge asked me for one live round. I gave Goodrich a new loaded 7.62 mm match round. He took it and the 6" square piece of paper from me. He then laid the paper on the dead sniper's forehead. He took the new unfired round and he drove it like a nail through the paper into the sniper's skull, nailing the paper to his forehead. He said, "Superman just made a big 'statement' here tonight! Our Superman just killed their Superman. See what I mean? And what a statement. We couldn't have planned it better! Intel. is gonna get a nut over this one! And for proof…look at this! He's been shootin' an old U.S. army M-1 long rifle."

Goodrich picked up the old W.W.II U.S. army M-1 sniper rifle Charley used. It had a big old ultra-violet scope mounted on it. It was in good shape except for a smashed lense from me putting a round right down the center, through the scope, into Charley's eye, through and out the back of his head! Goodrich opened the bolt and a round flew out. He said, "He was waiting for us all night. This was a set up! That's why they left us alone today. This sniper wanted to make a statement of his own!"

I replied, "No way!"

Goodrich said, "This weapon must have been sent through channels here, from the Soviet Union. After W.W.II. the Soviets got hold of a lot of U.S. weapons. They use to work with us, now they work with our enemy, the V.C."

Goodrich was a weapons expert. He went on to say after W.W.II, Russia got lots of U.S. weapons that were taken from U.S. soldiers by German soldiers when the G.I.s were captured. After we won the war Russia got hundreds of U.S. weapons from the Germans. Now the Russians give them to Charley to use on us. I just shook my head and I looked out into the open area once again just to check things out. The place was giving me the creeps.

As I looked around I saw a lone V.C. about five hundred meters away coming right at us. His AK-47 was slung over his shoulder and he was carrying a small bag, just strolling along totally at ease. I whispered, "Sarge! There's a V.C. dude coming, five hundred meters."

Goodrich asked, "How many?"

I replied "Just one."

He quickly picked up the dead sniper and said, "Grab the other stuff and follow me!" I picked up the old M-1 and I quickly looked around picking up anything else and I ran over behind some large rocks with Goodrich about twenty feet away. We got down to wait for our visitor. Goodrich and I watched him with our starlight scopes as he got closer and closer. Every eighty meters the dude would stop and wave his arms over his head like some sort of signal.

When he got within fifty meters of the tree and us, he whispered out something in Vietnamese. Goodrich kind of cupped his hands over his mouth and answered him right back. No way! I thought. This guy can speak Vietnamese just as good as they can! I almost chuckled. The guy walked up to the tree with his back to us and looked up…then he whispered something.

Goodrich quickly stepped out from the rocks we were behind and told Charley to "freeze!" in Vietnamese. I about swore I could hear the dude dump in his pants. Goodrich told him to give it up and drop the bag and weapon and put his hands up. When he did I went over to him and took his weapon and frisked him down. Just as easy as that we had a P.O.W. It was so cool I couldn't believe it. Neither could Charley, I guarantee!

Goodrich tied Charley's hands with a piece of rope that was tied around the bag lunch he was bringing for the dead sniper. Goodrich told me to watch Charley as he went back behind the rocks and got the dead sniper. He sat him down on the ground with his back against the tree like he was taking a nap. Goodrich said, "Come on! Let's get the hell out of here."

All three of us took off across the open area towards the location of the team. When we got to them I saw Commings and Sherman jump up out of a ditch they were in and run out to us. Then the rest of the team followed. Sherman said he saw the whole thing with the other starlight scope and they were all having a good time laughing about what just happened.

From there we could see the border of S.V.N. Shermam told us it was only a five-minute walk. Commings said, "Well…let's go home men?" We gagged our P.O.W. and headed back toward the village of Lao-Boa, South Vietnam.

CHAPTER 38

Snake Charmer

We all walked slowly and carefully because we knew our guest's buddies were around somewhere and you could never tell where you might run into them. But we still felt safer on the southern side of the war than where we just came from.

After about three miles of walking jungle edges and rice patty dikes we got to Lao-Boa around sun up. Just before we came into the village of Lao-Boa we ran into a Line Co. that was camped out for the night on their way to whatever village they were ordered to destroy next. They just loved doing that sort of thing, especially when they were ordered to do so.

They were a combat "leg" unit. A leg is an infantry soldier that is not airborne qualified. You could never talk them into jumping out of a perfectly good airplane for sex or money. And let me tell you they just loved sex and money! They would say that there were only two nasty things that fell out of the sky. One, bird s*#!; and two, airborne soldiers. They were regular non-airborne combat Line grunts that spent just about all their time in the bush because they were too dangerous for the army to let loose in a town unless the army wanted that town burnt to the ground! They had a very deep hate for all Vietnamese people and they were unleashed here and there by the army to destroy! Destruction was their job. They were very dirty, ill-mannered, ill-tempered, and ill in the head. They couldn't say one sentence unless every word in the sentence was a cuss word. They were very rugged, red-necked, anti-social military nasties that would just as soon kill a V.C. as look at him. For that matter they would just as soon kill anyone that wasn't directly hooked up with their unit. Even those in the unit had to be careful that one of the other men in the unit didn't turn and bite his throat out just to stay on top of the pack. They were like the animals you may have heard about around a campfire as a kid. The ones that eat their own young! Yes they did exist!

We all stopped for a short rest and to eat breakfast at their mess tent. Goodrich radioed back to the Special Forces Command Post near Hue to tell them that everything was okay and we needed a ride A.S.A.P. They told us they got the message and they wanted us to stay right where we were and they would send a chopper out to us as soon as possible.

Commings asked me to keep an eye on our guest because the line grunts would eat him for breakfast. I laughed and he said he was dead serious. He said as long as we were there we all had to watch out for the guy or he would be dead meat so fast we would never even see it happen. So we all sat around the prisoner in a circle and we guarded him as we ate. Around this leg unit was no place to be relaxed, I could just feel it.

While we ate our chow waiting for our ride to show up, I could see nearly every man in that unit looking at our prisoner as though he were the only piece of raw meat lying around inside a cage full of hungry lions. Every few seconds one or two of them would come in close to check out the enemy up close. (I think to see what one looked like when he was still alive.) They reminded me of a pack of wolves circling to make a kill. I got very dirty looks from each one as they walked by checking us out. I almost expected to hear growling any second. One dude even turned his head and spit on Charley as he and another guy walked by. I took my hand and I wiped it off his face. They were all sitting around in small groups or packs giving us dirty looks and mumbling all kinds of nasty things to us about how we should have slit his f*^#**! throat. Because he was a f*$#!* c*^$ s*$#!^ son of a f&%**#@** no good f*^*# c*#* S%#@*! (See what I mean about the language?)

I sat next to Charley and I pulled the gag down off Charley's mouth. I put some of the scrambled eggs and sausage I had into his mouth and fed him by hand. I couldn't untie him so he could feed himself. He was very thin and dirty, and he was shaking like a leaf. He looked like he hadn't eaten in a long time.

I knew by the look on his face that if the little dude had a chance to kill me he sure would have. I knew the line dudes were right in the way they felt and the way they looked at Charley and all. But I just felt so sorry for the guy, which really made me mad in a way. Feelings like that could get me killed in a place like that, and I knew that too. As I fed him the men in the Line company looked at Charley like he was some sort of deadly snake or scorpion or something, and in the bush he was! They looked at me like I must have been totally out of my mind for just being around him, let alone feeding him, heaven forbid!

I heard one of the dudes say, "Look at that a**hole! He's really feeding that f*$%*#! scum bag snake face son of a f^$#*!" Another guy said, "Yeah! maybe the f*^#*#! Lone Ranger wants ta be a f^$#@^! snake charmer when he f*$%#@! grows up some day, the dumb f&%*!!" They all laughed. They were right, in the bush Charley was a snake, a deadly enemy. Maybe they were right about me, too. In the bush I was also a snake. Maybe a snake charmer, a scorpion, something that I never will be able to put a suitable name on. But right there, we were just two lonely, scared, homesick, kids. Hell, we weren't even grown men yet.

As I looked at Charley and the packs of wolves around us, I felt as freaked out as Charley did. After all, I could see the faces of the wolves around me. At least Charley had a blind fold on. But I believe he could feel the hate all around him as I did. I didn't even have to open my eyes and look around to feel that. I also felt we were both telling each other mentally how tired, lonely and home sick we were. I could somehow feel that too. I felt just as far away from home right then as Charley did. Right then I was hated by my own kind just as much as they hated him. I could see it in their faces, just as Charley could feel the hate around him. I knew what my face felt like, what it must have looked like.

After Charley ate all the eggs I had, I squeezed and patted his shoulder. I could feel him vibrate he was shaking so bad. I said, "No sweat Charley, no sweat." He just put his head down and he started to blubber. Call me a pussy if you want, but I felt like my heart broke for both of us. I thought, maybe he would just give up now and wait the war out in a P.O.W. camp the best he could. But I knew in my heart if I was him all I would have been thinking of was how I could get away and kill more of my enemies! The fighting part of the war was over fo

Charley but still there for me. I wiped my eyes and got to my feet as I heard our bird coming in to land. I remember thinking to myself, God, please let me go home. I want to go home so bad!

When our chopper landed our guest was very reluctant about getting aboard. I patted his shoulder and I said, "No sweat Charley, no sweat!" He went right in. I thought, maybe I was a snake charmer. The chopper took off and headed for the S.F. Camp. We flew for about thirty minutes then far below I could see the Camp.

We landed and all of us jumped out. Commings took Charley by the arm and led him away. I never saw him again…where he went from there I don't know. All of us got the day off but were told to report to the briefing room at 1800 hours for a meeting on the mission. The first thing all of us did was to head to the hooch for some shut-eye. I slept like a dead man and I never got up until 1700, just about an hour before our meeting in the briefing room.

At 1800 hours we all gathered into the room. Soon Lt. Washington, the Intelligence officer, came in. He asked for our attention then said, "You men have done an outstanding job on the last mission, just outstanding! I am very pleased! From what Sgt. Commings and Goodrich have told me you men did exactly what was planned, with no casualties on our side and boo koo casualties on Charley's side. Just beautiful!

"And I have heard how our shooter was able to inflict numerous kills on the enemy and was solely responsible for the capture of the V.C. soldier that we have in custody." I thought, What? And I looked at Goodrich as he smiled. The Lt. said, "This was exceptionally fine work on your part, Jim. Sergeants Commings and Goodrich have put you in for a Silver Star with oak leaf cluster for this outstanding job. However, regrettably, I cannot put this recommendation through channels because this mission officially has never taken place. As a matter of fact, you were never even here. The record will show that you have been at Uplift the whole time with your own unit. The award would have only been a small token of our appreciation for the job you did while working with us. Both Commings and Goodrich believe that mortal danger would have fallen on the team without your expertise. Jim, you performed your job above and beyond the call of duty. I just wish that I could write a complete and formal award recommendation for you, but I cannot. I hope you will understand. I have asked that you be permanently assigned to us, but my request for your transfer was denied because of the high demand for snipers. You are needed elsewhere. But for the next two missions you will still be working with this team. We are now sending our own man through Sniper school. Jim, I want to thank you personally for a job very well done. You can be very proud of who you are!"

I remember I really didn't give two jumps about any award or medal, I felt the caliber of the people that were recommending me was so high, that was medal enough to me.

We all talked and discussed what we thought about the whole mission for an hour or so. Then the Lt. said we were dismissed for a two day rest. The Lt. thought we needed and deserved the rest. I agreed!

After the meeting was over the Lt. asked if I would stay for a minute. When everyone left I went up to him and said, "Yes sir. What can I do for you."

He said, "This afternoon I called Uplift to talk to your Captain. Your Captain, well, is a very hard man to please, is he not?"

I said, "I see you know him."

He said, "Even after I told him how well you operated, and all you have done to make this mission a complete success, he spoke ill of you. At one time you must have really, shall I say 'peeeed' him off!"

I replied, "Sir, he is ill alright…in the head! And oh, I've peeed him off, much more than once.

"Sir, I do my job, but just not good enough for him I guess. His idea of a soldier is a spit-shined, S.S. Waffin, sieg-heil, storm trooper no brain. No matter what, or how good you are, it is still never good enough for that, shall I say, A-hole. At one time I was an E-6! Now I'm an E-nothing! He put me back to E-0 because he didn't like the earring I'm wearing."

I told the Lt. what happened and he just shook his head. He said that what that jerk did to me was the perfect way to kill a good soldier quickly! He thought that harassment should be kept exclusively for the enemy alone. I said, "Enemy is just what he thinks I am. And now he is exactly right!"

The Lt. said, "I suggested to him that he at least promote you to E-5. But he suggested to me I mind my own business and he said he wouldn't even consider it."

I replied, "Sir, that's him all right! You definitely talked to my C.O."

All the Lt. had to say to that was, "What a waste." He told me that he tried to get me permanently assigned to the S.F. unit by contacting different people he knew, but with no luck. He said no one wanted to step on anyone else's toes. He said if he could have gotten me assigned to his outfit he could help me get all my rank back in no time. I felt good inside to think I was once again respected for the good job I knew I was doing. But the worst part was knowing I was going to have to go back and work for Captain A-hole soon.

I spent two months and part of the next working with the Special Forces team on a few more missions into Laos and Cambodia and another mission north that turned out just about like that first one. I was sent with the team into Laos and Cambodia to do the same thing as we did up north and we kicked butt! All the missions went very well. I got many more kills on those missions but none were confirmed or recorded because we weren't supposed to be there, period, let alone doing what we were doing. And I was not even there but back at Uplift, or so I was told. I really didn't care about any more confirmed kills anyway. I felt in my heart that I had enough to explain to God one day. I had a special chopper to take me to and from Sniper school each time for my re-zeroing and weapons check.

Soon I had only one more month to go before I was to go home and I was still thinking about extending for six more months to get my early out of the army. Then the day came for me to go back to L.Z. A-Hole. After I got packed to leave that morning, I was introduced to the Special Forces sniper that was replacing me. He had been around but we just never bumped into one another. If I was in, he was out, or vice versa. Lt. Washington, Goodrich and Commings said if there was a way to keep me, they would. But with no cooperation from my C.O. to begin with there was no way to help me. I said that was okay, being so short I really didn't care where I pulled my last thirty or so days in country anyway. They all wished me lots of luck and I left for the chopper pad.

I flew non-stop back to Uplift all the way, I didn't feel much like partying for some reason. All I kept thinking about was whether or not to extend six more months. I knew six more months with Captain A-hole would only get me killed or court marshalled for sure! I just didn't know what to do.

I finally landed at Camp Hippie or Fort A-hole....I really didn't know just what to call the place anymore. Fort Nightmare was starting to sound like the right name for the place. Anymore it looked more like Woodstock than a fire base in Vietnam. I walked across the road that led up Recon Hill toward the orderly room office to report in. The C.O. wasn't around but the clerk saw I was back and he signed me back in. Then I walked back down to the hooch to put my stuff away. When I got inside I looked around a second or two while my eyes built up some visual purple so I could see inside that damp, smelly, rat infested dungeon. It was as dark as Grant's tomb in there.

CHAPTER 39

Bad Medicine

As I looked around all I could see were new guys. I couldn't tell who was who. Then I spotted my old buddy Kabbatt who was sitting, talking to some of the guys. Kabbatt jumped up off a cot and ran over to me. He said, "There's that two digit midget. How the heck are ya, Jeeeeem?" He was from Hawaii and he had a long, funny sounding slang to his words that used to crack me up.

I said, "Good enough, I guess!"

He said, "I hear you're a regular hero now."

I said, "I'm 'here' alright but a 'hero' I ain't! A-hole must be telling lies about me again."

Kabbatt said, "He has been telling us a little bit about your C.I. Missions. He said he can't tell us much about the missions but he's very proud of you, Jeeem. And he wants us to follow your example he says....."

Shocked, I said, "What?!...He must have bumped his head and doesn't know what he is saying, or he has just finally gone totally insane!"

"I'm not lying," Kabbatt said, "He told us you're a regular hero! He said he's proud of you, you're a big hero!"

I just couldn't believe what A-hole said about me to these guys. I knew he hated my guts. The only thing I could figure out was that I had been doing a good job. I felt he only used that as an example to show the rest of the men that if they work harder for him, they could become his big buddy like he was trying to make it sound like I was. But I was not! That was the only reason I could think of that would make him ever pay me any compliment in any way. I asked Kabbatt if the C.O. had tried to sucker him to extend his duty there yet. He said, "Oh yeah, he talked to me last month. He asked me if I would extend to help with cherries in the bush. So I did. Now I have six more months to go before I go home. I'm going to stay to help."

I said, "My days are growing short too, with only twenty nine left to go. Two digit midget or not, I've been thinking about doing the same as you."

Kabbatt asked, "We still going to be snipers together Jeeem, for six more months?"

I replied, "Yeeeeah! I guess so!"

Kabbatt said, "I wish I could see the Captain's face when you tell heeeem that. I talked to heeeem about getting Bec into recon like you asked me."

He told me Bec was a sniper now and he was on a mission somewhere and was coming back in a few days or so. We both just talked and got caught up on the latest stuff around Uplift. I told him the "real" story about the missions I just pulled up north and all. He said he was getting ready to go out on a mission that day with the men inside the hooch. As he and the team got ready to go out he introduced me to the men I had never met before.

He told me Brink was at the supply bunker getting ammunition and supplies. He said that Brink was turning into a very good team leader. He said he noticed that Brink did a lot of things like I did. He said a lot of his ambushes and things were set up just like I would do it. And when they got into trouble he would ask Kabbattt what I would do in that situation. Kabbatt said, "He really respects you, Jeeeem, and what you taught heeeem."

I remember thinking that maybe it was like what I always believed about that 'thing" or that genealogy deal. Just like those "legs" that I ran into. The same thing, but in a negative way. One's actions would rub off on the other. Only in their case as one showed the other what he knew, how to abuse and mistreat people, the foul language, the leg grunts would just keep getting worse and more violent, more agressive, and less human. To me it was "war genealogy" You call it what you want!

I said, "No kiddin', Brink's doing well as a team leader?! He's looking out for the men?"

Kabbatt replied "Yes he is!"

Soon Brink came back down from supply. He spotted me and he said, "Sarge! How are ya?"

I said, "Good! I heard you're a darn good team leader buddy. That's cool. Maybe some of my good stuff rubbed off on you."

He said, "Well, you did show me a lot of stuff. But as far as it goes I'm average I guess. There still is a lot to learn. So far I've been able to get most of us back. So far."

I said, "Just don't forget! Getting everyone back is the most important part of your job. Screw the mission. If you blow one there will always be another one!"

He said, "You're right! I always watch my team closely and always keep them in mind. Sometimes I see them as more important, even more valuable than my own life."

I smiled and I said, "Brink! That's the real sign of a good team leader. You got it pal! You are seeing it just the way I would hope you would. Don't forget, those lives are all in your hands and they're all counting on you to keep them alive with your every decision and move."

He replied, "That's what always worries me! I always wonder if I am good enough to do all that or if I'm making the right moves."

I said, "As a team leader that kind of question will never leave you. You will have to ask yourself those questions every move you make! Don't worry dude, you've done real good so far from what I hear. Just keep up the good work!"

He smiled. Brink said that they were going out for a week or so, and he would see me when they came back in. I told them all, "Good luck! I'll see you guys soon." As they were leaving for the briefing room Brink told me there were four snipers now. Kabbatt, Becham, myself, and a man named Miller. I was told that snipers had their own hooch up at the top of the hill just below the C.O.'s office. He said like everything else, A-hole wants to keep everything separate. Then he left to join the team at the briefing.

I headed up the hill to find my new hooch and get settled in. I was beginning to feel like I was part gypsy I was moving around so much. Soon I could see a small new bunker-hooch with a sign by the door. It said, "SNIPER" with words under it reading, "If you're not a SNIPER, stay the f@#*# out." So being a sniper, I went right in. Inside I saw a new man. I guessed this was our new sniper Miller.

Miller got right up and introduced himself. He said he had come to our company by request of our Captain. He said he had eight months in country and he was no cherry. I said, "The name's Jim." I put out my hand, I wanted to be friendly in case he was one of A-hole's butt boys or something. He could talk and he was friendly.

He said, "Real glad to meet ya. I've heard a lot about ya."

I said, "Don' t believe anything you hear! Especially from Captain....!"

He said, "I've only heard good things about you, so far."

I said, "It's like I say! Don't believe anything you hear!"

I told him that there was a time when you could depend on what most anyone said, but not anymore. He just laughed and said, "Well, it's nice meeting you. That you can believe."

I said, "Same here."

The two of us rapped a while then went to chow and up to formation after supper. At formation I was told to report to the Captain directly following.

I walked up to the orderly room and I knocked on his door. He said, "Come in."

I walked up to him and saluted. I asked, "You sent for me, Sir?"

He replied, "At ease. Have a seat." I sat down and he said, "I've heard a lot of very surprising things about you from Lt. Washington."

I played dumb and said, "Oh, is that so Sir!?"

He said, "I was told you deserved a Silver Star, but you won't be getting it." He looked at me with a grin.

He went on. "And the Lt. requested I promote you back up to E-5."

I said, "Is that right, Sir."

He said, "Myself, I don't think you deserve E-5 but that's only my opinion, right?"

I said, "El correcto sir!"

He said, "As long as I am here, you will never get that E-5 promotion."

I said, "Why someone would put such a high value on a promotion is beyond me. All that gets a guy is more work. But, whatever turns you on, Sir!"

He said, "What would turn me on...." Then he whispered, "Is to see you leave here feet first." He went on, "But just to see you leave will do my heart a world of good. I'm the re-enlistment officer up here and I am obliged, well more like ordered by the army, to ask you if you want to re-enlist or extend your tour of duty here. But knowing you, I can't even imagine you doing that!" Then he snickered.

I said, "You're wrong again, Sir! I am going to extend for six more months. That way I can say goodbye to this chicken scratch outfit and the scum bags therein once and for all!"

His ugly mug instantly turned blood red. He looked at me like I just spit in his Nazi face. He yelled out, "You're f***in' s*%@!in'' me!"

I felt a grin start to come over my face I couldn't stop. I said, "Now why would I do that to my favorite...," then I stopped.

He said, "You're...You're serious?"

I said, "Yes Sir...I love it here, Sir!"

He said, "Well, you asked for it then!" He handed me the necessary paper work to extend my service six more months at Uplift.

He said, "I'll give you a tip."

I said, "I've already felt your tip too many times, Sir! Thank you no!"

He said, "Alright then, do you want your month R&R in Hawaii, Bangkok, or Hong Kong? The world is at your fingertips. Or do you want to waver your R&R, and apply it to your in country time?"

I asked, "If I waver my thirty days R&R, will it count as time in country and will I get out thirty days sooner?"

He said, "If you don't go on R&R for a month you will be out of the army in five more months, give or take a few days."

I felt as though I was dealing with the devil himself, and maybe I was. I felt I was being screwed without taking my pants off but it sounded so darn good I said, "That sounds real good to me, Sir."

He said, "That is all you and I have to talk about for now. You are dismissed!"

I just about ran out of there. The next day I was sent out on a Recon mission as a sniper for three weeks. For the next three months I was stuck on one mission after the other, the only break I got was when I had to go to An Khe to re-zero my 21, and on one of those missions I caught a bullet fragment in the hip. I remember that time like it was yesterday. It happened in the same place Moran got killed, in the Annamitique mountains. We ran into a huge V.C. Base camp. The team I was working with nearly got wiped out by the time we got back up help from Uplift. I blame A-hole for that. He had something to do with it, I just know! Our support company took so long getting there they must have come by way of China. In fact whenever we called back to Uplift for help A-hole would know it because the radio shack was part of his office.

I got nine days of R&R, and I had to fight with A-hole to get that. The doctor on post was the only thing that kept me out of the boonies that long. That was the only time I got to party or relax at all. I was turning into an animal. I hated everyone! But I loved to kill. Every time I pulled the trigger I saw A-hole's face in my scope. Whenever he re-supplied our team with men it was always new guys that he sent out to us. Whenever we got our new men and supplies, we were sent right back into another mission non-stop, never a break. Soon the only men with any experience left alive on the team were Brink, Thompson our radio man, and myself.

I remember a mission I was on one time after I became a sniper. I was working with a line company just on the outskirts of a small vill just a short ways above An Khe, up north. It was a place with a mile or so stretch between two very small vills and for a few weeks trucks and jeeps were being blown up left and right by land mines right under our noses. We didn't know if the mines were being set up during the day or night and no one could figure out how it was being done.

Our company decided to devise a plan. I would sit undercover watching a small section of road for anything out of the ordinary. Meanwhile, the line company squads would draw attention off me by hanging out in the area, making it look like they were just patrolling.

Very early one morning I was sitting in the bushes, watching the road just before the daily vehicle traffic started moving. I spotted a very young girl, about twelve years old, walking up and down the road acting nervous, like a shoplifter, looking around.

Suddenly she stopped and right in the middle of the road she dropped her pants and took a dump. As she was squatted down with her back to me I looked through my scope at her. I looked under her rear and could see her hands moving briskly. She was digging a hole between her legs while she was going to the bathroom. I'm no peeping Tom, but my job was to keep an eye out for anything strange and to me that was very strange. As she squatted there, I saw she soon had a fairly deep hole dug out of the dirt between her legs. She stopped digging and looked around. Then I saw her slowly and carefully pull a mine, or what looked like a mine, out of a fairly large black bag she carried on a strap on her shoulder. She proceeded to plant it. I watched her do the whole thing.

It was early and quiet yet and I didn't have a silencer on my weapon at that time. Most of the line squad with me were lying around sleeping or just getting up about three hundred yards away from me, near the edge of an open rice patty filed. I could see the girl's hands through my scope from underneath her starting to smooth the dirt back over the mine. I knew what I had to do and it was killing me. I knew I was going to have to kill a woman…a very young one. She was about two hundred yards away and if I could have yelled her to stop and freeze right there, she would have run so fast she would have been gone in a flash before I could even have gotten to my feet to stop her. She would be planting mines someplace else the next morning. I knew if the nightmare was to be stopped I was going to have to do it right then and there.

I held right on her back, dead center, and I was having a real hard time with it all. Killing a girl was really getting to me bad…I remember I didn't want her to suffer so I raised the cross hairs and I put them right dead on the base of her neck, right behind her head. I knew a hit like that right there would kill her instantly! Through the scope I could see more people were starting to walk up and down the road and I had to make my move.

Boom! The rifle barked out. The sound of the shot had the line dudes coming towards me fast. I jumped up and out of the bushes and I ran as fast as I could to the dead girl lying in the middle of the road and the many people that were now starting to circle around her. I knew if I didn't get there quick that mine would have "disappeared" so fast my head would have been spinning. The circling V.C. would have quickly carried the mine away. As I got closer to the body I kept screaming for everyone to get back and some of the line company dudes caught up to me quickly and they secured the area around the body.

When I flipped the girl over she was laying on top of a ten-pound land mine. It was a good thing that she hadn't actually armed it yet because her body would have set it off, killing many people around her as well. That really stuck with me for a long time. That was the only time I ever had to kill a woman. But I had no choice. She was doing what she felt she had to do…and so was I.

CHAPTER 40

The Mad Fragger

One day we got a "cherry," or so he called himself that anyway. He told us his name was Redd. He said he had never been in combat before, but you could never convince me of that! He would jump right into spider holes, caves or anywhere Charley was holed up and always come out with a dead V.C. If Redd was a cherry, so was Audey Murphy. He was a medic and a very good one. Redd was about 5' 6" and built like an ox. He shaved his head and his eyes looked weird…spooky. He also had a weird laugh and smile.

For some reason, right off the bat we both saw eye to eye, at least about our job. I knew not to screw with him as long as he didn't screw with me. He followed me everywhere. The only time that I got away from Redd was when I was sent to An Khe to re-zero. Myself, I thought he was quite insane. That is one reason why I stayed friends with him. Unless you had a death wish, staying on the good side of him was the only smart way to go. I knew the only thing I could do to get rid of him was to shoot him and that would be all out murder. I wanted no part of that.

I felt the only law that was keeping me out of the fires of hell then was the one that Babbles told me about; the one that he read about in the Bible. He said killing was acceptable as long as you killed because of self-defence during war or whatever. What did I know? At that time in my life Babbles was my "Spiritual genealogy" and I only knew what he taught me about God's laws.

I heard talk that Redd's brother was killed near Uplift in '66. He once told me he was sent to Nam by Satan himself to kill.

I asked, "To kill V.C., right?"

He replied, "To kill!"

I said, "Oh!" I knew right then this dude was a couple can's shy of a 6 pack. I figured when a guy started talking to Satan himself and getting orders from him, the guy was in real deep doo-doo.

My extension time was ticking away very slowly. I had three to three and a half more months to go and I was living in the bush at all times. I was barely keeping all of my brain together. I didn't know how much longer I could take it before I all out went up and shot A-hole.

One day while on bunker guard, during one of the few times I was out of the bush at Uplift, Redd came running up and sat down next to me. It was about 2200 and most everyone was laid back for the night. He just looked at me and smiled. I said, "So, what the heck ya lookin' at me like that for?"

He said, "I have a surprise for a sorry Captain within the next couple of days."

I asked, "Surprise? How's that?"

Just as he opened his mouth to speak, a very large blast went off just below us on the main post. I jumped up and started into the bunker. Redd just sat there. I said, "Come on you dope! It might be a mortar attack or somethin'!"

He said, "Naugh, just a blown ta hell Nigger is all. Black sum-b*!$*h bust my balls will he….I know he'll neva' mess with me again! The Mad Fragger just got some payback!"

I asked, "What the heck you sayin? That was you?!"

He said "Yep." Down on the main post I could see a lot of smoke and lots of men starting to gather around a hooch.

When I came back from Sniper school and I saw the big "change" at Uplift, I saw that blacks and whites were staying away from each other. Even the news from back home was telling all kinds of stories about race riots and Black Power against White Power and all that stuff. The hooch that just got blown up was mostly full of blacks.

I looked at Redd and I said, "You're kiddin' me!"

He just smiled and said, "My daddy is in the K.K.K. down in Georgia, an he's a big shot. He done told me to give them niggaz's hell over here. Ever think about joinin' the K.K.K., Jimmy?"

I asked, "The Klu Klux Klan…KKK? Are you nuts! or what?"

He said, "Yawl betta' stand up for our race while you still have a chance. There's gonna' be another civil war in America, Jimmy. One day yawl-er gonna' have-ta pick a side. Gonna' come a war one day, Jimmy, a war against Mexicans, niggers, spicks, chinks, and all that garbage!"

I was in shock and really didn't know what to say. I just said, "If I was you, I'd be real cool about who you tell stuff like that to! Especially now after this bombing."

He said, "You're the only good buddy I have, the only one I can really trust. I would sure hate to lose you as a friend, Jimmy. I would sure hate fer us ta become enemies, know what I mean?"

I said to myself, Man! Now this is just my luck, to know this all out madman! Not only did I have to watch out for Charley and Captain A-hole, but now I had to worry about this crazy son of a bug too! I knew right then that if our friendship, or whatever I could call it, ever got a little bit shaky, I would have to shoot this nut in the head or he would kill me. He just all out told me that by saying what he said. I was just too darn short to get blown up by this nut cake. I only had three to four months to go until I got out of there. Every time we came into the rear from that time on, the Mad Fragger, as he was soon called all over Uplift, would strike again on anyone he disliked - black, white or whatever. I had to live with knowing who he was but I could do nothing about it.

One day at formation A-hole announced that if anyone knew anything about who the Fragger was, all they had to do was drop a note on the ground anywhere around the area. He said it would get into his hands one way or the other and no questions would be asked. The whole time he said that speech he looked right at me. I knew that even if he didn't believe it was me, and I do believe he suspected me, I think he would have tried to pin the whole thing on me and never care less who it really was as long as he could pin an attemped murder charge on me. I think that because of the time I pulled my M-16 on him during that earring deal, let alone all the other times I drove him nuts!

In the military we went by a different set of laws than we do in our civilian life. In the military we had to deal with the Unified Code of Military Justice. That is a code that can usually never be beaten or broken. I read once over ninety percent of all court martials were convictions. They usually never brought you up on charges unless they had you set up air tight. If and when convicted, a man could spend the rest of his life busting very large rocks into very little rocks. In the military a person can still get a sentence with "hard labor" attached to it.

I believe that is the fate A-hole had planned for me if he could do it. So there I was, stuck with no one to turn to for help. I just had to live with it. Had I dropped the note telling the name of the Fragger, they would have compared my hand writing with the note and they could have matched it up and A-hole would have said I was just trying to pin it on Redd. Redd would have turned into a witness against me, and he would have said that he was the one in my shoes or in the predicament I was in. That kept my mug closed tight. But out in the woods Redd was the best fighting man I ever saw.

CHAPTER 41

Pussy Cat

One day after I came back from re-zeroing at Ahn-Khe, Kabbatt and I were sent out on a mission with two different Line Companies. After he and I reached our separate companies, we all moved out together toward our respective A-O's, or Areas of Operation.

Just before the two companies went off on their separete ways, Kabbatt jumped onto an A.P.C or an Armored Personal Carrier, a small tank sort of vehicle. We had been walking for quite some time and Kabbatt was hot and tired so he got on to ride instead of walking. He yelled to me to jump on and ride with him but I said that I was alright for then and we moved on.

About ten minutes went by. All of a sudden, a rocket came out of the thick jungle area right at us in the open and hit the A.P.C. dead center - right in the L.P. fuel tank. The A.P.C. blew sky high as I jumped for cover. As soon as I hit the ground I looked up and I saw Kabbatt sitting on top of a huge ball of fire about fifty feet in the air. We got hit from all sides by a big V.C. ambush. They hit us quickly and then vanished just as fast.

I ran over to Kabbatt, or what was left of him, and tried to do something. He looked like a burnt up marshmallow. I yelled for a medic. Kabbatt was burnt up badly and going mad with pain. His legs were fused together as was his right arm to his side. I darn near fainted! As I looked at the burnt up thing lying there, I almost barfed just knowing it was actually muscle-bound Kabbatt. It was unbelievably awful! He looked like something out of a monster movie!

We all got our stuff back together and evacuated the dead and wounded. When the medi-evac ship came in I tried to say goodbye to my good friend, but he was going in and out of shock and didn't give a hoot about saying anything to anyone.

The chopper flew away. That was the last time I ever saw him. It took me a long time to stop seeing that horrible picture of him floating at the top of that fireball and how he looked all burnt up. It played over and over, time after time in my mind, nonstop for days.

We had to call back to Uplift for another sniper, because Kabbatt was gone and the Line Co. needed one to continue the mission. About three hours after the attack we got a chopper with the fresh sniper. It was Miller, the new Sniper at Uplift. Both Line Companies spent that night about two hundred meters apart. In the morning the Line Co. that I was working with was going to be moving out about two thousand meters or two "clicks" further into the mountain area. The other company was going to work the valley area below the mountain.

That early morning, about 0300, Miller and I were awakened by the Line Co. Captains. It was still very dark. They said they had a job for us to do. We all moved toward the edge of a clear open area down at the base of the mountain where we were camped. One Captain said that it had been reported to him a few minutes ago that V.C. were seen about 300 meters out in front walking along a rice patty dike.

Miller and I went out to check it out. We both got down into position and looked through our night scopes. Sure enough, there were nine V.C. about 200 meters out crossing on top of a rice patty dike as the man had reported. I asked, "Miller, do you see 'um?"

He replied, "Got 'um."

I said, "I'll start on the right and you come in from the left. We'll work towards the middle, got it?"

He said, "Whenever you're ready."

I set myself up so I could move easily right down the line, towards the center of the line of V.C. So did Miller. I took careful aim and fired. Thud! I hit the first one in line. Thud! Miller hit the last one. Then I hit the second one, Miller hit the second to last one. And so on as we shot towards the center. They were all hit so fast, none of them ever realized what was happening to them until it was too late.

The last one to be hit was the one in the middle. He just stood there for a second, not knowing whether to dump in his homemade BVDs or go blind. Just as he went to jump off the rice patty dike, we both cut loose and hit him at the same time. We "double pumped" him. He went flipping about ten feet.

The two Line Co. Captains were watching the whole thing with their small P.V.S.-2A night scopes. One of them said, "I don't even believe that and I saw it!"

The other said, "It would take us a week of real hard work to zap that many dinks. Man, you guys are f*%#* scary!" Miller and I just smiled at each other. Then we got up and moved back to our area to sleep.

One captain said the bodies would be picked up the next day and sent back to Uplift. I often wondered just what they did with them. We always had to send them back if we could. Maybe they just ground them up and fed them to "legs," I never found out.

After breakfast that morning Uplift called and told the Line Company I was with to stay put for then, right there on that side of the mountain. They said that both Line Companies were supposed to do some sweeping maneuvers up and down both sides of the mountain, looking for base camps that had been reported by the local spies we had working for us. Miller and I were supposed to watch the low lands or valleys on either side, mostly at night. Uplift told my company to stay there an extra day and overnight to give Miller's company time to move around to the other side of the mountain, far enough away so we wouldn't bump into each other. They also wanted to drive any V.C. between us up the mountain to the top so an air strike could be called in and they could fry them.

That day Miller and the company he was with moved out and headed for the other side of the mountain. Also that day, a squad of guys in my company were supposed to go out and pick up the nine dead V.C. that Miller and I did away with the night before. But Uplift never sent a chopper out to us that day to come and get them, so they lay right where they fell dead. The Captain didn't want them lying around the camp all day drawing flies. He said they could run out and get them when the chopper came in the next day. So the bodies lay out in the open that night.

I didn't know it then but a very large tiger was eating the dead V.C. and had become a "man eater." All that night we kept hearing the loud growling and roar of a big tiger that was walking around just outside the camp area. Early the next morning, just before dawn, I was shaken out of my sleep by the line Captain. He told me that the "pussy cat" we had all been hearing was freaking out his men. It kept trying all night long to sneak into camp and snatch one of his men for a late night snack and we were all in danger of being attacked. He said that tigers could see at night and we couldn't. He said he had gotten reports all night long about the cat sneaking in close to the camp trying to snatch a man to two. I was instructed to take that "pussy cat" out!

Out about two or three hundred yards, fairly close to where the V.C. bodies were, I could hear the cat roaring and making growling sounds. He was guarding them as his own. One of the men on guard at the out skirts of the camp said, as he looked through a P.V.S.-2A, "He's right out there about a hundred fifty yards and he's a f^&$* monster!"

I got down into the prone position and I looked through my starlight scope. I spotted him right off the bat. He was so huge I couldn't believe my eyes. He looked like a large sofa with teeth. I watched him for a few seconds just admiring how totally awesome, huge and beautiful he was. He looked so strong and powerful he freaked me out to just look at him. I didn't want to pull that trigger any more then I wanted to go to blazes! But he was a threat and so big he could have snatched a man just as quickly and easily as a large Tom cat could have snatched a small field mouse. Besides, an order was an order!

I drew down onto the side of his massive head. He slowly walked broad side, looking right at me. He was growling with a very low guttural sound. He turned his huge head to the front and I put the cross hairs dead center in his ear.

Thud! I fired one round. He jerked and jumped sideways as he fell dead! I closed my eyes and I said, "Jesus! I hate this place."

That trigger pull felt like the time I pulled the trigger on that girl. It was even worse than when I pulled it on her. This awesome being killed to feed himself and stay alive. We killed just to kill.

CHAPTER 42

The Ancestor's Revenge

About 1100 hours that morning, after what was left of the V.C. bodies were picked up by chopper, we all headed out with the line companies and humped up the very steep mountain towards the top. It was a long and very hard climb because it was a big mountain. It usually took days to get over a mountain, especially in Nam, because the bush was so thick, making it slow going. You also had to keep an eye out for booby traps as you went, making the going even slower. It was a fight all the way to the top.

Just before we got to the very top of the mountain on the third day, the captain got on the radio to Miller's company. The officers planned that the two companies would link up for a day and just kind of relax before sweeping back down the mountain. All the way up neither company ran into a thing, which really isn't all that unusual because that many men made a gang of noise. A stone-deaf V.C. could hear us coming a mile away.

Suddenly, one of the men tripped a major booby trap. I was only about twenty feet from a sheer rock cliff when the blast went off. It was the biggest blast I ever heard. I felt enormous pressure being put on every inch of my body. I could also feel a lot of heat. I was picked up by the back blast of the explosion and thrown like a twig over the cliff to my right.

As I flew, I could see far below me into the valley. I was numb all over from the shock of the blast. All I could think was that this was my time to punch out the time card of life. I felt that my time was finally over.

When I came down and hit the ground I landed on all kinds of sharp rocks, roots, and sticks. I rolled and rolled down this steep cliff. Finally I came to rest on a small ledge. As I came back to my senses I could start to feel a lot of pain all over my body. My ears were ringing so hard it sounded like church bells ringing on Christmas morning. As I looked myself over for missing and broken parts I saw that somehow I still had my XM-21 with me. I couldn't believe I didn't lose it during my flight to the moon. I guess I remembered that there was a reward for my weapon as well as for me and I wasn't going to let Charley make a cent on that deal, no matter what. I don't really know to this day how I hung on to it. I saw many cuts and hunks of flesh torn loose from my legs and arms. My right knee hurt so bad I couldn't stand it. I thought I was going to die for sure. My right leg was pinned underneath me and I couldn't move it for the pain. It felt really weird, like it wouldn't bend out straight or move any longer. I used all the strength I could come up with to get my right leg to straighten out from underneath me. The pain was so bad I passed out cold.

When I came to, I sat there wondering how I would ever be found and if anyone up above me was still alive. I didn't know if the blast and ambush had killed everyone or not. I was hurt bad and I had no clue as to how I was going to contact anyone to get rescued. I thought that if I started yelling for help the V.C. would know just where to look to pick up a fat reward for capturing a "Superman" and his weapon. I knew I was in real deep trouble!

After I had sat there for about twenty minutes flipping out in pain, I heard American voices up above me. Then two men, one a medic, repelled down on ropes to where I was. They said some of the men saw me go flying over the cliff and they had sent word to Uplift for medi-evac choppers to come get the dead and wounded. They told me there were four men wounded counting myself…and three dead. They said that it really could have been much worse.

The medic told me that the captain thought that the booby trap was retaliation for the tiger he had me kill. The medic told me the captain felt real bad about the whole thing and he said he wished he never gave me that order. I had to agree. He said the captain thought and felt that was all true because of the size of the blast that was set. He believed that the enemy wanted to kill a massive number of us for killing one of their ancestors, especially one as noble and majestic as that tiger. (To the Vietnamese a tiger was something very special.) A charge that big was very seldom used because it was waste of explosives and a blast like that was used more to make a statement than anything else.

The medic helped me get my leg out from under me but I could see that my knee cap was off and on the inside of my leg, kind of off to one side. The more critical men were extracted first. As I waited my turn to be lifted out I asked what the heck happened up there. The medic said, "Someone tripped a very large mine up on top. We still don't know for sure who he and one other guy were, there's only a couple piles of burger left. Good thing all you caught was the back blast of that sucker!"

I replied, "Yeeeeeah! I'm real lucky."

The medic said, "Take it easy man, you're all done fightin' in this war for sure! You're going home!" The thought was just too good to be true. But it sure sounded good to me.

Soon I was in a medi-evac chopper and on my way to Ophu Cat hospital. Before I left I gave my XM-21 and my rut sack to the captain and he said he would make sure my things got back safely to Recon's arms room and not to worry. I was just happy to be alive and aboard a chopper out of that hell hole, hurt or not.

I saw two of the wounded guys riding with me. One had only one arm and his face was all bloody. The other man was real bad off. The total madness of it all really hit me and was just getting too much for me to handle anymore. I knew no matter how much I saw I would never get used to it.

Soon we landed in the hospital L.Z. We were hustled on guernies into a room where two nurses cut off all our clothing with scissors. Then we were moved into an operating room. Some doctors came rushing in and checked us out.

After I was cleaned up I was put into a ward with thirty other men. As I was pushed into the room towards my bed I could see men that were all blown up and shot to bits! I remember being put into a bed and given a shot. I fell asleep and didn't wake up until a day and a half later. I remember nurses trying to make me eat and drink, but I couldn't.

Finally when I did come to, I had tubes in my mouth and arms and my right leg was in traction. I looked down at my leg and I saw a large weight and rope tied to my ankle. I tried to sit up, but the weight that was tied to my foot pulled so hard it hurt like mad. So I just lay there.

Soon a nurse came over to me and asked how I was doing. I said, "Okay....I think?"

She said, "Don't worry, you have all your parts and you'll be all right."

I said, "Thank God!"

She said, "You'll be up in no time at all. Your knee is screwed up, but you'll be okay."

I said, "Thanks!"

She asked, "Can I get you something?"

I said, "I have to go to the bathroom."

She said, "You can't get up, but I'll get you a...," then she stopped. She asked, "Number one or number two?"

I said, "If number one means pee, you got it!"

She laughed and got me a stainless steel can to go in. That sucker was so cold between my legs I almost got frost bite. I decided then that that was the last time I would try that! So from then on when I had to go, I would unhook my traction and sneak into the john. The nurses would get all inflamed about that. The pain in my leg was terrible, but no way was I going to the bathroom in bed again!

For four weeks I stayed at Ophu Cat hospital trying to walk again. They would come in every day and stick a needle into my knee to draw out the fluid. My knee would swell up to the size of a cantaloupe each day, so they would have to drain it every day. I think that blasted needle hurt more than the damage to my knee did.

One day the Doc came in and said he was going to do a special test on my knee. He told me it was going to hurt but it was the only way to see clearly inside my knee. He said he was going to have to inject some dye into my knee in three places. When he first got started with "the test" the pain was bad but it soon got worse. I almost grabbed the Doc and broke his neck it hurt so bad.

For weeks I lay around and took every test they threw my way. Finally one day the Doc came to me and said, "I don't know if your knee will heal up by itself or not. You'll probably need an operation. The x-rays really don't show me what I need to see. I believe one of the tendons that run along both sides of your kneecap is damaged and possibly severed. One doesn't even seem to be there at all. I just can't tell for sure what damage has been done. The pain in the right side of your groin is a good indication that the tendon on the left side of your right kneecap has snapped up into the groin area. For now, there is nothing I can do. If it doesn't get better within three or four weeks, come back here and I will send you to Cam-Rhon Bay hospital for more extensive tests."

All that bologna meant to me was that I was still in pain and I wasn't going home.

CHAPTER 43

One More Time!

The doctor sent me back to Uplift on extra light duty for three weeks. After that I was told to come back and see him. At that time, I was up and walking, but the pain was still very bad.

I hitched a ride back to Uplift from Ophu Cat hospital and I went up to Captain A-hole and showed him my light duty slip. Right away he said I was just trying to screw off and I was trying to get out of mission duty. My knee was as big as a grapefruit but he still wouldn't believe me or cared less. For two weeks I got stuck on bunker guard every night. The third week the pain was very bad and my knee was turning purple, so I went to sick call down on the main post to see about going back to the hospital to get looked at again.

Before I ever got to see the Doc, Captain A-hole came down to sick call and came storming right in. He looked at a few of us that were there and yelled pointing his finger, "You! You! You! Get your butts back to duty! You're all just ghosting. You should be working, not ghosting down here! And you! Gibbore! I'll tell you when you can go back to the hospital. Move out!" So two of us walked back to duty, I limped back. Maybe the two other guys were ghosting but I sure as heck wasn't!

I only had fifty nine days left in country by that time and I figured for fifty nine days I could cope with about anything. Just knowing I was almost out of the army felt so good! I would have put up with anything. I didn't argue one bit, I just did any job I was assigned the best I could. At that time there was a lot of V.C. activity going on in the bush, guys were getting hit more and more each day.

The week I was supposed to go back to Ophu Cat hospital for a check up on my knee the Captain called me to his office. I walked up to the orderly room to see what he wanted. When I walked in he said, "Sit down! How's the knee?" I gave him a dirty look with no answer.

He said, "I'm going to come right to the point. I know you only have a short time left, but I need a favor from you. If you do this favor, I will get you a pass to Ophu Cat hospital with my personal recommendation to take you out of combat duty forever."

I said, "Who do I have to kill?"

He replied, "No, nothing like that. I need a team leader real bad."

I said, "Well get Brink or one of the other guys to do it." A-hole looked down for a second.

Then he said, "Brink...is dead. He was just killed about an hour ago."

In shock, I just stared right through him. I felt like I wasn't there, like nothing was real anymore, like it was all a weird sick dream. My "war son" was dead! As I heard A-hole's voice talking to me I kept thinking that I must have been some sort of jinx or something. I felt like some sort of bottom just fell out from underneath me. All the friends that I had were dead or dying all around me. I thought I must have been a bad "war father," a bad teacher, maybe cursed! I thought why not me?

Why was it always my friends that were killed and not me? The guilt was overwhelming! I could literally feel the blood run out of my face and I must have turned white as a ghost from grief.

A-hole said, "I have a very important mission to complete and I have no one left in the rear right now that can run a team. I need your help!" I wanted out of the army so bad that I would have done anything to get out! Anything!

I said, "If I go, you'll give me your word that you'll do what you say you will do?"

He said, "I swear it. I'll have you out of combat as soon as you get back in." So I agreed.

The next afternoon, messed up knee and all, I was ready to go. My team was made up of four new men that had never been out, two that had only been out twice, and myself. I said just what I had to say to them and nothing more because I was afraid to let them become friends with me.I thought all I could teach them was how to get killed! I planned to hump the radio and pull point. I was determined to get the team through that last mission if it killed me doing it. I was not going to take any chances at all! I planned to do the job as quickly and easily as possible and get out.

At about 1700 hours that afternoon, once we all got packed and loaded with ammo. and food, we headed out to the briefing bunker. Two teams were going out that mission, and we were going to be working together. Just before dark we were told we would be inserted into the Soui-Ca Valley. Locals reported large numbers of V.C. there almost every day and night. Our job was to plan, not do, an ambushing. We were sent out to get things set up for some line companies that were going to come in to do the ambushing in a day or so. All we were to do was get things set up and planned out, and to tell the line companies exactly where the enemy was moving most of the time, so they could get off a more effective ambush. Then we would be brought back in after the line companies came out to us to take over.

The only sense this made to me was that this was A-hole's last chance to get me killed. I just thought Screw it. It don't mean nothin.' Just one more time and I'm out-a-here! Our mission was supposed to be a quick in and out mission. We were told to do everything we could to avoid contact with the enemy. The Intel. men told us to take notes and plan ambushes and leave the combat to the line companies, which sounded real good to me.

After our briefing, I talked to Thompson, my usual radioman, who was the team leader on the other team, about what we were going to do. We planned to stay fairly close to each other and get in touch often. Both teams were going to plot four separate ambush areas to attack the enemy from many different ambush points. When set up right, these types of ambushes would usually send the enemy fleeing in panic into a second team's ambush.

About two hours before it got dark, we climbed into our choppers and moved out. We were flown into the Soui-Ca Valley southeast of Uplift and put down in the valley. I kept trying to think about the mission we had to do but it was very difficult to concentrate on what had to be done, thinking about going home and the pain in my leg. My messed up knee was killing me, which made the job almost unbearable.

After the choppers left both teams stayed together for the night and watched the valley below from our side of the mountain with a P.V.S.-2A. There was a half moon out that night so I could see very well. We were camped about four hours when we began to see many V.C./N.V.A. soldiers moving down in front of our position, about two hundred meters away. I grabbed Thompson and we crept to within twenty meters of the open area below. We sat there for an hour counting groups of five and ten V.C. passing right by us. In a very short time we counted well over one hundred moving within twenty meters of our position.

We then headed back to the teams to report to Uplift what we had seen. I called Uplift and told them what we saw and they told us that they would get back to us the next day. Both teams stayed together until late afternoon the next day. We moved about in short distances, planning and setting up many ambushes for the more open area below. The plan was to report what we were doing to Uplift, who would instruct the line companies and make the plan.

My team planned some ambushes that were designed to push the V.C. that were attacked first and got away into running into the other team's ambush. We stayed about two hundred meters from the second team the second night. We knew exactly how far each team was from each other at all times, so as not to hurt each other if any commotion started, we lost contact, or a fire fight broke out.

Near the end of the second day Uplift called and told us that they had changed our "watcher" mission to a "hunter killer" mission. All I could think of was how bad I wanted to kill A-hole. So we all went to work setting booby traps in different places and planning what we would do.

Around dusk my team spotted thirty or forty V.C. coming along a newly booby trapped trail we had prepared that day as Uplift wanted us to do. I called Thompson on the radio and told him to get ready because we might drive some V.C. his way. He said, "Roger that!" Thompson's team had an M-60 machine gun that spit a lot of fire power so he could finish off the enemy if they came his way as was planned. Soon the V.C. were in our kill zone. I grabbed my detonator and squeezed the switch. Baaaboom! All the mines went off together, surrounding the enemy team, as we had planned.

Suddenly...boom! Thompson's mines went off just after ours. I knew what was left of the enemy had turned and had been driven back to Thompson. We got up and threw fragmentation hand grenades at what was left of the screaming and mangled V.C. that didn't get away just below us. Fraggs would not give away our position. I ordered that no one fire an M-16, just throw hand grenades. Then I stopped our ambush to listen and to radio team #2 to see how they were doing. By then it was getting very near dark. I could hear the bark of Thompson's M-60, fraggs and small arms fire.

Thompson said, "They're everywhere! Were pulling back. I'm coming back to you while I still have a little light left." I told Thompson to move out and we would be watching for them. Then I looked at the men I had and I could see they were scared.

I said, "Just lie flat down. Don't fire your 16's until I say so. V.C. will see the flash and we'll be screwed for sure if they pinpoint our location! Whenever you see them or their muzzle flashes getting closer, lob a grenade and they will run right into it. We'll cause damage and won't give our position away!"

Suddenly I saw I had a man wounded and he needed help bad! One guy caught a piece of grenade or something in his chest. He was bleeding badly. Grenade fragments had been scattered all around. Thompson's team was giving Charley heck with the M-60. I could hear the 60 getting closer. I told the team to keep an eye out for anything as I helped the injured man.

The man I had on our radio said Thompson called Uplift and he said he already called in some gun ships and a reinforced platoon of men were on their way to us, hopefully they would get there before it was too dark. I told my team to keep low and watch and wait until help arrived. We just kept throwing grenades from time to time and doing the best we could to stay alive. The enemy was all around us and Thompson was having a heck of a time trying to get back to us. He said he had wounded men of his own to cope with as well. We fought there for about twenty minutes to half an hour before the enemy finally got chased off of us by the platoon and gun ships that came in.

Finally Thompson's team made their way to us. We moved into the lowland area below and we stayed there for the night and were air lifted out in the morning. After the reinforcement platoon swept the area the next day they found twelve dead V.C./N.V.A. soldiers and numerous bloodstained trails where Charley carried off his dead and wounded.

Somehow I lucked out again. How we got out alive I'll never know. My last mission only lasted two days or so, but it was just about the two scariest days I ever spent in the bush.

As soon as I got back to Uplift and off my chopper, I made a beeline for A-hole's office. I walked up and knocked on his office door, and he told me to come in. When he saw it was me he said, "Well, I see you didn't waste any time getting up here."

I replied, "Sir, I did my part, are you going to do yours? There is something wrong with my leg. It wouldn't be hurtin' like it is for nothin'!"

He said, "Now slow down, don't get all shook up."

I said, "Are you going to let me go to sick call or what?" He took a standard looking army form that was all typed out and he signed it. Then he handed it to me. I looked at it. It was my orders for passage to Ophu Cat hospital. Also on another paper was his recommendation that I be taken out of combat duty immediately and permanently. My eyes opened up like it was a check for a million dollars. In shock I said, "I never thought I would say this to you. But I just want to say, thanks a million."

He said, "You could in no way be any happier than I am!"

I replied, "Don't you bet on it!…Sir!"

I turned around and about ran out of the office to clean up and pack before he changed his mind. As I got cleaned up and packed I was so happy I couldn't even see straight. I just kept thinking about what the doctor at the hospital told me about going to the hospital in Japan if my leg was screwed up enough or it wasn't doing better by the next visit, and it wasn't! That was as good as a one way ticket home. The way my knee felt I knew it was messed up bad!

That last night there I went around to all my friends and said, "Goodbye!" That night we all partied big time. Just about midnight six of us Recon men were smoking a joint out on top of bunker #14, out near the edge of camp. We were all just sitting around way up on top stoned to the bone when a flashlight shined on us. We looked up and saw Captain A-hole with two M.P.s. He said, "How about if we join your little party there, Jim?"

I said, "Shiii…!"

He said, "Let's go boys."

He busted us all for smoking pot, which he could have done even without the M.P.s. He used them for backup because he was so spineless. He left one man on guard and took the rest of us to his office. We were fined two hundred dollars and then he told everyone but me to get out of his sight.

When everyone left he looked at me and said, "Not only are you fined two hundred dollars but, well your sleeves are mighty bare, aren't they? I guess there isn't much more I can take from you is there! It won't be long and you really will be able to call yourself a civilian. You're not far from that rank right now."

I just snickered and shook my head in disgust as I looked at him. I replied, "No matter what you think of me, I don't need you to tell me what kind of soldier I've been while I was here. Remember, actions speak much louder than words. I was a good soldier until I met up with you."

He said, "Don't worry about me stopping you from leaving tomorrow. I want you gone out of my sight. But if you are not sent home for medical reasons…If you ever come back to Uplift, you will find your stuff down on the main post in some Line Company. Don't ever come back up here. You don't belong here with real soldiers, all you do is set a bad example."

I asked, "Is that all, Sir?" He told me to get out of his sight. I was more than glad to.

I limped out the door down towards bunker 14. When I got near there I ran into the Mad Fragger. I said, "A-hole, I swear I could kill his azz!"

Redd just smiled and said, "I heard, and your wish is my command." Without even thinking about what he said because I was so steamed up, I walked over to a hooch where a guy I knew played old movies once in a while. The guy would send back to the world to get films then charge us a buck to see them. I went in and rapped with some guys for a while and laughed at the flick that was on as I tried to forget A-hole for a while.

Soon the Fragger came in and sat down next to me with that smile of his. I looked at him and asked, "What's up guy?!"

He just turned his head still smiling like the cat that ate….you know what I mean. I said, "So…What's so funny?"

He said, "Scratch one Captain!" I grabbed him by his arm and took him outside.

I said, "You didn't!"

He said with an ear to ear smile, "I did! That's one mother f#**#* that won't be in our hair anymore."

Just then….Baaaabooom! I said, "Oh no man! You must be nuts! Who do you think they're going to blame for that? I just left his office. I'm the one he just busted! Screw me, dude!"

With a laugh he said, "I can't help it. I'm nuttier than a Christmas nut cake! I didn't know what I was doing." Then he giggled.

We both ran around the end of our hooch and I looked up the hill at the orderly room. Up at the top of the hill I saw smoke and dust engulfing A-hole's hooch. Men were coming out of everywhere to look around. I said, "I sure hope that dude is dead! If not he'll think I done it for sure!"

Redd said, "Don't worry! If he ain't, he will wish he was. 'Sides he's gonna' have to prove who he thinks done it anyway. How's he gonna' do that? Naaaa. No sweat. Don't worry you're out-a-here in the mornin' anyway."

As everyone in the hooches came running out, we walked up the hill. As we walked up the hill the Fragger told me he put a grenade with a homemade time delay fuse on A-hole's window ledge as he was getting undressed for bed. The homemade fuse was just a rubber band around the handle of the frag, with a lit cigerette stuck behind the rubber band. You pull the pin on the frag and the rubber band holds the spoon until the cigerette burns down, melts or cuts the rubber band, and ten seconds later, ba-bam! The longer the square or the farther the cigerette's lit end was pushed above the rubber band, the longer the time delay before it went off.

I said, "Shut up! I don't want to know nothing!" He just laughed softly.

By the time we got up there we saw a medic and two other men carrying A-hole out of his hooch belly-down on a stretcher. His butt was completely blown off! I never saw anything like it. He had no butt cheeks left at all! The Fragger poked me in the ribs and then he snickered. As they carried A-hole past me all doped up, he looked up at me and fell back down out cold. He was hurt bad, but not bad enough to die. Which to me was even better! I thought from now on for the rest of his nasty life, every time he looked into a full length mirror and saw he had no azz, he would think of me! Everyone wanted him dead! But there was no doubt in my mind he thought I did it. I know that's what he thought.

As the Fragger and I walked down towards my hooch, he said, "How was that for a going away gift buddy?"

I shook my head and I replied, "Jesus. Man, you are something." The rest of the night everyone on Recon Hill got together and partied heavy just knowing A-hole wasn't going to be around bustin' rocks anymore. M.P.s showed up that night asking half-hearted questions about where we all were when the blast went off and everything. But they soon saw we were too stoned out to give a hoot about what happened to Captain Nobutt! They saw that no one was very "bereaved" or anything. They knew they had a whole L.Z. full of suspects and really had no idea where to start pointing a finger. They gave up quickly. Redd was right, no one could prove a thing. No one was going to bemoan him and no one saw anything or even wanted to know nothin'! The next morning I got up, ate breakfast and packed my stuff to leave for Ophu Cat Hospital. I said goodbye once again to everyone, then I walked down Recon Hill for the last time. Out in the road traffic was just as heavy as always. I put out my thumb and caught a ride.

As the truck pulled away, I looked back up at the hill and remembered the first time I ever walked up that blasted hill. For some reason I felt very lonely and farther away from those that made Uplift bearable. I could still see Schriff standing by the formation area waving goodbye. I could also see Lori walking across the yard toward the hooch, just after our night on bunker guard, waving to me so I would hurry. I could see Brink, my war son, my friend, coming down the hill with his rut sack on with his head down, trying not to worry about his next mission, or if he was a good enough team leader. And there was Kabbatt. And Babbles, the only one of my friends to really make it out unharmed, yelling down from the supply area for me to come and help him carry our meals and other goods down for the next mission. I could see and hear them all. Even Moran, who loved to hate me and bust my rocks non-stop. I could see them all as if they were there. I knew deep inside, love 'um or hate 'um, each of them would be inside of me forever. I thought, will I ever see any of my brothers again? Maybe these souls would all stay there to help the new men make it through Uplift's gates. Through this world's gates of pure hell.

I watched the very thick black smoke rising from the top of Recon Mountain as the truck drove north up the road. Uplift slowly began to fade from view. That was the last time I ever saw L.Z. Uplift, South Vietnam. It may have been foolish, but I waved my hand one last time to say goodbye to men that were not even there anymore.

Or were they?

CHAPTER 44
It's Not Over Yet

I turned around and looked up at the large puffy clouds in the sky and I wondered if they shaded my house back home maybe only yesterday. I wanted to go home more that day than ever before. I was truly alone, with no sure place to go. I planned on stopping at Quy Nhon on my route to Ophu Cat to say goodbye to my A.F. buddy Ted Springer. Then it was non-stop to Ophu Cat, then Japan, I hoped. The ride felt very long that time, longer than usual anyway.

I thought back to the times I had gone back and forth to all my schools. And all the times I went to re-zero at An Khe sniper school. Many good and bad times, many good and bad people passed through my mind as I rode down Highway #1. I knew this was going to be my last trip, no matter what! Even if I had to smash my knee with a bat, I was never coming back down this road again. The whole way to Quy Nhon, I felt as though someone or something was hot on my trail and I felt I just couldn't stop or I would be caught and killed.

Soon I could see the village of Quy Nhon just ahead. The truck stopped and I got out. I walked onto the A.F.B. and headed towards Ted's hooch. I went straight to Ted's hooch and not to where he worked because it was late Saturday morning, about 1200. I knew Ted would be getting off work soon and I thought I would just meet him at the hooch and surprise him. I walked down the hallway and into his room. Inside the room were two rolled up mattresses and two empty lockers. I said, "What the heck!" Maybe he went home or got moved to another hooch, I thought.

I walked down to Walter's room at the end of the hall, the room we used to play cards in. I knocked and Ted's friend Walter came to the door. I said, "Hey guy, what's up?"

He said, "Hey Ranger! Come on in. Long time, no see." I went in and sat down.

I was in pain big time. I moaned, "Oh, my blasted knee is killing me from all the humpin' around!"

He said, "Where you headed?"

I replied, "I'm so short, I have to stand on a chair to shake hands with Tom Thumb! One way or the other, I'm homeward bound!"

He said, "Good deal man. I never thought you would make it!"

I replied, "I never thought so either, but then I might."

He said, "I'm so glad for you."

I said, "Where is that lazy azz bomb jockey?"

He said, "You've heard about the attack on the A.F.B. about two weeks ago, right?"

I replied "What, no?"

He went on, "Oh yeah…It was maybe about 0800 one morning we got hit by rockets and mortars big time! Ted was crossing the field in his truck with a whole load of stuff. One of the rockets, or maybe a mortar, no one knows, hit right near his fully loaded truck. A large part of one side of the Air Base was wiped out because of that blast and the shelling. They never found Ted, just pieces of his truck."

I felt I was in a dream world listening to Walter. If only I could find the right meaning for the word Nam. I just couldn't believe my ears. Another one of my friends was gone! Stunned, I got up and I said goodbye.

I really had no feeling left inside me right then. No sorrow, no hate, no nothing. I was a total blank mentally, I was so stunned. I never wanted Ted's job shuttling bombs, but Ted was in a place where I never worried about him getting a scratch, let alone being killed. I was crushed!

I slowly walked back down the hall and out of the building. As I walked along in a daze I just kept trying to stay strong, telling myself that it didn't mean anything. But it did mean something! It meant that another good friend was dead! No matter how hard I tried to shake it off it just wouldn't go away. I kept trying to convince myself that the Nam never existed. But it did, it was really there.

I was soon at the main gate. I looked back once again to make sure the place did exist. I wanted to keep the memory of a kind and very generous friend alive forever within me. I could see the time, even the truck the day he pulled up just about where I was standing. He stopped to give me a lift when he didn't have to. We instantly became friends and now he was gone forever!

When I got to Highway #1, I easily got a ride that took me north towards Ophu Cat. When I got there I went straight to the hospital. After I got all checked in and all I just sat down to wait my turn to see the doctor. More than two hours went by as I sat there.

Finally my name was called. I got up and made a scene as though my leg was about to fall right off. I grimaced with pain every step. I figured if I couldn't dazzle them with my brains, I would baffle them with my bologna. One way or the other, I was done with everything the army stood for. I was a P.F.C. alright! But that didn't mean Private First Class, that meant Proud F#**#in' Civilian to me from that day on. I wanted out of that chicken scratch army and this good for nothin' country as soon as possible!

I hobbled into the Doc's office and moaned to him about how bad my leg was and how Captain Nobutt made me go out on missions with it screwed up anyway. I told the Doc that even if he got his degree out of a Cracker Jack box he could see my knee was puffed up twice the size of normal! He totally agreed and said he wanted to draw some fluid out and that would help relieve some of the pain. I also showed him the papers Captain Nobutt gave me. After that he told me that if there was any blood at all in the fluid I was as good as on my way to Japan en-route home! I said, "Doc, I'm not, well, weird in that way, but if you get my hurtin' azz out of this hole, I'll kiss ya!"

He laughed and said, "Don't worry about having to do that, I wouldn't let you anyway. Besides, with a knee like that, I don't see how you could have been sent back to duty in the first place! I can't believe you weren't sent home when this first happened!"

I replied, "Keep talking Doc, this is all sweet music to my tired ears! You sound like the only one that I've bumped into in a very long time that knows what he is talking about!" He withdrew some liquid from my leg. It was dark red with blood.

He said, "Ranger, how does the word 'Home' sound to you!?"

I said, "Doc, I always keep my word. I'm gonna' kiss ya!"

He just laughed and said, "You Rangers really are nuts, aren't you?"

I said, "Doc, I'll never be able to tell you how you just made me feel!"

He said, "Your face just told me! Go take this slip to the desk out front. The guy out there will set you up with a bed until you get your transfer papers." I thanked him a million times in the two seconds it took me to fly out of his office. Then I got my bed and room assigned to me from the dude out front.

About two days went by and my Doc came to talk to me each day and would tell me how he was pushing for me to go to Japan and all. Finally one day he came in and told me that I was going to be flown the next day to Cam Rhon Bay Rehabilitation Center for lots of sun and fun! He said that I would spend a short time there to relax and to see if my knee would stabilize somewhat and for more tests to see if I really needed an operation. He told me that he really feared that I was going to need surgery on my knee. But he said that wouldn't ever be done in that country. He said that when I got home I could have it done there, if need be. He told me I would be leaving for Cam Rhon Bay hospital at 0800 in the morning. He said my days as a combat soldier were over! I thanked him another million times for all he had done to help me. He told me to forget it and we said goodbye.

The next morning I was put on a flight to Cam Rhon Bay rehabilitation center. As I looked out the window aboard the plane, I felt very sorry for everyone still there. There was a Jimi Hendrix tune playing over and over in my head, "There must be some kind-a-way-out-a-here." I thought, Dear Lord I found the way.

After the airplane landed in Cam Rhon Bay, I could see some sights that were familiar to me from long ago. It was almost the exact spot I landed in when I landed in country. It all seemed like a million years ago. If I only knew what was ahead of me when I got here, I said to myself. But how far I had come. All the things I went through seemed so far away and more dream-like than real. Maybe it was all just in my mind, just a dream, all that I'd seen, tasted and smelled. Maybe so. All I knew for sure was that I was out of the nightmare called war forever.

We were all loaded onto a bus and taken to the Cam Rhon Bay Rehabilitation Center. The place was right on a beach on the South China Sea. The sand was hot but still felt so good. The sea stretched out as far as the eye could see. The water was a beautiful shade of blue. The place was beautiful all the way around. The hooches were all wood buildings with only screen walls. They were about fifty yards long. Down in front of the hooches was the beach and ocean. We were all assigned a bunk and locker and were told the only rule was no smoking, drinking, or eating in the hooches. Everywhere else I looked, I could see men drinking, smoking, eating and having a good time. I also saw dudes lying all over the beach soaking up sun and having a great time.

There was an open-air auditorium in the middle of the beach. They would show movies and have rock concerts or live bands at least once or twice a week. Most every night they would show a movie, or let some G.I. get up there and do some sort of comic act or whatever. All we did everyday was party hardy! The only work for most of us was physical therapy for an hour each morning. That was just to try to keep our muscles strong. There were all kinds of bone and muscle injuries there. Each night at the movies there would be two hundred men or more at the auditorium beach area smoking pot and relaxing at each show. During the day we would go to different hobby centers for relaxation. The food there was very good and you could have all you wanted. Every mess hall had a sign in it. It read, "Take all you can eat, but eat all you take." That was all they had to tell me. In no time I put on ten pounds, bringing myself back to normal weight.

The place let my mind and body unwind somewhat. There was no fear of Charley there. We all really needed the peace of mind. Some guys were so screwed up, mentally and physically, I didn't believe they would ever fully recover. The memories of Nam haunted every one of us. During my stay at the Rehab Center, I met Army, Marine, and Air Force G.I.s. There was no rivalry there. No one fought or argued about anything at all, except who was "bogartin" (hogging) the joint or who had the prettiest chick back home.

I had many tests and X-rays there to try and determine the extent of the damage to my knee. But none of the Doctors would say for sure what was wrong with my knee. They all kept telling me to exercise it and not to skip any of my therapy classes.

After a week or two I started to get very restless about going home. I knew I had it good there but I wanted to go home! One day a friend and I got the idea to sneak downtown to do something different for a change. So we changed from our cut off shorts to our regular army clothes and headed out the gate towards town. We passed by an In-Country Processing Station.

As we walked towards the main gate two cherries came up to us and asked if we had any joints to sell or if we knew where they could get them. We said we were headed downtown to party and to buy some pot ourselves. So they asked us to get them some weed and they would pay us twenty dollars extra for doing it. So we told them we would meet them back there about 1500 that afternoon. They said they would be shipping out about 1600 and to make sure we got back by 1500 or so.

I asked, "How much do you guys want?"

They said they wanted to split a quarter pound. The one guy gave me two hundred dollars. When I saw all that cash my eyes popped out like two headlights. Being cherry, they said, "Is that enough?"

I said, "Oh yeaaaaah! I can get a quarter, all right and maybe you'll even get some change back."

They replied, "Good deal!"

As we walked away I said to my friend, "Talk about cherry! These guys

282

are used to buying pot in the world. Can you believe this?! For two bills here we could get them a carload of weed. Brooother!"

My friend said, "Hey, for two hundred bucks we could buy a field of pot!"

I replied, "You got that El correcto dude!" So with our new-found way of making a lot of money very easily, off we went. We partied on the two cherries' money all day long and had a ball! We got back in plenty of time to make roll call but we missed the two dummies that got shipped out earlier. Needless to say, we had a very good money-making business there for a while. We would take cherries orders each day and the army would ship them out of our hair the same day.

One day when I went to see my doc, he asked how my leg was coming along, as he twisted and bent it in every direction he could think of. I replied, "It felt better until I stopped in to see you!" He said, "It will be tender for a while, but I think it will be okay if you give it time."

I said, "Look Doc, I've been here for a month now sitting around this place, just waiting to get the heck out or go to Japan or whatever. I'm so short now, I have to look up to see down! When can I go home?!"

He replied, "You're headed for Japan on Friday, is that soon enough?"

I threw my arms up and yelled as hard as I could, "Yeaaaaah! hooooo!"

He said, "You don't have to sound so depressed about it!" I reached over and hugged the snot right out of him. Then I limped out the door.

That was Tuesday. I had only three more days to go! I couldn't get it out of my mind. At long last! I just couldn't believe it was true. Only two days before I left to go to Japan.

That afternoon I was walking along the beach by myself thinking about being home. As I walked I saw two guys on the beach, and a chopper parked next to them. They were just sitting there catching a buzz and soaking up the sun. As I got closer I stopped because I knew one of them. I thought, are my eyes playing tricks on me? I yelled, "Brad?"

The guy looked up. "Jim!" He yelled back at me as he jumped up.

I said, "I knew it was you, you joker!"

It was my old friend Brad Feelen. I couldn't believe it. We sat down and we talked for quite a while, trying to catch up on all of the things we had done since the last time we saw each other. The last time I saw Brad was at Uplift, the night I almost got blown to heck by a rocket, and lost my M-16. He said he re-upped in the army to get a better job. He took a job on a chopper as an M-60 gunner. He still had a long time to go, five or six months before he was going home. I told him about Bec and how he was getting along. I told him of my getting hurt and all about how I was going to Japan in two more days.

As we sat on the beach talking he showed me an article in a newspaper put out by the army called "Stars and Stripes." This paper was put out by the army once a month, telling about different things that were going on in country and about U.S. troops. He said, "Check this out, here is a story about two Recondo teams from Uplift. Was this about you guys?" I took it and read it.

It went something like this:

OUTNUMBERED RECON TEAMS KILL 12 N.V.A.

Two Recondo teams from E Co. Recon, Special Operations Group, or S.O.G. 173rd Airborne, operating in the mouth of the Soui Ca Valley Southwest of L.Z. Uplift forced contact with nearly fifty V.C./N.C.A. enemy soldiers.

They ended up getting themselves surrounded but still managed to kill at least twelve of the hapless enemy last month. Once again Charley failed to take back what he used to control.

Inserted by helicopter before dark, the Recondo teams quickly moved to their ambush areas. A few hours later they saw several groups of four to eight V.C./N.V.A. soldiers moving along a trail one hundred meters to their front. Silently, two of the Recondo paratroopers moved to a new position ten meters from a V.C trail and counted one hundred three V.C./N.V.A. soldiers moving in one group. Before dark their total count of enemy soldiers was over two hundred. The next day the two teams split up and set up ambushes about three hundred meters apart. The plan was to spring the first ambush, sending the enemy into the kill zone of the second team. It was planned that if large groups of enemy were present, both teams would spring their ambushes simultaneously.

Luck was with them. A group of fifty enemy came along the ambush trail. Coordination between the two teams was excellent. Both teams detonated their Claymore mines together. They followed the blasts of the Claymore mines with hand grenades. At that point they had the enemy's attention. Soon they realized they were extremely outnumbered. They withdrew and took to higher ground behind them. Suddenly the enemy opened fire from all points of the compass. One team had an M-60 machine gun. Thanks to its firepower, they were able to break through what the enemy thought was an air tight kill zone.

The lead team was not quite so lucky. Without an M-60 machine gun and one man wounded, they were completely pinned down. But because of cool leadership, instead of giving their position away they used fraggs and blew the enemy to bits! By tossing hand grenades they inflicted numerous casualties on the enemy without giving their position away.

Meanwhile, help was on its way! Helicopter gun ships that had been put on alert came to their aid. The gun ships began firing on the nearby hedgerows and thick jungle area. Then a Reaction force, from A Co. 503rd Airborne Inf., was inserted to back up the two teams.

By the time they reached the teams the enemy had vanished. The dead and wounded men were extracted. Then the Reaction force swept the area, finding 12 dead V.C./N.V.A. and one wounded V.C./N.V.A. soldier. Also they found many blood-spattered and crushed down drag trails of V.C./N.V.A. that had been carried away by their comrades. If Charley wants the Soui Ca Valley, he'll have to try a lot harder than that a lot harder."

After I read the story, I explained to Feelen that my team was the one that was pinned down and the rest of the whole story. He said, "Man, I'm sure glad I got out of that bull when I did. My first day there I could see that job was for a man who didn't want to live too long! That's why I got the heck out when I had the chance!" He said his job wasn't all that safe now but it was better than getting chased through the boonies by crazy little people with guns. I never told him about the time I saw the prisoner of war hooches on my first C.I. mission with Special Forces. I didn't want to worry him about getting shot down and captured.

Soon it started to get late. Brad said, "I probably won't see you again for quite some time but maybe we'll meet back in the world again someday."

I said, "I am getting out of the army as soon as my toe touches earth in the world, so come to Upstate N.Y. if you ever want to see me again!"

He said, "I just may do that someday! I just might!"

I said, "That sounds real good! Do that will ya!?" So we said goodbye. It was real strange how we first met and how we kept bumping into each other. That was the last time I ever saw Brad. I often wonder whatever became of him.

I walked back to my hooch and rested. Soon the day to leave Nam came. Along with me, there were about two hundred fifty men leaving for Japan that day. As I sat staring out the window of the aircraft, I thanked God I was gazing into the hell called Vietnam for the last time. I closed my eyes and didn't open them again until we left the ground. I didn't want to ever gaze into that evil land again, not even by accident. I was so relieved and relaxed just knowing I was headed in the right direction for a change.

I slept just about the whole way to Japan. We landed in a very large Air Field near Tokyo. In fact it was the only airfield that could handle the U.S. Air Force's largest jet called the C-5A Galaxy. This jet was large enough to transport a whole battalion of men fully equipped for combat. Its wing span was about three hundred feet from wing tip to wing tip. When it turned around to head out for take off, the wing would stretch all the way over the air port terminal. As I sat in my seat waiting for and watching this monster turn around to head out, I could see the tip of one wing pass right over the terminal fence. It was some airplane.

Soon the C-5A got out of our way and we taxied over to the terminal. We were off loaded and put on buses that took us to our hospital a short distance away. After we got to the hospital we were sent to chow. After that we were sent from room to room as we all got processed into the hospital. We went nuts at how everything looked: all painted, with new looking beds and furniture. Things most people would normally take for granted was a very refreshing sight. None of these normal everyday things were seen where we had all just come from.

The nurses were either U.S. army personnel or women from other countries. All of us looked at them as though they were beauties out of "Playboy." Aaaaaah! Round eyes and round everything. I could feel the word "ghostin" starting to take on a much stronger meaning as I looked around. I started to remember that there really were nice things in the world and not just an ugly world like I had just come from. Everything was so beautiful compared to Nam.

We were all eventually assigned a room and bed. We got unpacked and comfortable. Many days for most of us were filled with all kinds of tests. Some tests were done to find out if any foreign viruses or parasites were living inside of us. We were tested for nearly anything they could think of.

After the first three days of tests, they finally got to looking at my knee. The first doctor that took X-rays and tests on it said I had severed one main tendon on the inside of my right leg. He also said my medial and lateral menisci were damaged.

He asked me, "Who re-set your knee, Doctor Frankenstein?"

I replied, "Worse! It was me!" I told him the whole story about how I got hurt and while in a state of confusion and panic, I set my own knee trying to get it straightened out. He said he thought if I didn't have corrective surgery done, one day I may never walk right again. He also told me that an operation of that type could not be done there in Japan. When I got back to the States, he recommended I have it taken care of. I told him I would think about it and see. He said, "Do more than just think about it!" He said that it was never going to heal by itself.

After I got the good news from Doc Bedpan, I went down to the cast room for the cast the Doc ordered for my leg. After it was put on, from my crotch to my right foot, I walked around like a ruptured duck for weeks. For the first two weeks all I did was lie around. The cast was killing my foot to walk around with it. But I finally cut and broke enough of it off at my ankle so that it didn't hurt as much, and I soon started walking around much better.

I played cards and all kinds of games down at the Day Room once I got more mobile. There were times I would go out on the lawn to sit and talk with some of the other men that could get around by themselves.

I became pretty good friends with a guy there that was in the Navy Sea-Bee's. He worked as a carpenter building hooches and all kinds of buildings. One day a hand held circular saw he was using kicked back and took off four of his five fingers on his left hand. The tops of what fingers he had left were stitched up with wire stitches. He would sometimes get the wire stitches wound up in his blankets or sheets, which was so funny to me. I couldn't stop laughing every time it happened. The nurses would usually have to cut him free with scissors to get him unhooked. The pain for him was very bad; it wasn't funny at all to him. I used to tell him to stay away from electrical outlets and batteries, so he wouldn't short out the hospital's electric system and fry himself! He never thought that was too funny, but I used to laugh about it!

We were eventually allowed to go anywhere on post. We could go to movies or hobby centers to build models or race model slot cars. There were nightclubs that we were able to go to and eat or drink just about anything we wanted.

One day the Sea Bee and I were sitting on the lawn near the day room. After we got tired of sitting around, we headed back to the hospital. We saw the day room exit door was open about two inches, and instead of walking all the way around the hospital, we headed for the day room door, only about twenty yards away. We were rapping, not really paying attention to anything in particular as we opened the door and walked right into our day room. As we shut the door behind us, we could see we were the only white dudes in a whole room filled with about forty black dudes. They were having a Black Power meeting! It was like two black men barging into a K.K.K. membership rally! I looked around as the room filled with chatter quickly got dead quiet. I said to myself, "Ohhhh baby!" I was about deafened by the silence. Slowly we moved, both of us holding our breath as we made it to the large double doors that lead into the main hallway of the hospital.

I slowly opened the door and when I did I caught a black dude's toe under the door and pinched him bad! He let out a yell like I just stabbed his butt. He was no big monster, but he acted like King Kong. He yelled, "Hey! you f@#$%%^^&** You just smashed my f@##$%%^! big toe!"

I said, "Sorry man, I'm sorry! I didn't see that your foot was under the door."
He jumped back and smacked me in the face as I was looking down at his foot.
Instantly, I saw the whole Milky Way start to appear before my eyes. I reached out
and put a headlock on him. Like flies on a can of dead worms every black dude in
the room came crashing down on my friend and I. In two seconds, we were beat
and kicked to a pulp. I still had the guy that punched me in a headlock. As I pulled
myself out the door on my belly, I pulled this bonehead right with me. I would bet
his neck stretched two feet. I was determined that he was not going to soon forget
the dumb white boy that pinched his toe. Even if they killed me, they would have
had to pry my dead, lifeless arm off his dead, lifeless throat! I was locked on like
a trained pit bull.

The commotion brought doctors, nurses and orderlies running into the hallway.
They tried for five minutes to get those black dudes off us. My cast was smashed
to white powder and my friend's hand was bleeding very badly. I looked like I just
got into a fight with a freight train and won!

All the way to the emergency room I just kept thinking, why did those men do
something like that to us? We were all U.S. soldiers; we were all in the same boat.
I only did what I did by accident. I never had any intention of doing anything more
than passing right through that room. All of those guys came from the same hellhole
I just came from.

But I knew that there was a difference…I was white, and they were black.
None of that ever made any difference to me but I guess to them it did. I remembered
how back in the Nam only weeks ago, we all worked to help each other stay alive.
That was the first terrible shock I got that made me realize the world back home
was going through a drastic change, as L.Z. Uplift did. I didn't know it then but I
would soon get a greater shock than even that. I found out that I was at war with
my own countrymen.

I spent an extra two weeks in bed, just recuperating from my warm welcome
into the day room. But soon I was good as new again.

Weeks later, my cast finally came off. One day I was called into the Records
Room to talk to a Sgt. about where I would be stationed back home. Stationed! I
thought. Stationed was only for someone still in the army. So I went right down to
see him.

I walked into a room labeled "Records." The E-7 inside told me to have a
seat. So I did. He said they were starting to prepare everyone's orders for active
duty back in the States. He looked at my records then said, "You will be stationed
at Fort Bragg, N.C. and will be assigned to such and such Ranger/Recondo Co."

I yelled out in shock, "Fort Bragg! Ranger Company! Are you nuts!? I'm out
of the army, Sarge!"

He replied, "No, you still have about a year left to pull!"

I yelled, "WHAT!!! I extended back in Nam to get an early out!"

He said, "According to your records, you never made the whole extra six
months of that half tour. If you hadn't taken your R&R you would have made it no
sweat. You now have, one year, 4 months and 28 days in country. You need a total
of one year and six months to be eligible for early separation."

I said, "I never took R&R so I could count that time."

He said, "According to your record, you did go on R&R for a month. Your company commander, your Captain said so right here." All I could see was my Captain and his ugly face smiling at me.

I screamed, "That no good son of a #*%*#*$! " After the Sarge calmed me down enough to go on, I told him the story of what happened.

He said, "I'm very sorry! But I can do nothing to stop or change your orders for Fort Bragg, N.C. You have no proof at all of what you have told me."

For two weeks I was so mad, I swore I would hunt down and find that so called Captain and kill him with my bare hands. But soon I just got used to the idea, because as always I did what I was obliged to do. But I remember saying to God that he would have to forgive me once again. If I ever saw that no good man, I would kill him for sure!

Time passed but my leg still wasn't any better. After awhile I could get around and was soon able to get passes to go into Tokyo to party on weekends. With the money I saved while in Nam I planned to really go nuts in Tokyo. The city itself was very nice. It was almost litter free and most people were very friendly. All the clubs were very fancy with very fancy ladies. Japanese ladies were so much more fancy then Vietnamese women that it wasn't even funny. At that time in Tokyo, most hookers didn't really act like hookers at all, but more like women that just hung out downtown to meet guys to party and have fun with, just like in the states. As long as you treated them good - bought dinner and took them dancing, that was usually all you had to pay for.

For the first three weekends out in Tokyo all I did was party big time. The girls treated me like I was a king. I really couldn't believe it. They were all very good looking and never gave me any bull about anything. The girls showed me all the sights of Tokyo and I went to many bars, shows and concerts. Most everything cost me an arm and a leg, but I was so starved for good times I spent money like it was water. I got drunk and stoned every night and stayed as close to that as I could even in the daytime. Pot was available anywhere, but it was very expensive! Just a small matchbox full would cost ten dollars or more. It was good weed but not that good. I kept my nights full of women and I stayed as high as possible.

I saw many things as I traveled around by train. I went all over the Tokyo area having fun. After a while I got tired of it all, as is usually the case with too much of anything. I wanted to go home once and for all.

One day I called my girl back home from Tokyo. When I got her on the phone, it took both of us a while to stop talking to each other at the same time, because we both had so much to say after so long. But I finally told her I would be home in a few weeks and I would tell her all about my journey into the Twilight Zone then. We both said goodbye for then and we said we would see each other soon.

After I hung up all I could think about was if we would still know each other like we did before. A year and a half can change people drastically. I just hoped I didn't seem too crazy to her. And I hoped that she didn't think I'd gone insane by the way I acted. I just prayed I would be able to cope with the army and everyone that was protesting the war in Vietnam once I got to Fort Bragg. Every time I saw a news program in the Day Room on Japanese television all I saw were films of how people back home were protesting the war. I couldn't understand Japanese but I could just tell the protesters were mad about the war. I would soon learn first hand just who and what these people were and what they were all about.

CHAPTER 45
Welcome Home Mother F*%#*^#!

Finally the day came for me to head back home to the place I held so dearly in my memory. I was tired and worn out from being so hopeful of getting out of the army for good. Now that wasn't going to happen. The day I got my orders to leave Japan I was not as excited as I always thought I would be. I guess by that time I would only believe what I saw and not what anyone told me. I trusted no one anymore. No one!

My final destination orders were for a Navy hospital in Queens, New York. It was here that they would determine whether or not I needed surgery for sure. Even though they said I might be a cripple for life without surgery, I knew somehow someday with God's help, I would eventually heal up completely. I didn't know how and I couldn't explain any of what I felt, I just knew it. I also knew right then that no one was going to mess me up again. From then on, I was going to take care of myself. From that day on my motto was F.T.A.! All the way! That was the way I felt and it was going to be that way forever.

We flew from Japan with one stop in Alaska for fuel. The next time our landing gear hit the ground, it was in Washington, D.C. I spent a few days at Womack Army hospital, then on to New York. All the men on that plane were wounded Vietnam veterans. Some of the men could get around by themselves but some were in very bad shape. As soon as we landed in New York, they had a bus waiting for us at the airport. We were all congratulated by the pilot and crew of the airliner.

Our Captain said, "I want to say that for myself and crew, and for all Americans, we're very proud and honored to welcome all of you wounded heroes home. You are the kind of men that our country should always be very proud of. You men had an impossible job to do. But you all did your duty and should be very proud of what you have done for our country. For all of us I just want to say, God bless all of you and thank you all for what you have done for our country. I am proud to be the one that has had the privilege to bring you men home again."

Everyone that could walk got out of the plane first. Outside were three buses with large signs plastered all over them saying, "Welcome Home Wounded Vietnam Vets." Far off in the distance just beyond the airport fence, we could hear people yelling and shouting. As we got off the plane and into the buses, we felt as though we were going to get a hero's welcome with all the people that turned out at the airport. After all the men were loaded into the buses, they headed towards the gate. The closer we got, the clearer we could hear what the large group of people were saying. There were cops everywhere trying to hold back the crowd.

As we started to pass through the airport gate, we could see the people were acting violent as heck. They yelled out things like, "You no good f##**!!in' baby killers." And things like, "You f##**!!ers deserve to be wounded after what you did! You all should have died in Vietnam, you scum bags!" They began throwing bottles and cans, rocks, and bags of dog poop! They didn't seem to realize that we, like them, didn't want to fight a war, and we were not responsible for the war. I thought they were mindless idiots, the victims of ignorance egged on by agitators. Their actions seemed so coordinated but that was no excuse for their actions.

We all looked at each other as though we didn't have any feelings left inside of us. The wounded that were so screwed up that they had to lie down were trying to get up to see for themselves what they were hearing. Most of us burst into tears as we drove past the people outside. Our people were doing that to us, not the V.C. We were all in such a state of shock we could not say one word. But I could feel the hurt and sorrow and I could smell the salt of tears and I only wished God had taken me before I got to see my own brothers doing what they were doing. They had no idea what they were doing to us.

Years later, I now believe, Jesus was asking me if I could forgive them for what they did. But at that time, and for many years after, I just could not! They were mostly young people, as we were. But we were the ones that either by choice, by force or by draft had to do what was expected of us. None of them had any idea of the pure hell we just went through. And now they made our home hell too. I felt as though I had nothing left to look forward to. My sacred dream of the world I once longed for was gone forever! We had no dream left to come back to, only more pain than we could have imagined back in the Nam.

I vividly remember looking into the faces of my American brothers outside the window of the bus that day and how sick I felt. I remembered back to the times I felt nothing in this world could ever feel worse then the hot breath of Charley's AK-47 breathing into my face. Many times Charley would be so close to me when his AK-47 went off, I could feel the heat and smell the exhaust from the muzzle blast as he popped up out of a spider hole or hidden bunker, or did a kamikaze charge at me. It was awful! So close to being killed, but yet not. The feeling was real bad and sickening!

Many years have gone by since then, and at times I wonder which was worse, Charley or those protesters outside the window of the bus that day. Up to that point in my young life nothing had ever hurt me all the way to my soul as that did. My heart instantaneously froze solid. Again I was reminded of the hate I had nurtured through the war. This hate stayed with me for many years. The feeling of wanting to come home had left me. At that point I didn't even want to be home or even call America itself my home. I along with all the other wounded men on that bus died that day. I could see it in their faces. We were still breathing, but we were dead inside.

After six weeks I recuperated in the hospital, and I got a two week leave. I came home and within that two weeks I got married to Deb, the girl I went with in high school.

CHAPTER 46

Back in the World

We were married for about twelve or thirteen years but for the last three or so years we had a very rocky marriage. For the first year after I came home from Nam she would not even sleep with me because of my violent nightmares. I would wake up screaming all covered with sweat every night from terrifying dreams. My temper was violent. I never hit her once, but I was verbally abusive and that is just as bad. I know now no one could be close to me or peacefully live with me then. That's what ended our marriage.

The horrors of Vietnam were burned deeply into my brain and there was nothing I could do to erase the evil images out of my mind. There was nothing I could do that could erase the hate I felt for all people. I felt a sense of being left behind by all the people that had found good jobs after high school, while I was pulling my tour in Vietnam getting nowhere, risking my life for nothing! Then after coming back home I had to work hard just to find a job, never mind a good one.

For years, I dealt with the problems and troubles all by myself, then I went to V.A. hospitals for help for Post Traumatic Stress Disorder. But until the late 1980's, the V.A. would not admit that P.T.S.D. did in fact exist or was a serious affliction. I went from 1973, when I completed my military duty, to 1996 fighting the Veterans Administration before they finally said that I did have P.T.S.D. Throughout this time I lost countless jobs. The bottom finally fell our when my wife threw me out after thirteen years of marriage. Because of this disorder, I lost everything I saved and worked for all those years.

The day my wife threw me out, I left home with nowhere to go. With only my guns and my clothes, I left everything else, including my beloved son of five. I died that day, even more so. I believed in God and hell, even though I didn't understand them. That and my son were the only things that kept me from ending my life. I was a survivor but I was just barely hanging in there.

For the next few years, I went from one relationship to another. They were all the same and went nowhere at all because of my attitude. I lived to ride Harleys, race motorcycles, and to party. I never let anyone into my heart because I knew I hated the feeling of a broken heart, so I kept it stone hard and cold.

By 1990, I was basically living out of my car and had nowhere to go, so I went into the Wilkes-Barre, Pennsylvania V.A. Medical Center for a four week stay in a mental ward/de-tox center there. I was soaked with booze and dope and I was desperate. Doctors there said that my liver was shot and I was a dead man if I didn't quit right then. They gave me numerous tests, medication, exams, you name it. Nothing helped. Nothing. When I got back home, the love I had for my son got me to slow my drinking slightly so that I might live a little longer and spend more time with him. Still my life was headed nowhere. I was an empty shell of a man.

Then one day in 1992, I came down with Viral Encephalitis. I was renting a small apartment in Endicott, NY at the time. About two weeks before, I was out walking in the woods at my hunting spot. A bug there must have bitten me.

I was taken to the hospital where I was pronounced clinically dead and had a near death experience. I remember everything vividly. I didn't fly down a brightly-lit tunnel, as some do. I was instantly and literally slammed to the ground, as though I had fallen from a high place. When I came to my senses, I realized I was no longer in my normal body or in a place that was at all familiar to me whatsoever. But the place was as real as it is here on earth, even more so. This was a very spooky, very dark, and terrifying place. Countless husky darkly shaded beings attacked me and tied me to a long pole and began to carry me. While I was tied to the pole, as a tiger may be bound to a pole, they scratched me, bit me, punched and kicked me. These beings resembled what I had seen in books before. They looked like cave men. They were very muscular, stocky and ugly. They had very long fingers and razor sharp long fingernails, which they used to stick into me, like sharp rods or sticks. And they had huge fanged teeth, which they used to bite me all over my body. My "tormenters" had no love or mercy in their faces or in their evil looking eyes. For that matter they showed no emotions at all and they radiated evil.

The whole time, I was being carried, along this dark, twisty, spooky road, they would stop now and then to curse me, bite me, scratch me, punch me, and kick me. Their fingers were like long knife blades. I could see their fingers entering my body like knives. The pain of it all was beyond description; the worst I have ever experienced. Their scratches were like fire burning into my flesh. It seemed like this torture lasted years and years, yet there was no real sense of time at all, just a long drawn out ordeal. I remember hanging there in absolute excruciating pain and all I did was scream with agony. These creatures were on me like hundreds of mad dogs.

Then, I really don't know why, but I began to scream, "Jesus! Help me!" over and over. Somehow, I knew in my soul that he was my last hope. I knew he was the only one that could save me.

Instantly the creatures that were attacking me let me go and stepped back away from me hissing and snapping their teeth. They shrieked as though I was now the one that was ripping them to pieces. As I watched them back away from me I saw our Lord standing between the creatures and myself with his arms outstretched to me. As soon as I touched him I instantly became clean as new snow. I also knew inside my soul I was on that spot, that very second, forgiven everything…everything! I saw a flash and I looked up as I felt myself re-enter my earthly body.

I saw a nurse looking down at me. I remember saying, "What the…what happened? Where am I?"

She said, "You are a very sick man, but I think you will be all right."

That night I was up eating and drinking like a pig. I was still very disoriented, but getting stronger quickly. My family was there and told me all that had happened. They told me how the doctor told my mother that for a while there was little hope of saving me. The doctor said all they could do was pray. The day I went into the coma, my son called me and when he called, I apparently knocked the phone over and he heard me screaming in agony. The last thing I remember that day was having the worst headache imaginable. Then everything went black. My mother said that all I did for days while in the coma was scream uncontrollably until the day I came out of it. She told me that the last day, all I kept yelling was, "Jesus help me! Jesus help me!" over and over. Then it was over.

At that time, none of it ever rang a bell. I still didn't understand what had happened to me. I thought it was all just a nightmare. But since then I know it wasn't a dream. I died clinically, and I did a tour in hell. There is no doubt about it. It was all very real! More real than this world.

It took months for my head to clear. When it did I became curious as to what happened to me. I went back to the hospital and paid to get all my records to see if they would tell me anything. When I read them, I got a shock in black and white. The papers told a story about all the drugs and antibiotics they had poured into my body to keep me alive and how for a period of time, I was clinically dead. It then told how they resuscitated me back to life. It was all there. The papers told me in black and white that I had died. That's when I knew for sure that I did a tour in hell, but I didn't understand why I was brought back.

At that time, I was working for a maintenance company subcontracting for IBM, doing maintenance at their powerhouse. That work soon ran out and I was laid off again. For a few months, I worked as a welder/pipe fitter during the construction of a Frito-Lay wastewater treatment plant in NY. When that job was finished, I got laid off yet again. I then worked for a while building a mall in Vestal NY, putting in air conditioning units and I got laid off yet again when that job was finished.

I was still fighting off the bad dreams I continued to have ever since Vietnam and trying to deal with my nowhere life. I felt more and more worthless by the day, as if I were completely abandoned. To lose one job in a lifetime takes a lot out of a person. But all my working life I had never made it more than five years at one place before being laid off or quitting. My life was a cycle of abandonment, despair, loneliness, depression, always wondering what to do next, over and over again. Everyone suffers this but I was vulnerable to defeat.

In 1993, I got a job with a Foundry doing heavy maintenance. I was working for them about eight months when I fell down a long flight of stairs, smashing a disc in my lower back. My left leg and left toes went numb. After surgery on my lower spine and months of pain and rehabilitation, I tried to go back to work. It only lasted six months or so. Then the pain got too bad to work anymore. After a second and now final operation, I became 100% disabled. I fought the Social Security people for over two years for help before they finally accepted me as being disabled. While on workman's compensation, I made only $465 a month for over two years. Times were very hard. I could not work, I could barely pay my bills and food was a luxury item. They were hard times, especially when $350 of the $465 went to pay the rent.

Eventually, I started getting help from Social Security, and with my workman's compensation and a small 30% P.T.S.D. pension from the V.A., (after a thirty-year fight) things got a little better. Then I received some back pay from Social Security. I put that together with a V.A. loan. That got me a nice, ten year old double-wide with some land in the country.

Still, I was empty inside. I kept blaming God for making me suffer all those years. I hated everyone and everything for the lack of money, lack of strength, and lack of friends. I still thought God was punishing me for all I had done in my life.

I kept hearing a little voice inside my head saying, "So, you have your own house, but you still don't have enough money to really enjoy it. It took all you had just to get the place. Now you have to make it livable. You're still stuck in the house with nowhere to go and no money to do anything with. And how does it feel to be paralyzed from the waist down by unremitting back pain that spreads? Makes you feel real good crawling around like a snake with all the pain and all. Look at your car, it's junk. How far are you going to get with that? And now you have to pay taxes and upkeep on the house!" These words just kept running through my head over and over.

In March of 1999, I was driving to a V.A. hospital in Syracuse, NY when my motor blew. It had already blown previously that year and I had just spent $2500 putting a new motor into it. I had to take out a loan to get that first mew motor. I was then truly broke and devastated.

After having my car towed back from Syracuse, I found out that the warranty on the $2500 motor and labor job, would only cover $350. I had to come up with the rest of the money. Then, that same week while I was stuck in my house waiting to get my vehicle back my furnace died. I learned it would cost me $2500 for a new one. It was late March or early April and thirty degrees outside, and I had no heat. Rage and suicidal tendencies took on a whole new meaning. Now what if my pipes freeze, I thought.

I was about to cash in my chips. Between the pain in my back, in my heart, in my mind, and in my wallet, I had had enough of life. Satan was reeling me in fast. I was about to become his personal possession for all eternity. If I would have pulled the trigger, nothing and nobody could have brought me back. I was about to be lost forever.

One afternoon, my sister stopped over to my house. he is much younger than I am and we never really talked much. She knew I had many problems, but was afraid to really talk to me about them. After having the most in-depth conversation I had ever had with her, she told me that no one on this earth, not a doctor, nor a psychologist, not a psychiatrist, a psychotherapist, or any drug could fix my problems. She said only God could help me. I almost laughed. We talked for a while and before leaving, she said that she would pray for me.

That night I was buried deep in sorrow. My son called me and we talked a long time. He also could tell how down I was. I said I believed God was still punishing me for what I had done in my life, by allowing my motor to blow up twice and now my furnace on top of that.

He exclaimed, "Stop blaming God! It's not him! It's the devil!" You see, my son had come to our Lord Jesus before me. He said, "Who do you think would try and push the blame on God or Jesus? The devil! That's who. He is the one that lies to people. He's the one that tries to get you to believe it is anybody else but him. Who would benefit the most if you killed yourself, huh? The devil, that' s who! The second you pull that trigger, you are damned forever and I will never see you in heaven! Listen to me! Hear what I am saying!" He didn't even sound like my son.

CHAPTER 47

Miracles

Suddenly, like a bolt of wisdom out of the blue, it all made sense to me. After all I had been through in my life, all the mental agony and torment, not being able to see; suddenly I could see it all. All in one split second! It was like a light in a pitch-black room just came on. Now, this kid, this twenty-year old kid, that the Lord Jesus gave me, finally got through my solid iron head! I knew that right then, through my sister and my son, Jesus had worked a miracle. I finally saw the light, as if being born again. All my life I had always believed only what I could see, whether it was with my eyes or my mind.

My son and I talked a while and I told him how it all just came to me. I told him that Jesus must have worked a miracle or something because I now knew what was happening to me for once in my miserable life. As usual, we both said we loved each other and we hung up.

I felt very different. That night, just before I went to bed, I felt so much sorrow for blaming God all my life for not helping me. I felt so bad I fell to my knees sobbing uncontrollably. I begged God for forgiveness and pleaded with Jesus to forgive a sinning wretch who was not worthy to even untie His sandals. I meant it with all my heart. I was truly sorry. I knew, not felt, right then that Jesus was my Lord and only Savior! "Praise our Lord Jesus! Praise Almighty God forever and ever!" I kept repeating this over and over until I fell asleep at the foot of my bed from exhaustion.

The next morning I heard the phone ringing. Without thinking, I flew out of bed and stopped dead in my tracks. I stood there a second wondering why I wasn't grimacing in pain. Normally I would have to wake up, open my eyes, slowly and carefully sit up, slowly swing my legs over the side of my bed, slowly twist and turn to limber up, then slowly stand up. I was up to that point, paralyzed by pain from the waist down!

Usually I would say, "Oh man, I woke up again. I have to face another blankadee blank, blank day, give me a break!" I would truly be sorry that I was still alive. I would be sorry that God hadn't shown me mercy and taken me in my sleep. Usually the voice in my head (the devil's words) would say, "No such luck pal! You're in for the long haul."

I looked at the clock and it was early. It was 7:30 or 8:00, something like that. As I picked up the phone I knew who it was. I said, "Hello."

"'Dad! How are you doing?" It was my son and I already knew it. He was calling to check on me. We talked a few minutes. Nothing real special was said except that he said he loved me, as usual. He had said this many times before but now I knew it was different. I knew for sure that someone in this cold, hard world was thinking about me. Someone really cared that I was still breathing! I could see clearly. My son loved me and God loved me.

As I was standing there talking to my son, I noticed that I was standing, not sitting down and I had no pain in my body at all. For two years I couldn't stand for more then a few seconds before pain caused me to sit down, or fall down - one or the other. For two years I crawled around on my belly or on my knees as I would fix my meals or whatever because the pain was so bad! Suddenly that day I had no more pain at all.

Because of everything that was flowing through my mind, I was somewhat in a daze as my son and I talked. I told him about my back, not quite believing it myself. I heard my son chuckling and he proceeded to tell me that he prayed really hard for me last night and that maybe Jesus answered his prayers.

Right then, I knew that this phone call was the most meaningful one I ever got. It was a phone call from a person of God that just helped save my life, my eternal life. Little did I know just then how prayer would completely change my entire life forever. A few days later I found out that my sister and her family prayed for me that night as well.

I want to say 'God bless' to all those who helped pull me back out of hell and away from the claws of Satan! I praise God for putting these people on earth to help save me so that God can use me in his way and I won't be useful to Satan any longer. Thank you Jesus!

My son and I finished our talk and we hung up. That morning I looked out the window. Usually I just get the same feeling about the day, blah, big deal! It wasn't a very sunny day, but somehow everything seemed to glow. The air was a hazy gray, but everything out there somehow had a glow to it. It was like when you are on vacation and look out at the lake or ocean and think about how lucky you are to just be there. You just feel as though you're free from work and free from the everyday blahs, you just plain feel good about the upcoming day.

From that day on I always feel like that. I never have a bad day. I sometimes have things go wrong, but I never feel like I used to. Whatever the problem I have the belief that Jesus is there with me, and now no day could ever be too hard for me to accept or deal with. To me nothing is impossible, as long as Jesus wants me to do it. Who could possibly stop me from doing something God wants me to do? Who can stop God? No one, that's who. I now have no worries.

As far back as I can remember, I've always wanted all the money that it would take to pay all my bills and maybe even have a little extra to do some of the things I like to do, like most people I would guess. But from that morning on, I feel filthy rich! I have no personal desire for money at all. That in itself is very strange to me. Since that day, I have felt so good and so at peace with everything; I just don't feel at all like my old self and haven't to this day. I have no more hate for anyone or anything. I don't even hate the people that always made me mad, like Captain A-hole or Charley. I've stopped hating the people that have done me wrong in the past, or those who have more than me. Now I can barely remember those things, and if I do, I can quickly erase those thoughts without any bad feelings at all.

For years now I have been going to V.A. psychologists and psychiatrists at two V.A. medical centers. For years they've prescribed numerous types of drugs for P.T.S.D., social problems and for my sleeping disorders. I used to take Vicoden, a very strong pain killer for my back, which I no longer take. I have not taken drugs of any kind since Dr. Jesus fixed me. I used to smoke, two to three packs a day for thirty nine years, and I quit that morning. I smoked pot every day from 1970 till 1999 but not anymore.

Now I breathe fresh air, I dig holes to plant trees and flowers and I mow my lawn. I have to be careful to save some work for tomorrow, when a short time ago I could not do any work at all. I could barely clean my house at one time.

Recently I had a physical with my regular doctor at the VA. After a blood test, he looked at his computer for the results. "Hmmmm," he replied.

I asked what that meant and he said, "Your liver is looking really good!" Not one doctor had ever told me that before, only the opposite. I am looking far beyond this life now, and I am gazing into eternity. Not just sixty or seventy or whatever amount of years God allows me to work for Him here. The real glory of God is the change in this life. It extends to eternity.

Before I became saved, I tried once or twice to read the word of God. Even back in Nam I tried to read it like Babbles suggested I do. Then I was blind to the understanding that no one can read anything in the dark. I never had a clue to what I was reading! Until the all-powerful Spirit let me see some of the mysteries of God's thoughts, I didn't have a clue. How could any blockhead like me possibly comprehend the thoughts and words of Almighty God until the Spirit enters them? Being blind without sight or light, the enemy can come to you at will and rob you right to your face, and you'll never know it.

Evil will walk up to you, give you a big fat kiss and run you through. But, when you are equipped with the full armor of Almighty God, you can walk into a room full of demons and they will stampede over each other trying to flee from you. When God is with you, who can possibly stand against you?

CHAPTER 48

Soldier of God

One night out of the clear blue, the Lord decided to start me on my spiritual education. That's the first step of becoming a Soldier, boot camp if you will. On this night I woke up for no reason, or so I thought. It was exactly 1:00 am and I was wide-awake and full of energy after being asleep only two hours. I felt an uncontrollable desire to watch TV. (Yeeeeah! I know, tell me about it! Above and beyond ridiculous right?) However, I calmed down and I fell back asleep. It seemed like hours went by and I opened my eyes again, only to find that I was absolutely drenched, bed and all, head to foot! In a total rage, I flew out of bed and into my living room, expecting to find someone standing there with an empty bucket of water. I found no one. I sat on my couch with a towel drying the sweat off myself when I noticed the time was 1:05 am; only five minutes had passed.

Just knowing sleep was out, I pushed the "on" button on my TV remote. That night, before I went to bed, I was watching a pay-per-view western on channel 529. It was now on channel 372, the Trinity Broadcasting Network. This is a Christian TV network and to this day I praise God for those people and their station. That night on TBN, I was introduced to one of my five spiritual teachers. I was introduced to a way of learning God's work in an incredibly strong and forceful manner. For over a year now, many times a week I listen to five Pastors: John Hagee, Rod Parsley, F. Price, Benny Hinn and Charles Stanley. These men are my spiritual genealogy. They are Bible teachers and God is giving me (with their help) a free Bible education. I now see the great truths about life that exist there.

Now, let me tell you some of the miracles that the Lord has done for not only me, but for others that I have prayed for. Slowly but surely, now Jesus is beginning to let me "work" with him. I'm beginning to build some rank in his army.

The first miracle was one that my son, my Veterans Administration Representative, and I all saw, or realized to be a miracle. My V.A. Rep. only shook his head in total amazement.

When I was in Vietnam I was wounded and sent to a hospital in Japan for a while, then sent to a hospital stateside. My medical records, along with the records of the wounded soldiers on my flight, were "mysteriously" lost in passage. We all lost important papers, without which any wounded veteran has no chance of proving a claim or receiving help or compensation from the Veteran's Association.

One important form is called #DD173. This is a station to station travel and assignment record. This form was lost from my file in 1972. Because I didn't have this form, I was subjected to a thirty-year fight with the V.A., one that I had no chance of winning without it.

I asked the Lord to help with all that. In 1999 I went to my V.A. Rep. and asked him if I could get a hearing in Washington, D.C. It was a long shot because I had no new "material evidence," but I had nothing to lose. After contacting the

V.A., they told me I could get a hearing, but I would have to wait up to two years to get it. They're very busy I guess (turning people down). Being a believer in God's power, I went over the V.A.'s head and went straight to God. Three weeks later, I had in the mail a scheduled appointment for a hearing in Washington, D.C. The first thing that came to my mind was thank you, God!

I went back to my local V.A. Rep. just to show him the letter and ask him what I was to expect in Washington. While he and I were going through my folder, which we had both been through hundreds of times over thirty years, he said, "Hey...hey, what's this?" Low and behold, there was my form #DD173, lost for over thirty years. I thought he was going to fall out of his seat. He shouted "Jim! Do you know what this is?" Then he explained that had I turned in this form, (which I never had before and we both knew it), I would have won my case back in 1972. All I could do was praise God. However this happened, God was teaching me to help myself through prayer.

I went to Washington and won my case hands down! But, don't forget, we're still dealing with the V.A. system. They said I won, BUT, now they want me to go through the maze (again) of medical and mental evaluations, and doctors, tests, you name it, to see what my current rate of disability is today.

CHAPTER 49
The Vietnam Memorial

It has taken me over twenty years to get up strength or guts enough to visit the Vietnam Wall in Washington, D.C. I had passed through D.C. earlier but could not bring myself to view the Vietnam Memorial. By myself, that never would have happened. But with God by my side I finally went.

There are four particular men's names on that lonely wall. Three men I was friends with. One took his last breath and blew it into my face while I held him in my arms. Another I carried over two miles down a mountain, but he died two days later in the hospital from a second bullet I never knew hit him. The third man I once hated as he hated me. The fourth is a fly boy who I thought was out of harm's way. The wall is a place of very bad memories and heartbreaks for me. Only the power of the Holy Spirit could have gotten me through it. I can now face myself and the park.

While I was there at the Wall, I held out my hand and touched the name of the friend that died in my arms. I prayed, "Dear God, Please allow me to help other people as long as I live. Let me do your work, the work of our Father. I know these men are in your arms now and there is nothing I can do for them anymore. But, there are so many who are spiritually dead or dying. With your power I can work to bring them to you. I ask this favor in Jesus' precious name....Amen."

At
The
Wall

More
Than
Twenty
Years
Past

Suddenly a feeling of peace, love and warmth came over me like fire! I felt short of breath, as though I were not there....like I was invisible. I can't explain it any other way. I didn't know it then, but from that second on, all kinds of new unexplainable things were about to happen to me. From that time on, my life has totally amazed me. I started (and I'm still doing) things I would never have done before.

The rest of that day I felt as though my body was on fire. I was so spiritually pumped up, I felt like I had done some sort of powerful drug or ate a super atomic energy pill like Ted Springer and I used to do back at the A.F.B. in Nam. That day my son and I went around Washington, D.C. preaching to anyone who would listen.

A black man came up to us and began peddling porno tapes, dope and whatever else he was carrying. I began peddling the Word of God faster than he could peddle his goods (or bads). This guy shut his mouth, then stood there apologizing for doing what he was doing, just because I told him Jesus just told me, (and He did) that He was very sad and disappointed in this man for doing what he was doing. Before he ran away, he said he would take back the big bag of 'Tricks' he was carrying. Whether he did or not, I can't say. I prefer to believe he did.

My son and I got tired of walking and I hailed a cab. The black cabby kept adjusting his mirror and looking back at us. He asked, "Where you two headed?" I told him we were hot, tired and hungry from walking around all day and we wanted to go to a good restaurant. As he looked in the rear view mirror he asked, "Were yawl two actually walking around this area today?"

I answered "Yeah, why?"

Well he replied, "Yawl do realize yawl is white?"

My son and I chuckled, "Yeah, last time I shaved I noticed that, why?" I replied.

He shouted out, "'Cause yawl is white and the streets yawl is walkin' on is the most dangerous black streets in da U.S.A, according ta da news!"

I had wondered why we were the only two white guys in sight all day. smiled at him and replied, "The Lord encampeth round about those who fear Him."

He asked, "Say what?"

I replied, "No weapon formed against me shall prosper."

He roared with laughter and slapped the steering wheel and said, "Yawl is about the two bravest white boys I seen in a long time, or the craziest! Folks get shot and stabbed all the time around here!"

My son Jesse said with a big smile, "Take us to the Hard Rock Café." The cabby laughed and shook his head. We had a riot talking with that cabby. He soon pulled up to the Hard Rock. He dropped us off and he wished us luck. We walked right in and ate a good supper and walked around looking at all the rock memorabilia all over the walls inside the cafe.

After we ate, we decided to walk the two miles or more back up New York Ave. (The deadliest street in America?) to our hotel. ll the way back we kept praising the Lord for giving us both such a great day together. That day was worth all the world to me. All day long, we passed groups of black people and we were totally at ease. They never said a thing except "hi" or "hello" to the two "brave or

302

crazy" white boys, as we went on our way. For the Lord sends his Angels to protect those who love him.

When I got back from Washington, D.C. I bumped into a good friend of mine at a wedding. He looked more like a guy that I should have been looking at during a wake, not a wedding. I was shocked that it was the same guy who was my friend. I asked, "Dude! What happened to you? You look sick." He told me that he had some sort of "liver ailment." To me he looked as though he had lost his liver completely.

I began to talk to him about the power of God. He got all nervous and embarrassed. I knew Jesus would help him, so with all kinds of nosy unbelievers watching, I grabbed his head by his cheeks and said, "In the name of Jesus and by the power of His blood shed on the cross, I command this sickness to leave this man now!" His face lit up, red with embarrassment. I actually saw people standing around shaking their heads in disbelief and disgust. My friend and his wife quickly said good-bye.

I stood there alone asking Jesus to forgive this man for not becoming a preacher like he once told me he set out in school to do, but quit. I asked Jesus to heal my friend, because he was a true combat veteran like me.

One day a few months later, this man called me and told me he was off all his medication and doing fine. 0He told me he had not felt that good in years. I asked him if he thanked Jesus for what he did for him. He told me he did. He told me he knew in his heart that he would not have gotten better any other way. He told me the doctors tried everything but nothing worked. I felt so happy! I prayed for that guy many times and I hoped he would see the light. All I can say is, "Thank you God for giving my friend one last chance." I've talked with him since and he's doing very well and gaining weight and said he even goes out now and has much more energy.

I was born on this earth January 2, 1950, but I never even realized what it meant to be fully alive until April 4, 1999, just about midnight. That night Jesus came into my mind and body and I became saved. I have now become a totally new creature and feel born again. The first part of the story of my life is a story of continuing anger, abuse, hopelessness, hate, darkness, suffering and real stupidity. I was at war with myself and at war with the world. It is a reflection of so many other people's lives throughout this world! As a soldier of God, I am going to do whatever I can to help bring light to other spiritually dead or dying people. I believe I am actually looking through Jesus' own eyes now because He said we are all one with Him. This is why I can now look at heaven and earth in a totally new way. He has made me a totally new creature.

I am a follower of Jesus. Some of you may laugh, but I am a living Witness to God's power. He healed me – physically, mentally, and spiritually from everything that plagued my life, for over thirty years in just one day. I have learned what many others already knew.

Now I see "Life," the real life, not just here and now…but I see life everlasting. God is in all ways forgiving and strengthening and never destructive.

Soldier of God, James Gibbore.

CALLING ALL SCOUTS—Endicott Police Sgt. Charles Garland shows James Gabbore, Cub Scout, how patrol cars are contacted from police headquarters. The youngster, along with other members of Cub Scout Pack 204, Den 2, was a visitor to the police station and central fire house yesterday.

Confirmation

High School Picture

Author James Gibbore - 2001